SUCCESSFUL METHODS IN COST EN
    Hira N. Ahuja and Michael A. Walsh
QUANTITATIVE CONSTRUCTION MANAGEMENT: Uses of
Linear Optimization
    Robert M. Stark and Robert H. Mayer, Jr.
ENERGY MANAGEMENT AND CONTROL SYSTEMS: Theory and
Application
    Manuel C. Macedo, Jr.
PROJECT MANAGEMENT: Techniques in Planning and
Controlling Construction Projects
    Hira N. Ahuja
COST ACCOUNTING FOR THE CONSTRUCTION FIRM
    Bill G. Eppes and Daniel E. Whiteman
TRANSPORTATION INVESTMENT AND PRICING PRINCIPLES:
An Introduction for Engineers, Planners and Economists
    Martin Wohl and Chris Hendrickson

TRANSPORTATION INVESTMENT AND PRICING PRINCIPLES

TRANSPORTATION INVESTMENT AND PRICING PRINCIPLES

An Introduction for Engineers, Planners and Economists

MARTIN WOHL
Professor of Transportation System Planning

CHRIS HENDRICKSON
Associate Professor

Carnegie–Mellon University
Pittsburgh, Pennsylvania

A Wiley-Interscience Publication

JOHN WILEY & SONS

New York • Chichester • Brisbane • Toronto • Singapore

Library of Congress Cataloging in Publication Data:
Wohl, Martin.
  Transportation investment and pricing principles.

  (Construction management and engineering, ISSN 0193-
9750)
  "A Wiley-Interscience publication."
  Includes index.
  1. Transportation—Cost effectiveness. 2. Transportation engineering—Cost effectiveness. I. Hendrickson,
Chris. II. Title. III. Series.

HE152.5.W64 1984 629'.04'0681 84-7347
ISBN 0-471-87989-4

Printed in the United States of America

10 9 8 7 6 5 4 3 2 1

FOREWORD

Thirty years ago the study of transport economics consisted largely of observing and chronicling the behavior of the ubiquitous "authorities"—the FCC, the FAA, and so on—and distilling the principles which emerged from their voluminous and bewildering processes. It was a tiresome but necessary toil. And such research was the precursor of many blessings, such as the deregulated air transport industry which, with increasing efficiency, gives us ready and cheap access to all parts of the Union.

But, and just as important, in the last three decades transport economics has become firmly wedded to the underlying technologies of the transportation industries. It has become an essential tool (or if you do not object to the disgraceful mixture of latin and greek roots, a "methodology") for decision making. Thirty years ago the main criteria for investment were to be found in certain rules of thumb, such as the rule that "rubber pays for the highways" or that "when traffic exceeds x thousand cars per day per lane, then build additional lanes." The new melding of technology and economics exposed the egregious errors, as well as occasionally exposing the underlying truth, in such propositions. New alternatives and fresh perspectives were revealed in great profusion. We now know much more.

This book can be construed as a culmination of that marriage of method and infusion of ideas. It shows us how to arrange our thinking on transport techniques and solutions. But above all it provides *insights*—and some surprises—into the oldest of human needs: the moving of the body as well as the soul.

SIR ALAN A. WALTERS

Personal Economic Advisor
to the Prime Minister
of the United Kingdom (1981–1983)

June 27, 1984

v

SERIES PREFACE

Industry observers agree that most construction practitioners do not fully exploit the state of the art. We concur in this general observation. Further, we have acted by directing this series of works on Construction Management and Engineering to the continuing education and reference needs of today's practitioners.

Our design is inspired by the burgeoning technologies of systems engineering, modern management, information systems, and industrial engineering. We believe that the latest developments in these areas will serve to close the state of the art gap if they are astutely considered by management and knowledgeably applied in operations with personnel, equipment, and materials.

When considering the pressures and constraints of the world economic environment, we recognize an increasing trend toward large-scale operations and greater complexity in the construction product. To improve productivity and maintain acceptable performance standards, today's construction practitioner must broaden his concept of innovation and seek to achieve excellence through knowledgeable utilization of the resources. Therefore our focus is on skills and disciplines that support productivity, quality, and optimization in all aspects of the total facility acquisition process and at all levels of the management hierarchy.

We distinctly believe our perspective to be aligned with current trends and changes that portend the future of the construction industry. The books in this series should serve particularly well as textbooks at the graduate and senior undergraduate levels in a university construction curriculum or continuing education program.

JOHN F. PEEL BRAHTZ

La Jolla California
February 1977

PREFACE

Engineers, planners, and policy analysts, among others, often have little formal training or education in investment planning and pricing. Indeed, one can hardly expect otherwise when, for the most part, a single course in microeconomic theory or engineering economics is required to become degreed or certified in most engineering and planning fields. The textbooks, handbooks, and manuals used in both the teaching and practice of engineering and planning rarely devote more than scant coverage in a chapter or two to investment planning, to pricing, to benefit–cost analysis, and similar topics. We might ask: Can these matters be so unimportant in the process of planning, designing, evaluating, constructing, operating, and maintaining structures and facilities which together represent annual resource committments of hundreds of billions of dollars? We believe not.

Perhaps as a result of this lack of attention, conventional wisdom on this subject is often misleading. For example, consider the following set of widely held beliefs about how to efficiently plan, justify, or price alternative investments:

Buildings, bridges, and other such structures should be designed so as to fail or physically collapse only under the most catastrophic and improbable conditions.

Once built, a facility should be used until the end of its physical life; to discard or abandon a still useful facility or piece of equipment is wasteful.

Those who benefit from facilities or services should pay the costs, and those who benefit more should pay more.

In designing facilities sufficient capacity should be provided so as to meet the demand.

Of several investment choices, the one whose ratio of benefits to costs is the highest is the "best" one.

The operators of heavy trucks should pay for the extra pavement and construction costs which were incurred on their behalf.

In an economic analysis of new alternatives or improvements, one need only analyze the extra benefits and extra costs over and above those for the existing system.

Once some large and integrated program (such as the Interstate Highway System) is begun, it *must* be completed.

Downtown traffic congestion should be reduced, if not eliminated.

All steps should be undertaken to reduce air pollution, energy consumption, and the loss of lives and limbs.

However appealing or dearly held one or another of the above beliefs may be to one group or another, the fact remains that *economic efficiency principles do not necessarily support any of them.* Some of the conclusions may be desired or reached for reasons of fairness or equity, but this is quite a different concern from that of improving the efficiency of systems.

In writing this book, it was our hope to clarify the relevant economic issues and to provide a useful conceptual framework for addressing the problems of investment, pricing, and evaluation. Reflecting our own backgrounds, many of our examples are drawn from the realms of roadway or transit passenger services. However, we should emphasize the more general relevance of the material presented here. The principles and analysis procedures we discuss are generally applicable to a wide range of investment and pricing problems, whether in the public or in the private sector and whether in the transportation, construction, utility, water resource, or other such industry.

In presenting these principles, we have relied upon descriptive presentations and graphical illustrations as well as mathematical formulations. After an introduction to the issues in Chapter 1, the general framework for considering investment and pricing options is developed in Chapters 2 to 8. These chapters contain discussions of the importance of equilibrium, the economic benefits and costs of particular facilities or services, and methods for choosing among alternative projects. The following two chapters (Chapters 9 and 10) discuss financial considerations and multiobjective decision making. Estimation techniques and their associated accuracy are introduced in Chapters 11 and 12. Finally, a discussion of some practical problems and innovative possibilities in pricing and investment appear in the final two chapters. Appendices summarize the mathematical methods used in the book, the problems associated with the internal rate-of-return project selection method, and the use of ordinary least-squares regression for statistical estimation. The mathematical methods used are generally restricted to algebra and simple calculus with graphical illustrations.

For an introductory course in transportation economics, transportation planning or public investment planning, the material on estimation techniques (Chapters 11 and 12 and Appendix III), and on multiobjective analysis (Chapter 10) might be deferred to a second course. Appendix II might also be omitted for those who are not concerned with the pitfalls of the internal rate-of-return method due to the adoption of simpler analysis alternatives.

Preparation of this text benefited from discussions and work with numerous teachers, colleagues, and students over many years. Deserving special thanks is Tung Au, our colleague at Carnegie-Mellon University. We are also grateful to Frances Bukes for typing and retyping the manuscript through its many stages.

Finally, we have tried to free the text from errors and misstatements, but we are well aware of both our own imperfections in this regard and the complexity of the subject matter. Any errors of fact or judgment are our own responsibility and embarrassment. Besides asking for the reader's indulgence, we would very much appreciate letters pointing out any such mistakes or making suggestions for improvement.

MARTIN WOHL
CHRIS HENDRICKSON

Pittsburgh, Pennsylvania
June 1984

CONTENTS

TRANSPORTATION INVESTMENT
AND PRICING PRINCIPLES

CHAPTER 1

AN INTRODUCTORY STATEMENT

Increasingly, planners, managers, and legislators are employing economic analyses (e.g., "benefit–cost", "cost-effectiveness", "breakeven", "financial", "impact", or "alternatives" analyses) as part of the overall planning and policymaking process. On the one hand it is obvious that knowledge of the economic impact of various transport investment and operating options is useful and important. On the other hand it is also obvious that such analyses are poorly understood from the standpoint of what economic consequences should be incorporated, how they should be measured, when a particular method of analysis is appropriate, and even how to apply the various analysis methods. Moreover, there is ample evidence that a lack of sufficient understanding of these matters makes it exceedingly difficult (if not impossible) for analysts and policymakers alike to make rational decisions among different projects, among agencies competing for limited available funds, or about funding levels.

This text is aimed at narrowing these gaps, at clarifying the issues and methods involved, and at reducing the inconsistencies among economic project analyses. Further, attention will be given to those matters which are capable of analysis and to those which are not and thus which can be dealt with only judgmentally. Essential objectives of this text are to develop consistent tools for "alternatives analysis"; improved techniques for analyzing transportation investments; and better methods for conducting benefit–cost and cost–effectiveness analyses. Also of crucial importance is the integration of technical material and concepts so that the interrelationships between and among the various components of transportation investment planning can more readily be understood and applied.

The key issue being addressed—that of developing and explicating better analysis methods and techniques for ascertaining the desirability of different policy actions—has as its aims the improvement of our understanding of the overall management and policymaking process, the elimination of internal inconsistencies, the assurance of completeness with respect to accounting for multiple and often conflicting criteria, and the specification of the crucial assumptions and concepts to be incorporated in the analysis process.

To carry out these objectives, it will first be necessary to detail the components of an economic analysis. In a sense this discussion will be aimed at identifying what internal and external aspects of concern should be considered and incorporated. Second, it will be necessary to provide a framework for measuring or predicting the various benefit and cost items (broadly construed) to be included in a benefit–cost, cost-effectiveness, or alternatives analysis. Third, it will be necessary to outline the manner in which these benefit and cost aspects are interrelated and affect each other for various policy actions (e.g., for pricing or control options) and to describe how their totals and increments vary over the long run (as demand shifts, as capacity is changed, or as new alternatives are introduced). Fourth, it will be necessary to develop procedures for placing present and future benefit and cost values on a commensurate value scale (e.g., by making use of appropriate discounting techniques). Fifth, some considerable attention will be devoted to the different benefit–cost analysis methods which can be used for assessing the worthwhileness of various projects and of additional increments in investment. Finally, means of incorporating multiple objectives or attributes will be assessed.

While most of the text will be focused on methodological development (e.g., on how to conduct cost-effective analyses or benefit–cost analyses, and so forth), it will also be necessary to deal rather specifically with a number of empirical issues and with matters of practicality and application. For instance, it will not be sufficient to simply deal with functional definitions of costs and, in turn, cost functions; what is also needed is some attention to the appropriate way to estimate such functions and to incorporate both resource and user costs. Nor can one overlook the significant way in which travelers' "value of time" relates to this development. Similarly, demand functions will be treated in more than abstract terms and placed in a more understandable and useful form. Their development will be undertaken such that analysts more fully understand their nature, makeup, and importance, and that they have a working knowledge of the applicability and utilization of demand relations and cross-relations. While these empirical issues will be dealt with briefly during the methodological developments, we shall treat them more extensively in the final chapters, which concern the practical difficulties of analysis.

By way of highlighting some of the problems at stake and some of the issues which will be dealt with in this work, some illustrations may be helpful.

Far too often, analysts, when evaluating alternatives, use cost-effectiveness analyses when benefit–cost analyses should be used. The essential difference in these analysis methods is that of assumptions concerning demand and travel volumes. Cost-effectiveness analysis assumes that travel volumes are unaffected by the alternatives being considered, whereas benefit–cost and other analyses consider the effects of volume changes. Alternatives being compared often have service or price differentials that will lead to different levels of usage (even though volume is assumed to be constant), thus giving rise not only to cost differences but also to differences in user benefits. Comparison of alternatives in such an instance by only considering differences in investment cost, maintenance cost, and user travel time is incomplete and inappropriate. More properly, demand elasticities and cross-elasticities should be used to estimate the extra patronage and net benefits resulting from the service or price differentials, and then this increment should be used in the total accounting. While it is easier and simpler to carry out only a cost-effectiveness analysis, it nonetheless is often incorrect. (This is not to say, though, that cost-effectiveness analyses would never be useful; for instance, when the service or price levels of the alternatives do not give rise to differentials in patronage, a cost-effectiveness analysis would be sufficient.)

Another common and important problem faced when conducting either cost-effectiveness or benefit–cost analyses involves the treatment of travel time savings. In virtually all cases analysts assume (by example or by the analytics employed) that the marginal utility of any time saved is constant; that is, they assume that the value of a minute of time saved per trip is equal to one-sixtieth of the value of an hour saved. In effect, this assumption leads one to value, for example, a $\frac{1}{2}$-minute saving in travel time at about 2 cents per trip if the value of an hour saved is assumed to be $2.40. Such an assumption is often incorporated in analyses for alternative public transport proposals, and when such values are magnified by tens or hundreds of thousands of trips per day and 30-year horizons, the results easily give rise to rather questionable user benefits of tens of millions of dollars. Needless to say, such practices need to be dealt with more explicitly and with more attention to their conceptual rigor.

As a third example, the subjects of subsidy, of proper pricing, and of the practicalities of implementing different pricing policies (e.g., free transit vs. peak-load or variable cost pricing) need to be dealt with in a more understandable, complete, and less theoretical fashion than is now common. Further, these topics should be covered from other than an advocacy viewpoint, and they should be dealt with in terms of their effect on economic efficiency, on practically, on equity, and on transport financing.

While this text deals primarily with the economic impact of different policy or technological options, that focus should not be construed to mean that decisions about building or not building more roads, airfields, or subways, or those about user charge or pricing policies, and so forth, *should* be based solely and exclusively on the basis of their economic consequences. Rather, the contention is simply that the economics of choices is important, is relevant, and is an essential *part* of the decision-making process. Certainly, political, legal, and other impacts are and should be considered in making decisions. We simply argue that economic considerations should also be properly included. Some methods of including other considerations in an analysis are described in Chapter 10.

Further, our hope is that analysts will better understand the appropriate set of questions to be asked and the methodologies to be employed in order to obtain good answers. Relevant alternatives should not be assumed away; "policy" should not be made in a vacuum; "conventional wisdom" and commonsense notions should not stand in our way. Three examples may be helpful in understanding such problems.

First, when transportation suppliers are faced with rising costs, seldom does either the supplier or the public regulator (who often must approve proposed rate or fare changes) consider—much less analyze—other than a fare or rate *increase* as a means of offsetting cost increases. Similarly, when a transportation facility or its service is improved, the "conventional wisdom" usually leads one to assume that the improvement "should" be accompanied by a rate or fare increase. In neither case, though, can one *necessarily* conclude that a rate or fare *increase* will produce net economic gains, either to society or to the suppliers of transportation. Rather, it can be shown that in some instances (and perhaps many) both parties will benefit from a rate or fare *decrease*.

Second, most observers of the transportation scene seem to feel, if not believe, that urban traffic congestion "should" be reduced, if not eliminated, and thus that something "must" be done about the traffic congestion problem. For years this line of reasoning led many to believe that the answer was to build more highways; more recently the conventional wisdom has turned to reduced transit fares, to the construction of subways, to downtown auto bans, to the encouragement of car pools, and to a host of other nonauto "solutions" to achieve this widely acclaimed goal. While it is quite appropriate to consider more than just highway–type alternatives as means of reducing traffic congestion, it is of equal importance to consider or question the goal *itself*. That is, it is not clear that we "must" or even "should" reduce, if not eliminate, traffic congestion. It just may be, for example, that the extra costs or losses in accessibility, privacy, comfort, or what–have–you which accompany such "solutions" may outweigh the benefits or gains which accompany them. In short, it may be better to do nothing and continue to live with congestion, however bad it may seem to some, than to do something about it.

The same kind of argument and an identical conclusion might also be used for air pollution and traffic safety issues. In none of these cases can one simply assume that to do something is better than to do nothing, at least as an economic matter.

Third, when conducting a benefit–cost analysis for *various* alternatives, policymakers or analysts frequently overstate the "benefits" accrued from an alternative by including as a "benefit" item those costs which are said to be saved by not building a rejected or less preferred alternative. The usual reasoning is that by virtue of building one alternative, we avoid the *necessity* of building another and *thus* can include the costs saved as "benefits" when analyzing the consequences of building the preferred facility. However, the reasoning is illogical and leads to an incorrect identification of the benefits and costs. First, it must be recognized that *all* of the alternatives *can* be rejected, thus foregoing the benefits and costs of each. Thus, not to build one facility does not imply the necessity of building another. Second, if we were to add the costs saved from the rejected alternative as a "benefit" item for the preferred alternative, it would be possible to justify any alternative simply by rejecting an alternative which has costs that are higher than those for the alternative being analyzed. Third, the merit or self-sufficiency of each alternative is independent of the other options. That is, the benefits and costs of alternative A result only from the construction and operation of alternative A and are independent of alternative B; the net benefit of A must be nonnegative if alternative A is to be judged desirable or "feasible."

The above examples hardly exhaust the list of questions or aspects of transport economic analysis to be considered, but simply highlight the type of issues and thinking which is to be explored in more depth. In some cases it will be possible to reach a definitive answer about the appropriate structure and/or methodology to be employed; in others it will not. In either case the intention here is to clarify the issues and the proper approaches to economic analysis of pricing, financing, and investment options, as well as to indicate where the theory ends and the judgment begins.

1-1 SCOPE OF THE TEXT

This is an introductory text on transport pricing, financing, and investment planning. While it is meant to be comprehensive, and to illustrate the linkages among these aspects of transport planning (broadly construed), it is also somewhat simplistic—in defining cost, price, and demand functions and in dealing with all the ramifications of "the real world." Moreover, it has been necessary to overlook (other than cursorily) some important issues, such as regulation, political consensus, interfirm competition, urban development, and management. Nevertheless, the objective has been to carry the "theory" far enough to provide a fundamental understanding and to be practical.

Essentially, our purpose is to present those principles, relationships, and methodologies which are necessary to provide a framework for answering the following essential questions:

1. Should *any* investment be made?
2. If so, how large should an investment be, and when should it be made?
3. Once it is built, how should a facility be operated and priced?

Also covered is a fourth question: How should we conduct benefit–cost analyses for alternative projects or policy options?

The first three questions deal with *optimality* (e.g., the best facility size, or the best way to price and operate a facility), while the fourth deals in a more limited way with the *feasibility* or worthwhileness of any project among a specific set of projects. The distinction between the two issues is important. Benefit–cost analysis involves an evaluation of the stream of year-by-year benefits and costs which accompany or stem from a specific project (to include its technology, operating policies, and pricing strategies) and, in turn, a determination of whether the project's benefits (however measured) outweigh its costs. Also, a complete benefit–cost analysis for a given set of mutually exclusive alternatives will include determination of the feasibility of undertaking projects having higher initial capital outlays than the lowest cost one which is feasible. By contrast, investment planning is concerned with optimality; that is, with determining the best project, pricing policy, and operating strategy from among a virtual infinity of alternatives.

Two other key points are worth noting at the outset. *First*, the primary, though not exclusive, concern will be focused on pricing, financing, and investment for *publicly* owned, operated, or regulated facilities (e.g., public highways, public transit systems, inland waterways). Necessarily, though, the interaction between the public and private sectors must also be considered because of their inseparability and interdependence. This would certainly be the case for public highways when used by privately owned and operated vehicles, as well as for public roads and streets used by publicly regulated but privately owned and operated taxicabs. While our central concern in such instances is to determine which public facilities should be built and how they should be maintained, operated, regulated, and priced, the fact remains that decisions about public facilities can properly be made only by accounting for the full set of consequences to both the public and private sectors. *Second*, we will primarily concern ourselves with the *economic* consequences of different investment levels, pricing policies, and operating strategies. In a sense, then, we will consider or include only those consequences and objects of concern for which (someone within) our society would be willing to pay or forfeit something else of known economic value in order to obtain them or keep from giving them up. This is not to say, as will later be explained, that social consequences or objectives—as opposed to economic ones—are irrelevant when considering investment, pricing, or operating alternatives. Rather, it is simply to emphasize that our principal concern is with identifying economic well-being rather than with the distribution of economic resources or other social objectives. To use somewhat common terminology, we are more interested in increasing the *size* of the economic "pie" than in *splitting* the "pie"; that is, we are more concerned with identifying total economic gain than with who gets what share of it. However, Chapter 10 does deal with the problem of incorporating other social objectives within the analysis.

Among the more important aspects of transportation economic analysis to be covered are the following:

Development of Travel Demand, Benefit, and Revenue Functions

In order to forecast the amount of tripmaking which will result from one project or another, and in turn to estimate the travel benefits and revenue associated with this amount of travel, it is necessary to make use of travel demand, benefit, and revenue functions. As we shall see, these relationships are intimately related, both conceptually and analytically. More simply, trips are demanded (under different conditions of price and service) only because they have value or give benefit to travelers or shippers; thus, one might say that the prospective value of trips inherently gives rise to the demand.

Also, it is important to view travel demand as a conditional tripmaking relationship, dependent upon the price of and service afforded by the transport system, attributes of potential tripmakers, and the characteristics of the potential destinations.

Development of Cost and Price Functions

Cost and, in turn, price functions are fundamental to an appropriate analysis and evaluation of technological alternatives, operating strategies, and pricing policies. Moreover, they are requisite to investment planning in which the aim is to search for the "best" project.

Such functions must be developed in three stages. First, engineering knowledge is required in order to specify the various technological devices and facilities which can be built and operated to handle varying amounts of volume and levels of service. From this knowledge, the labor and material inputs (i.e., the factors of production) required to provide different levels of volume and service can be determined.

Second, by applying factor prices (i.e., the prices of the factors of production) to the material and labor inputs, cost functions can be determined; these functions indicate the costs of providing different levels of volume and service.

Third, it is necessary to develop the relationship between price and cost for different pricing policies and then to apply these relations to the cost functions; the resulting price functions can be used to determine the price at different levels of volume and service for each cost-related pricing policy.

Travel Forecasting or Determination of Equilibrium and Performance Conditions

Once the demand and price functions have been specified for a region and its transport system, they may be interrelated in order to determine the resultant or equilibrium travel volume and performance conditions. In some sense we may think of this process as forecasting the expected travel volume, price, and service levels which will result from the interaction of "supply" and "demand," as well as the accompanying totals for costs, benefits, and revenues. Ideally, we need to understand how "supply" and "demand" interact, and thus how cost, benefit, and revenue totals change, with respect to different technological conditions, service or quality levels, pricing policies, and socioeconomic levels. It clearly would be desirable to be able to pinpoint both year-to-year (or intertemporal) and hour-to-hour (or intratemporal) variations in the resultant usage, service, and thus cost, benefit, and revenue totals.

Determination of Commensurate Values for Present and Future Benefits and Costs

For most transportation projects policy or improvement actions will affect volume levels (of the project in question, as well as other services) and, in turn, benefits and costs over a fairly long time horizon. Also, the cost and benefit streams are likely to vary over the years, depending on the scale of any initial construction, on future maintenance or rehabilitation, and so forth. Given the time value of resources (i.e., the fact that resources today are valued differently than equivalent ones at a later date), it will be necessary to place the year-to-year benefits and costs that will accompany the project over its planning life on a commensurate value scale. This is especially important when attempting to evaluate alternative projects, some of which are more capital intensive in early years and others of which require heavier capital commitments in later years, and so forth.

Examination of the Incidence of Benefits and Costs

Earlier a distinction was made between efficiency and distributional matters, that is, between overall or aggregate economic gain and who gains or loses from one policy action or another. While the issue of incidence is important and will affect political decisions about which policy is or is not appropriate, the fact of the matter is that the issue is not easily amendable to objective analysis. Put simply, what seems fair or equitable to one man may not seem fair or equitable to another. There is no universally accepted yardstick for defining equity.

Despite this disagreement, it seems reasonable to suggest that the analyst, while determining the aggregate economic effects of different policy actions or programs, should endeavor whenever and wherever possible to examine and to provide information on the differential impacts of projects. This information should be as explicit and detailed as is possible so as to indicate which people or groups of people will accrue the benefits and which will pay the costs, without regard for any judgment about the "goodness" or "fairness" of the outcome(s). To follow this approach is to recognize the importance of equity issues but to avoid having the analyst make normative judgments.

1-2 PROBLEMS IN DEFINING THE ANALYST'S POINT OF VIEW AND IN IDENTIFYING RELEVANT COSTS AND BENEFITS

At the outset it is of critical importance to pinpoint which consequences stemming from any policy action should be included in the list of benefit and costs to be used for judging economic feasibility. Essentially, this involves a judgment about *whose point of view* should be taken and, in turn, about which costs and benefits should be considered as internal to the project and which would be regarded as external. For instance, when deciding whether it is worthwhile to use (limited) available funds and resources in one way or another or to withhold their use until some future time, an individual tends to allocate his total resources in a fashion which is the most desirable *to him*. On a larger scale a private industrial firm operates in a similar fashion but considers each alternative use of its resources from *its own* "point of view" or in terms of the most "worthwhile" or profitable investment to *its owners* (or to those whose funds or resources are being risked).[1]

Importantly, as the individual or group of individuals making investments changes, a shift in "point of view" may occur and the final decision may change accordingly.

The problem of specifying whose interests are at stake or to whom the investment is worthwhile is more complex when public projects are considered. For example, *should* a state highway agency, in deciding among various highway projects (including that of doing nothing), consider the consequences to the agency, those to the state highway users, those to the entire state populace, or those to the nation (or world) as a whole? Also, *should* the state highway agency consider the economic feasibility of only the *state agency's* expenditures on construction, maintenance, and administration or should it be concerned with the feasibility of the total outlays and with the overall consequences, whether state, federal, or local and whether public or private?

The arguments for and against different viewpoints are numerous. E. L. Grant persuasively argues that the economy of public works proposals (whether city, country, or state) "ideally, perhaps," should be considered

---

[1]This view is somewhat oversimplified since it fails to take account of the fact that a firm's managers or officers may follow a different strategy in order to assure job security, gain power, and so on. See Herbert A. Simon, "A Behavioral Model of Rational Choice," *Quarterly Journal of Economics* **69** (1955).

from the point of view of all of the people in the country.[2] T. E. Kuhn takes
what at first glance appears to be a stronger stand:[3]

> *Any public body should, logically, adopt the viewpoint of the economy as a*
> *whole. The very term* public *(authority, agency, or enterprise) implies respon-*
> *sibility extending over the community at large. Indeed, "promotion and protec-*
> *tion of the public interest," or similar principles, are by law supposed to guide*
> *the conduct of public bodies. Perhaps even more compellingly, public enter-*
> *prise agencies are creatures of legislatures and through them answerable to the*
> *community. Indeed, under common law all business is public; only an arbi-*
> *trary distinction separates private and public business. The distinction is*
> *suspended when "private" businesses, such as power, gas, telephone and tele-*
> *graph companies, are regulated "in the public interest." That public enterprise*
> *should adopt a public viewpoint appears, then, to be self-evident. The point is*
> *salient: it has significant practical implications and invokes basic principles. It*
> *dictates that normally no costs or gains in public enterprise can be classified*
> *as external and disregarded.*

While in the above paragraph Kuhn makes no distinction between
local, state, or federal (public) agencies, and thus implies that *all* public
agencies (whether local, state, or federal) *should* take the *national* economy viewpoint, the manner in which he distinguishes between internal
and external costs and gains (benefits) elsewhere in his text suggests that
at times he feels it is proper for a public agency to view only the costs and
benefits to its own economy. This implication is supported by a metropolitan transport example in which intergovernment transfers are treated as
benefits.[4]

An alternative position might be to consider the feasibility from the
point of view of *those whose funds or resources are being risked*. That is,
the feasibility might be judged in terms of the welfare of those who must
bear the burden of having foregone more worthwhile opportunities or of
financing capital investments or future operating expenses, should the
expected benefits not materialize. This would appear to be the position of
Richard Zettel, who noted:[5]

> *The appropriate objective is to maximize benefits to the users who are called*
> *upon to finance the program. In some circumstances it may be appropriate to*
> *seek contributions from the general treasury to finance that portion of the*
> *project which is justified on the grounds of general (rather than user) benefit.*

[2]E. L. Grant et al., *Principles of Engineering Economy*, Wiley, New York, 1982, pp. 494–495.
[3]T. E. Kuhn, *Public Enterprise Economics and Transport Problems*, University of California
Press, Berkeley, 1962, p. 13. Earlier on page 8, Kuhn noted, definitionally, that "external values
can be defined as signals not received by the decision maker but by other parties, and internal
values as effects that are of definite concern to him."
[4]Ibid., Table 2 and pages 55–56.
[5]Richard Zettel, "Highway Benefit and Cost Analysis as an Aid to Investment Decision," Reprint
No. 49, Institute of Transportation and Traffic Engineering, University of California, reprinted
from Reports, International Study Week in Traffic Engineering, 3d, Stressa, Italy, 1956.

Following Zettel's position, with a pay-as-you-go or fully self-financed highway user tax financing program, only the user's viewpoint would appear to be relevant. However, should the highway program be financed out of general state or federal funds (or should highway bonds be floated and backed by the full faith and credit of the state or federal government), then the viewpoint of the entire state or federal populace would be appropriate. In general, to take the point of view of those whose funds or resources are being risked will result in taking a "total public viewpoint," but the definition does permit a more restrictive position to be taken where it is appropriate (such as with privately financed toll facilities or with public facilities supported entirely through user tax revenues).[6]

It is our view that worthwhileness should be defined from the point of view of those whose funds *or* resources (present or future) are being risked, which may include only the users or the users, taxpayers, and other affected individuals. Thus, we suggest two principles for economic analysis of projects:

1. The relevant items of "cost" or "benefit" are those specific factors or elements which are both affected by a project and valued by those whose resources are being risked (i.e., the "owners").

2. Cost and benefit items should be valued in relation to the relative importance and value which the affected individuals (the owners) place on them.

In practice, the "owners" of a project (or a higher authority) place constraints on the system; in such cases these constraints must be considered in analysis. Rather than include some arbitrary objective alongside the other terms and give it some relative scale value, the "owners" may prefer merely to maximize their net benefit, for example, subject to some specified condition. In a sense this specification would be somewhat analogous to certain types of government regulation and is directly akin to establishing certain social objectives, *regardless of the impacts*. While these constraints, or social objectives, will not directly enter the economic analysis, their economic consequences should be accounted for in the overall decision-making process; the economic value of social objectives can at least be determined by imputation.

It should be evident that analysis for private projects is distinctly simpler and more straightforward than for public programs. Generally, "costs" for private projects include money outlays which must be made to obtain the capital, labor, and service inputs, or to compensate others for

---

[6]By contrast, the Doyle Report emphatically concluded that "in consonance with the basic objective of Federal policy, governmental actions at *all* levels should be taken in the national public interest. Conflicting interest *must, of necessity, yield to the greater good of all*." [Emphasis added] from *National Transportation Policy*, Report for the U.S. Senate Committee on Interstate and Foreign Commerce, U.S. Government Printing Office, Washington, D.C., January 1961.

damages of one sort or another; the "benefits" include the money revenues (or other savings or types of payment) received as a result of the project investment. In general, only items which in some way are actually translated into or can be expressed in money terms are included in the economic analysis.

For the case of public projects at the federal level, all factors or elements of concern which have value to the "owning" public and which the *public would willingly pay* (in a broad sense) to gain, or to keep from losing, will be included. Thus, social and political objectives can meaningfully be included in economic analysis, provided, of course, that the owning public would be willing to pay for them or at least to trade off some other object of interest or value where conflicts occur. Generally, then, social or political factors should enter the analysis only in those instances where society would be willing to forego dollars and cents, other assets, or other values in their stead. This assumption is made, first, since most tangible and "intangible" objects of concern have a history of experience and have been valued at the marketplace (at least implicitly); thus, there is a place to start in establishing relative if not absolute value scales (a problem that simply cannot be ignored, one way or another). Second, this assumption is made to point out that factors of presumed concern to the owning public and for which they are *not* willing to forego something else of value (which *must* be foregone to achieve the object of concern) are just that—presumed rather than real. For instance, a commonly expressed view is that we *want* to keep our air clean and our views unobstructed. Having said this, however, it does not follow that society does *in fact* value clean air or an unobstructed view to the point that it would be willing to forego the resources necessary to retain the unobstructed view or to keep the air clean. That is, if we would be unwilling to forfeit other resources in order to keep from losing our view or clean air, then the value of the view must be regarded as presumed rather than real.

By this discussion, it is not implied that decisions involving "political" or "social" values are improper or avoidable. Rather, it is to emphasize that decisions to expend additional resources in order to meet or achieve some social goal or objective imply at least a limiting value of the social ends (since the extra costs could have been avoided by sacrificing the social objective). Also, the earlier remarks were intended to emphasize that lack of willingness to "pay" for some social objective (or at least to forego something else of value in order to achieve that goal) suggests the lack of real value associated with the objective. In any case the analyst bears the responsibility of defining and quantifying (directly or by imputation) as many of these aspects as is practical.

Also, with such a view being taken of the transport problem and of public investment in transport facilities, one might ask whether it is appropriate to include within the analysis and framework some consideration of other city planning (or community) objectives and to account for any interactions between transport investment, the spatial organization of business, industry and residences, and the resulting economic or social effects. Clearly, these system effects should be part of the overall system analysis if the public welfare (in terms of economic efficiency or incidence of costs and benefits) is affected over and above that as measured by examining only transportation costs and benefits. While these sorts of external effects differ only in character and extent from other more readily identifiable externalities which stem from transportation facility improvement and usage (such as air pollution), it must be said that it is considerably more difficult to establish reliable relationships between transportation and land use.

In fact, the present state of the art in transportation and land-use planning is such that at best only limited statistical correlations can be shown and only approximate and tentative hypotheses about dependent relationships can be made. This is not to say that such relationships never existed; the historical record of the impact of new transportation technologies contradicts this. However, there is considerable doubt whether new transportation investments will have substantial land use or locational impacts in an environment with relatively good general transportation facilities such as the United States. Moreover, any development which does occur due to such new investments is *not* likely to represent a net change since the development may only be relocated from other sites; changes in land rents near new facilities are quite likely to be of this nature and thus represent no net benefit.[7] Accordingly, little attempt will be made to introduce these diverse sorts of planning issues unless there appears to be sufficiently strong evidence of dependent relationships and of measurable and identifiable externalities.

[7]The literature on this subject is substantial and controversial. For reviews of the literature, see A. Altshuler et al., *The Urban Transportation System*, The MIT Press, Cambridge, Mass., 1979, Chap. 10; M. D. Cheslow and M. L. Olsson, "Transportation and Metropolitan Development," Working Paper 5049-07, The Urban Institute, 1975; or G. Fromm (ed.), *Transport Investment and Economic Development*, The Brookings Institution, Washington, D.C., 1965.

CHAPTER 2

THE USAGE OF TRANSPORTATION SYSTEM FACILITIES—USER COST AND TRAVEL DEMAND

An essential component of transportation system design and investment analysis is an estimate of the patronage or vehicular volume which will be attracted by different facilities and operating policies. "How many people will be attracted?" is one of the most common initial questions asked of planners, and the answer provides a starting point for detailed design and analysis studies. Unfortunately, our knowledge about travel demand is meager, and obtaining accurate forecasts of future user volumes is quite difficult. This does not imply that a planner can ignore the problem of estimating volumes, because the benefits and costs stemming from different transportation system alternatives are quite sensitive to the resulting volume of travel. Nor does the difficulty of forecasting imply that a planner must devote a great deal of time and resources to the prediction of future travel volumes; in many cases experience and a proper understanding of the factors influencing travel demand may be used to obtain sufficiently accurate demand forecasts.

To understand the factors influencing travel demand, it is important to consider tripmaking decisions from the point of view of the users or tripmakers. Adopting this perspective is not easy. For example, a transit manager is concerned with the proper operation of and costs incurred for the transit system as a whole. In contrast, a patron makes the decision to use the transit system on the basis of the door-to-door service provided between his specific origin and his particular destination, rather than on just the average service quality of the transit portion of the trip. Moreover, the patron considers aspects of his trip which are not affected by the transit system's operation, such as his safety in walking to and from the transit stops and the relative attractiveness of alternative travel modes. Also, users consider the time and effort involved in travel, in addition to the fares charged for service. In this chapter, then, we shall consider tripmaking from the point of view of travelers and the resulting effects on volume and costs to users (as distinct from the costs to society, which are dealt with in Chapter 4).

2-1 DEMAND FUNCTIONS

A demand *function* expresses the dependent relationship between the
volume or quantity of tripmaking to be demanded and the various factors
which influence the quantity demanded, including the price of travel.[1]
(Here, the *user* cost is regarded as being equivalent to the price of travel.
The terms will be used interchangeably.) Thus, travel *demand* is a measure of the desire of a group of people for tripmaking under a particular set
of circumstances. If these circumstances change, then the travel demand
also changes. The usefulness of a demand function is that the resulting
volume may be predicted for a wide range of conditions; that is, the
demand function expresses the number of trips (or travel) which will be
desired (i.e., demanded) at each level of the various factors influencing
travel demand. Note that travel demand is *not* a fixed level of "need"
which must be satisfied; as underlying circumstances (including the price
of travel) change, the amount of tripmaking also changes.

Figure 2-1 illustrates in its simplest form a demand function for tripmaking between, say, a given pair of origin and destination points, at a
specific time of day and for a particular purpose. It is not necessary that
the demand function be a straight line, although this is a simple and fairly
useful functional form. This demand function (or curve) assumes a particular level and distribution of income, population, and socioeconomic
characteristics. It is an *aggregate* demand curve, representing the volume

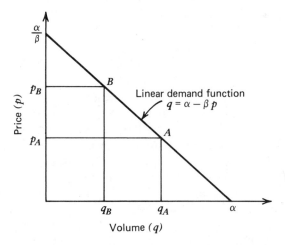

Figure 2-1. An illustrative demand function.

[1]Appendix I describes the use of such mathematical functions throughout this book.

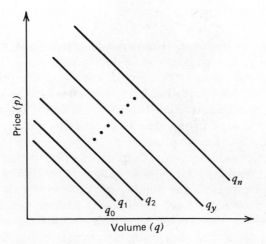

Figure 2-2. An illustration of demand function shifts. Note: the slope β_y is not necessarily constant; $q_y = \alpha_y - \beta_y p$ for $y = 0, 1, \ldots, n$.

of trips demanded at different prices by a particular group or aggregate population, including travelers having high or low urgencies for tripmaking. Some people among those wanting to make trips will value the trips differently due to variations in income or the ability to pay for the trip, and others because of differences in the urgency of the trip or the value of getting to their destination, and so forth. Functionally,

$$q = \alpha - \beta p \qquad (2\text{-}1)$$

where q is the quantity of trips demanded when the price is p; α and β are constant demand parameters, which, in practice, must be estimated to find appropriate numerical values. This demand function is useful in predicting the effect of price changes; at a price of p_A, a volume q_A of trips will be demanded. With a price increase to p_B, volume will decline to q_B. Note that there is a price level such that the volume demanded is zero in Equation (2-1); this price level is α/β in Figure 2-1. Above that level one can assume that no trips are purchased.

Changes in population, income, or other socioeconomic characteristics could result in shifts or movement of the demand curve, as shown in Figure 2-2. That is, the demand could increase (or decrease) in response to such changes. We could illustrate these shifts by a three-dimensional drawing in which the quantity of tripmaking was jointly dependent upon the trip price and level of population. Such a drawing would be complicated, however, so a functional form is used to represent a demand function:

$$q = f(p, \text{SE}) \qquad (2\text{-}2)$$

where q is the quantity of trips to be demanded when the trip price is p and with socioeconomic conditions SE. For the simple linear function of Figure 2-2,

$$q_y = \alpha_y - \beta_y p \qquad (2\text{-}3)$$

where α_y and β_y are the parameters for the socioeconomic conditions of potential travelers in year y.

Trip price in the demand function may be thought of as the overall or combined payment in time, effort, and money expenses which a traveler considers when making a trip. When combined, these components represent the "user cost" a traveler will face. Importantly, it is not necessary to combine these components of "user cost" into a single price; in the same way that a different demand curve could be shown for each level of the socioeconomic variables, a demand curve might be constructed with respect to money expenses or fares, given a particular level of effort and travel time. However, an overall price or user cost measure is useful for explaining demand changes, and we shall use it repeatedly. As we shall later see, the analytical framework is greatly simplified by making use of a combined price including time, effort, and money. Obviously, though, constructing a measure of trip price or user cost implies that the various time, effort, and money expenses can somehow be placed on a commensurate value scale, a problem discussed in Section 2-3.

It is possible to construct demand functions for individuals as well as groups. Thus, the demand curve in Figure 2-1 (with a suitable change in the parameters α and β) might represent the annual number of trips demanded by an individual from his home to a destination, given his socioeconomic circumstances. It is also possible to focus on a particular trip and consider the *probability*, or chance, that an individual might take the trip as a function of the trip price. Such *disaggregate* or individual demand functions may be summed or combined to yield the aggregate or market demand function for a population. Mathematically, the aggregate demand function is the sum of the individuals' demands; thus,

$$q(p) = \sum_{i=1}^{N} q_i(p) = q_1(p) + q_2(p) + \cdots + q_N(p) \qquad (2\text{-}4)$$

where $q(p)$ is the aggregate demand at a price p, N is the number of individuals in the population, $q_i(p)$ is the demand for travel by the ith individual at a price p, and Σ indicates a summation of $q_i(p)$ for $i=1$ to

$i=N$ (as described in Appendix I). Assuming that an individual's demand is linearly related to the price, the aggregate demand would be

$$q = \sum_{i=1}^{N} q_i(p) = \sum_{i=1}^{N} (\alpha_i - \beta_i p)$$
$$= (\alpha_1 - \beta_1 p) + (\alpha_2 + \beta_2 p) + \cdots + (\alpha_N - \beta_N p) \tag{2-5}$$
$$= \alpha - \beta p$$

where α and β are simply sums of the individual α_i and β_i parameters.

The unit of measurement for the quantity or volume of tripmaking deserves some attention. Unless otherwise noted, the measurement units used here will be *separate* and *different* person (or, where appropriate, vehicle) trips *per hour* desiring to move between a particular pair of zones or points along some transport system facility. An hourly time interval for the quantity of trips is somewhat arbitrary, but it is important in many urban and intercity travel situations in order to reflect the changes in congestion and other service conditions that affect tripmaking. For example, to use the volume of daily trips would often mask large peak and off-peak differentials in travel time and comfort. Use of other terms such as *trips*, *travelers*, *tripmakers*, or *tripmaking* are all intended to correspond to this definition and description. However, it is also important to note that this specification of measurement units implies that each vehicle trip will involve an equal number of passengers (that is, identical car occupancy). This point is discussed further below.

As a numerical example, suppose that a group had an aggregate demand function of

$$q = 100 - 10p \tag{2-6}$$

At a price $p = 5$, a total of $q = 100 - 10(5) = 100 - 50 = 50$ trips per hour would be demanded.

2-2 SENSITIVITY OF TRAVEL DEMAND

Generally, demand functions are downward sloping with respect to price, as illustrated in Figures 2-1 and 2-2. Thus, as a trip requires greater effort, time, and/or expense, tripmaking will decline. A useful descriptor for explaining the degree of sensitivity to a change in price (or other factor) is the *elasticity* of demand. Definitionally, the elasticity of demand with respect to price, or ϵ_p, is

ϵ_p = percentage change in quantity of trips demanded
which accompanies a 1% change in price

$$= \frac{\partial q/q}{\partial p/p}$$

$$= \frac{\partial q}{\partial p}\frac{p}{q} \tag{2-7}$$

where ∂q is the change in the number of trips which accompanies ∂p, the change in price. Also, for small changes in price and volume, $\partial q/q$ and $\partial p/p$ (when multiplied by 100) are the percentage changes in volume and price, respectively. The calculus derivative, $\partial q/\partial p$, indicates the effect on q of a very small change in price; Appendix I contains a further explanation.

In practice, there are several slightly different definitions of elasticity, depending upon the information used to estimate the elasticity. *Point* elasticity uses the calculus derivative to describe the elasticity at a point on the demand function and applies, strictly speaking, only to infinitesimally small changes in price; or

$$\epsilon_p = \frac{\partial q}{\partial p}\frac{p}{q} \tag{2-8}$$

Arc elasticity uses two points on the demand curve to calculate elasticity; one common definition is

$$\epsilon_p = \frac{\Delta q/\overline{q}}{\Delta p/\overline{p}} = \frac{\overline{p}\Delta q}{\overline{q}\Delta p} \tag{2-9}$$

where $\overline{p}$ and $\overline{q}$ are the average of the "before" and "after" prices and volumes, respectively, and Δq and Δp are the changes in q and p, respectively, between the two points. The various elasticity definitions yield values which are usually quite similar, but the values are identical only for very small price changes.

When the elasticity is less than −1 (i.e., more negative than −1), the demand is described as being *elastic*, meaning that the resulting percentage change in quantity of tripmaking will be larger than the percentage change in price. In this case demand is relatively *sensitive* to price changes. Contrarily, when the elasticity is between 0 and −1, the demand is described as being *inelastic*, or relatively insensitive, meaning that the percentage change in quantity of tripmaking will be less than the percentage change in price. The demand is perfectly elastic when the elasticity is minus infinity, meaning that small changes in price will result in infinitely large changes in tripmaking. Finally, if the elasticity is 0, then the demand is perfectly inelastic, meaning that small changes in price will have no effect on the quantity of tripmaking. While many of our planning processes and benefit-cost analyses assume—implicitly if not explicitly—that the quantity of tripmaking remains constant even though the prices may change (i.e., the demand is perfectly inelastic), it should be recognized that it seldom would be accurate to characterize demand as being perfectly inelastic.

For illustrative purposes, these and other relationships will be examined while using a simple linear demand function, though little violence will be done to the development of general principles by assuming linear demand.

For a linear demand function we can determine the elasticity with respect to price for Equation (2-1) by using Equations (2-5) and (2-7); by taking the derivative, we determine the point elasticity or the elasticity when the price is p, which is

$$\epsilon_p = \frac{\partial q}{\partial p} \frac{p}{q} = \frac{(-\beta)p}{q} \qquad (2\text{-}10)$$

or, after substituting for p, using Equation (2-1),

$$\epsilon_p = 1 - \frac{\alpha}{q} \qquad (2\text{-}11)$$

so that price elasticity is only a function of q and the parameter α in the latter case.

For the linear demand case it can be shown that when q is equal to zero, the elasticity is equal to minus infinity, when q is equal to α (the intercept on the horizontal or x axis) the elasticity is 0, and when q is equal to $\alpha/2$ (half the intercept on the horizontal or x axis), the elasticity is -1, or what is called unit elasticity, the point dividing the elastic and inelastic portions of the demand function. Thus, the upper half of the demand function is elastic and the lower half is inelastic (Fig. 2-3). For example, with the parameter values of Equation (2-6) and a price $p = 5$, the elasticity is $\epsilon_p = 1 - 100/50 = 1 - 2 = -1$, which is the unit elastic point.

From all of the above, the practical application and usefulness of knowledge about demand functions and elasticities should be all too evident. For instance, demand functions together with the user price permit us to determine how much travel can be anticipated, while elasticities permit us to estimate the percentage change in tripmaking which stems from a price change. Moreover, since the facility costs are dependent upon the expected level of usage, demand functions are necessary to anticipate costs as well.

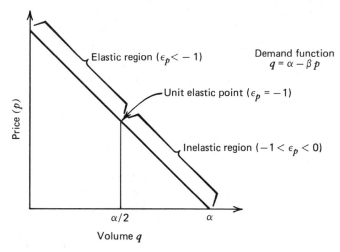

Figure 2-3. Price elasticity ranges for a linear demand curve.

2-3 "USER COSTS" OF TRAVEL

Earlier the sensitivity of the amount of tripmaking to changes in the price of travel was emphasized. Travelers and potential travelers are responsive or sensitive to levels of and changes in price, where the price of travel is interpreted as the full private user cost of travel, including time, effort, and monetary expense.

The user costs of a trip are usually estimated as a weighted linear combination of travel time components and monetary payments for a trip, such as

$$p = vt + f \tag{2-12}$$

where p is the price or user cost of travel (in dollars) for a usage level of q, t is the travel time, f is the fare or monetary payment, and v is a user time cost parameter. Also, v represents the unit value of travel time (in dollars per unit of time). For a user cost function, it is not necessary to assume a linear combination of time and fare as in Equation (2-12); it is done mainly for simplicity at this stage of the presentation.

The value of the parameter v in Equation (2-12) is usually called the value of time and may be estimated by observing user choices (as discussed in Chapter 12). For example, it is usually the case that (up to some point) travelers would willingly pay a toll or higher parking fee in order to reduce their trip time or walking time on a given trip.

Once the various travel time components, monetary charges, and appropriate parameter values are known, it is a straightforward calculation to find the user cost of travel for a particular trip, by using Equation (2-12), for example. That is, given knowledge about the fare and trip time, the user cost can easily be calculated. However, estimation of travel times requires considerable attention, due to the effects of crowding or congestion.

On virtually all transportation facilities user travel times increase as greater volumes use the facilities. For a roadway, vehicles begin to interfere with one another, causing each vehicle to slow down. The resulting congestion or traffic jam may increase average travel time enormously, especially as the volume of usage approaches the roadway capacity. Moreover, transit systems, terminal operations, and virtually all other facilities exhibit similar congestion effects. With transit systems, for examples, additional patrons mean that vehicles must stop more often and longer, thereby increasing passengers' waiting and riding times. At still higher volumes patrons experience severe crowding in the vehicles and some may have to wait for following vehicles before boarding.

The consequence of such congestion effects is that the user cost of making a trip tends to increase as the volume using a particular facility increases. Each person or vehicle using a facility must endure the average delay and expense of using the facility, including the congestion effects caused by the total volume or flow of the facility. Thus, the introduction of additional traffic or flow onto a facility will increase user costs (for each and every tripmaker) to the extent of both the costs incurred by the new tripmakers and the additional costs imposed on all others due to congestion.

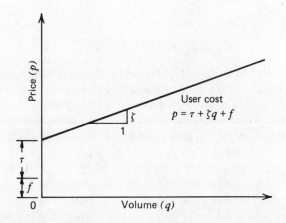

Figure 2-4. An illustrative user cost or price–volume relationship.

In the literature of transportation systems analysis this dependence is summarized by price–volume functions, or relationships which express the user cost or price of travel on particular facilities as a function of its usage. To calculate price–volume relations, it is often useful to first develop performance functions, such as Equation (2-13), which are mathematical expressions relating the travel time to different volume levels on a facility. Assuming a linear relationship between travel time and facility usage (again for analytical simplicity), we get

$$t = t_0 + \delta q \qquad (2\text{-}13)$$

where t is the average travel time for a usage level of q, t_0 is the travel time for low or near-zero volume levels on the facility, and δ is a travel time congestion parameter for that facility. In turn, a performance function [such as Eq. (2-13)] may be substituted into a user cost function [such as Eq. (2-12)]. The resulting user cost or price–volume relation would be as follows:

$$\begin{aligned} p &= vt + f \\ &= v(t_0 + \delta q) + f \\ &= vt_0 + v\delta q + f \end{aligned} \qquad (2\text{-}14)$$

or

$$p = \tau + \zeta q + f \qquad (2\text{-}15)$$

where p is the user price at a usage level of q, f is money expense, τ is a constant parameter representing the value of the minimum trip time, and ζ is a parameter representing the joint effects of travel time increases and the unit time value (so that $\zeta = v\delta$). Figure 2-4 illustrates this user cost or price–volume function.

As indicated in Equation (2-15), the user cost or price will be dependent both upon the level of usage, q, and the monetary charges, f. To make matters worse, the money charges (whether for transit fares, tolls, or parking charges, etc.) may be and often are dependent upon the usage of the facilities as well as their capacity. Discussion of this aspect will be deferred to later chapters which deal with pricing and investment policies.

2-4 DETERMINATION OF EQUILIBRIUM VOLUMES AND TRAVEL CONDITIONS: AN INTRODUCTION

Given some transportation facility (as well as fleet size, operating schedules, etc.), the volume of travelers which use it (that is, the equilibrium flow as opposed to its potential flow) is determined from joint consideration of both the user cost and demand functions. Simply, equilibrium flow will be determined by the interaction of demand functions (which indicate the volume of tripmaking at each price level), on the one hand, and of user cost or price–volume functions (which describe the prices which will face the tripmaker at different volumes or aggregate levels of tripmaking), on the other.

Determination of equilibrium flow or the actual volume which will use a facility (and of the benefit or value which will actually accrue to its users, as well as the ultimate costs of providing the transport service) depends on a joint consideration of price and demand functions. Also, it is necessary that the price and demand functions introduced above have dependent and independent variables which are measured on a common scale; for example, the unit price travelers will have to pay for using a particular facility (as shown on the price–volume curve) must be stated in the same overall units as the price travelers will be willing to pay (as shown on the demand curve).

Similarly, there must be a correspondence between the output or quantity units for the price–volume and demand functions, which in this case will be person trips per hour moving between a common set of origins and destinations. Further, only passenger movement will be appropriate for this two-dimensional analysis of the interaction between price–volume and demand functions. Restriction to passenger-carrying vehicles will greatly simplify the construction of suitable cost and price–volume functions, but suggests the necessity of adding another dimension to the demand functions, at least for private automobile transport. Specifically, with the output measure in person trips for both the price–volume and demand functions, implicit in any two-dimensional demand curve (such as the one in Figure 2-1) is that the number of passengers per vehicle is presumed to remain constant for all trips made during the hour. We should recognize that the number of passengers per vehicle trip varies from hour to hour, from one vehicle to another, and from one income level to another (and thus from year to year as incomes and preferences change, etc.), but we shall ignore these variations in this introductory chapter. If a mixed stream of freight and passenger vehicles of different types were used, the price functions would have to be formulated in terms of the volume of each type, and would have to be related to demand functions for each type of movement with all cross-relations and interactions being accounted for. These less simplified conditions would complicate this presentation to the point of blurring the framework and methodology.

To illustrate in a general way the interaction between price–volume and demand functions and to indicate equilibrium conditions, consider the price–volume and demand conditions as they presently exist for many if not most public highways and transit facilities and as they are portrayed in Figure 2-5 for some facility x. Facility x is assumed to have a fixed

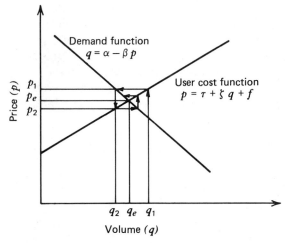

Figure 2-5.   Illustration of equilibrium demand and supply.

amount of capacity, a particular operating schedule, and so forth; thus, changes in the user cost or price stem merely from changes in travel time and delay due to changes in usage. We assume that demand is stable or constant from hour to hour and can be represented by one hourly demand function. This implies that demand does not fluctuate either hour to hour or year to year and that our pricing policy is such that the price–volume function is constant. Also, for the moment, we will consider only the short-run equilibrium conditions and leave until later an exploration of the consequences of system expansion or contraction.

For the simplified case in Figure 2-5 the equilibrium flow will be q_e and the equilibrium price will be p_e. That flow and price will stabilize—aside from stochastic or random effects—at (approximately) this level can be seen by assuming a different level of flow and considering the consequences. If the flow were q_1, for example, the resultant user price would be p_1; but if the price were p_1, only q_2 travelers would be willing to make that payment and travel. And, in turn, a flow of only q_2 would require a payment of only p_2, a price which would cause a flow above q_e but below q_1 to travel; and so forth. Iterations will continue in such a fashion until a price and flow level is determined which will be consistent with both price–volume and demand functions. The resulting movement towards equilibrium results in a distinctive "cobweb" appearance of lines as shown in Figure 2-5.

As a general rule, the volume of travel expected on a facility as well as the average price or user cost of travel is indicated by the intersection of the price–volume and demand functions, q_e and p_e in Figure 2-5. If more than one intersection exists, then multiple equilibria are possible, as discussed in Chapter 3. Usually, only one volume and price combination results in a stable or long-lasting equilibrium. A stable equilibrium exists whenever a slight perturbation—as described in the previous paragraph—results in price and volume changes which cause a return to the original equilibrium point. Not all price–volume and demand relationships will directly converge in a cobweb fashion on the equilibrium point as shown here. Certain very steep or very flat combinations might not do so. Chapter 6 discusses one such case.

Using the demand function ($q = 100 - 10p$) and price function ($p = 1.4 + 0.14q + f$), the equilibrium volume at a toll of, say, $f = \$0.50$, can be found as

$$q = 100 - 10p$$
$$= 100 - 10\,(1.4 + 0.14q + 0.5)$$
$$= 100 - 14 - 1.4q - 5$$
$$= 81 - 1.4q \qquad\qquad (2\text{-}16)$$

or

$$q = \frac{81}{2.4} = 33.75 \qquad\qquad (2\text{-}17)$$

with $p = \$6.63$ per trip and travel time $t = 0.4 + 0.04q = 0.4 + 0.04(33.75) = 1.75$ hours.

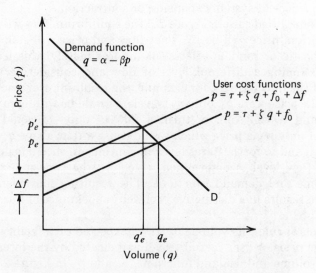

Figure 2-6. Illustration of the result of a fare increase.

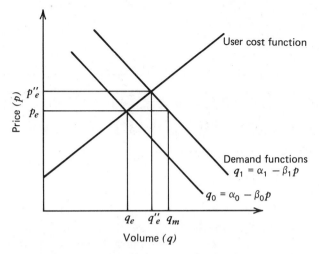

Figure 2-7. Illustration of the result of a population increase.

A few other examples may indicate the general procedure for estimating changes in equilibrium tripmaking. In Figure 2-6 the effect of a fare increase is illustrated by an upward shift in the user cost or price–volume curve. The demand curve remains unchanged, and the new travel volume is q'_e, or $q_e - q'_e$ less than the former volume. With an increase in population the demand curve will shift up in two-dimensional price–volume graphs. Such a shift is depicted in Figure 2-7, with a resulting increase in travel volume to q''_e. Note that the equilibrium travel price has also increased, to p''_e. Without considering a change in trip price, a volume of q_m would have been incorrectly estimated. Thus, changes in trip prices *must* simultaneously be considered in forecasting travel volumes; otherwise, forecasts are likely to be quite inaccurate.

CHAPTER 3

FURTHER DEVELOPMENT OF USER COST AND DEMAND FUNCTIONS

The previous chapter introduced the general concepts of travel demand, user costs, and equilibrium in the travel market. This chapter is intended to provide extensions and elaborations of those basic concepts. Discussion of the practical and empirical problems associated with estimating demand and user cost functions will be deferred until Chapters 11 and 12.

3-1 INTRATEMPORAL AND INTERTEMPORAL SHIFTS IN DEMAND FUNCTIONS

The determination of equilibrium volume and price levels described in Chapter 2 applies to a particular facility in a single time period. As will be seen, this analysis may be applied to analyze the effect of different facilities or services, a matter of great usefulness in evaluating alternative investments or operating policies. In addition, it is possible to analyze multiple time periods.

During a given time period or, say, during a year, demand may fluctuate dramatically from hour to hour, from day to day, or from season to season. These intratemporal demand fluctuations produce peak-load situations which commonly result in traffic congestion and crowding. Together with intertemporal or year-to-year fluctuations, this peaking phenomenon adds greatly to the complications of determining equilibrium flow and price levels. Yet its proper consideration is important for pricing, for the efficient utilization of facilities, and for investment planning.

Part (a) of Figure 3-1 illustrates demand functions during three different hours of the day and their interaction with the price–volume function; if the demand functions for all 24 hours were plotted, the quantity demanded versus time-of-day results would probably be somewhat as shown in part (b). The use of only one price–volume function in Figure 3-1a implies that the same amount of transport service is available in each of the three hours shown. To the extent that the available facilities change

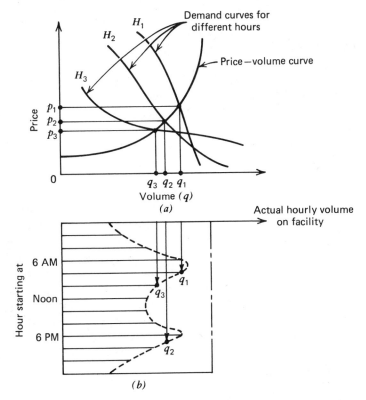

Figure 3-1. Illustration of short-term intratemporal demand and price–volume relation-ships. Note: for simplicity, demand curves for only 3 hours are shown.

from one hour to another (e.g., because of scheduling changes, express services only available during certain hours, ramp closings, etc.), then a separate price–volume function would be needed for each hour.

Different demand functions for different times of day have been hypothesized to reflect differences in trip values for various trip purposes and preferred times of travel. For example, it is reasonable to argue that work trips are more valuable and urgent than shopping trips and that they are somewhat restricted with respect to the times of day at which they can be made. Second, as will be discussed below, these hourly demand functions are interdependent and have cross-relations. (These interdependencies are not shown on Figure 3-1.) That is, the tripmaking during hour H_1 is partially dependent on the equilibrium flow conditions during the other hours of the day, and vice versa. Put on practical terms, the exact time of the home-to-work trip depends not only on the trip price and value of going to work exactly on time but also on the trip prices and values of

going to work somewhat earlier (and avoiding congestion) or going somewhat later (and avoiding congestion but getting one's pay docked); similarly, evening-out-to-dinner trips and shopping trips depend not only on
the trip price and trip value of travelling during the most "suitable" hour
but also on those during earlier and later hours. These cross-relation (or
cross-elasticity) problems clearly cannot be ignored in any realistic study,
just as those with respect to *modal cross-relations* cannot be overlooked in
any full analysis. (That is, as conditions get better or worse on one mode,
they affect not only the absolute amount of tripmaking but switches from
or to other modes as well.)

Shifts in demand from time period to time period (or, say, from year to
year) or intertemporal demand fluctuations can be represented by using
different demand functions for each time period. However, to simplify the
graphics, let us assume that we can represent the hourly demand functions
(as shown in Figure 3-1) for each year by some sort of aggregative or
averaged demand function; in this case, year to year or intertemporal
demand fluctuations would be as shown in Figure 3-2. The shift of the
demand function upward and to the right implies that population growth,
shift in land use, shifts in consumer preference patterns or income growth,
and so forth, would singly or in combination produce increases in demand
at a given price. For the hypothetical demand curve shifts and price-
volume curve shown in Figure 3-2, it is evident that the (aggregated or

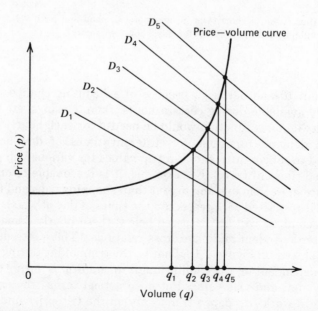

Figure 3-2.   Illustration of intertemporal demand and price–volume relationships. Note: D_t
is the demand curve for the tth year.

averaged) equilibrium flow during the early years would increase faster than during the later years (in both absolute and relative terms); such a result would be the usual result for *uniform* increases in demand and for facilities or systems whose capacity remains fixed over the years. Also, if the price–volume curve were vertical in the region of equilibrium, then no increases in equilibrium flow would occur over the years. Thus, shifts in demand—that is, shifts of the demand function—do *not necessarily* mean that shifts in the equilibrium flow (or volume actually using a facility) *will* occur.

3-2 DEMAND IN CHOICE SITUATIONS

The demand functions formulated earlier need to be extended in order to represent the conditions for choice situations in which the decision to use a particular alternative (such as a transit service) is dependent upon the price of that alternative as well as the price of competing opportunities (such as taxi service).

To begin, let us assume that travelers are choosing between two competing alternatives (say, between two modes or two times of day for travel) and that they consider the prices of both alternatives when deciding whether or not to travel, as well as which alternative to select. Then, an appropriate *set* of demand functions for alternatives x and y might be as follows:

$$q_x = \alpha_x + \beta_x p_x + \gamma_x p_y \qquad (3\text{-}1)$$

$$q_y = \alpha_y + \beta_y p_x + \gamma_y p_y \qquad (3\text{-}2)$$

where q_x and q_y represent the hourly volume of trips demanded for alternatives x and y, respectively, when the price of choice x is p_x and the price of choice y is p_y. The coefficients (α, β, and γ) are the parameters of the demand functions and must be estimated. Graphically, the first of these demand functions would be as shown in Figure 3-3 with volume q_x dependent on both modes' prices (p_x and p_y). Purely for analytical convenience, we have used a linear aggregate demand model and a binary choice situation. Disaggregate nonlinear demand models or multiple-choice situations might also be used, although the appropriate set of functions becomes more complicated. Chapter 11 contains examples of different demand model types.

The interpretation of such demand functions is straightforward. Assuming that the choices x and y represent two competing modes, it is clear that the volume on mode x depends not only on the mode x price but also on the mode y price (i.e., the price of the competing mode), unless of course the demand function coefficients are zero. (Where travelers are

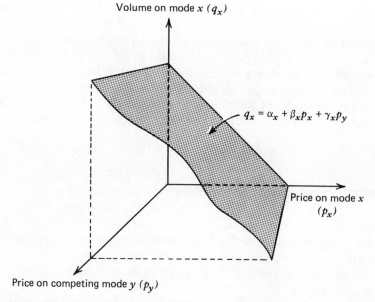

Figure 3-3.   Illustrative demand function for a binary mode choice situation.

choosing among many modes or times of day, some of the demand function coefficients may turn out to be zero.) Each of the two demand functions contains a *direct* demand relation and a *cross*-relation in which the former describes the effect of the price for the mode in question upon its volume of tripmaking and the latter describes the effect of the price for the competing mode upon the volume of mode x tripmaking. Thus, for mode x, the second term—or $\beta_x p_x$—is the direct relation and the third term—or $\gamma_x p_y$—is the cross-relation. *A priori*, we would expect the coefficients for the direct relations to be negative and those for the cross-relations to be positive. In this instance—for Equations (3-1) and (3-2)—the set of two direct relations and two cross-relations permit us to assess the absolute changes in tripmaking for both modes which result from a price change to either, as well as the shifts which occur between the two modes. Suppose that the price for mode y were to be *reduced* by Δp_y. Accordingly, the volume of mode y travel would increase by an amount $\gamma_y \Delta p_y$, and the volume of mode x travel would decrease by an amount $\gamma_x \Delta p_y$. (Recall that it is assumed that β_x and γ_y are negative and that the other coefficients are positive.) Moreover, the additional mode y travelers (equal to $\gamma_y \Delta p_y$) include some people who made no trips prior to the price drop and some who simply shifted from mode x; the latter trips are represented by the cross-relation term of $\gamma_x \Delta p_y$ and the former by the difference between the two terms, or $\gamma_y \Delta p_y - \gamma_x \Delta p_y$.

Elasticities for this set of demand functions can be computed in much the same fashion as indicated in Section 2.2, except that in choice situations there will be both direct elasticities and cross-elasticities; the former describes the sensitivity of a mode's volume with respect to its own price while the latter describes its sensitivity to the price of the competing mode. For competing modes x and y with demand functions as represented by Equations (3-1) and (3-2), respectively, we would have the following point elasticities:

$\epsilon_{p_x}^x$ = (direct) elasticity of mode x with respect to p_x

$$= \frac{\partial q_x/q_x}{\partial p_x/p_x} = \frac{\beta_x p_x}{q_x} \tag{3-3}$$

$\epsilon_{p_y}^x$ = (cross) elasticity of mode x with respect to p_y

$$= \frac{\partial q_x/q_x}{\partial p_y/p_y} = \frac{\gamma_x p_y}{q_x} \tag{3-4}$$

$\epsilon_{p_y}^y$ = (direct) elasticity of mode y with respect to p_y

$$= \frac{\partial q_y/q_y}{\partial p_y/p_y} = \frac{\gamma_y p_y}{q_y} \tag{3-5}$$

$\epsilon_{p_x}^y$ = (cross) elasticity of mode y with respect to p_x

$$= \frac{\partial q_y/q_y}{\partial p_x/p_x} = \frac{\beta_y p_x}{q_y} \tag{3-6}$$

The definition and interpretation of these elasticities is similar to the direct elasticity defined by Equation (2-7) in Chapter 2.

Whereas the direct demand relations and cross-relations provide information about the absolute changes in quantity demanded which stem from price changes, the elasticities describe the changes in percentage terms (i.e., the percentage change in quantity demanded which accompanies a 1% change in price). *A priori*, we would expect the direct elasticities to be negative and the cross-elasticities to be positive.

As a numerical illustration of demand functions in a choice situation, suppose that we are considering the demand for travel in different time periods over the course of a day. Price changes in one time-of-day period might affect the demand in other time-of-day periods. Thus, the aggregate hourly demand during the hth time-of-day period might be represented as follows:

$$q_h = \alpha_h - \beta_{h,1} p_1 - \beta_{h,2} p_2 - \cdots - \beta_{h,h} p_h - \cdots - \beta_{h,r} p_r \tag{3-7}$$

in which $h = 1, 2, \ldots,$ r. (In other words, there would be r time-of-day periods and r separate demand functions.) To illustrate the intricacies of such a set of demand functions, let us make use of the ones shown in Table 3-1.

Note that the demand in any one time-of-day period is not (necessarily) dependent upon the prices during *all* time-of-day periods but only upon the prices during those time-of-day periods which can be regarded as competing choices or substitutes. For instance, people who are considering whether to travel during the first time-of-day period (or from 6 to 7 AM) generally only consider two time-of-day choices, either then or from 7 to 9 AM. They are unaffected by the price during the third time-of-day period from 9 to 10 AM because they do not consider that choice as a reasonable substitute. Put differently, they would rather not travel at all than shift to a period later than 9 AM. By the same token, people who are considering travel during nighttime hours of 7 PM to 6 AM only think about the price during that time-of-day period, thus implying that there are no other time-of-day substitutes.

Most of the demand functions in Table 3-1 include both direct demand relations and cross-relations. The former tell us about the absolute volume changes which result from a change in price for the time-of-day period in question, while the latter tell us about the absolute volume changes which result from a change in price for other time-of-day periods. If you will, the later tell us about shifting peaks. As an example, consider the demand function for the first time-of-day period, or

$$q_1 = 4000 - 25p_1 + 15p_2 \tag{3-8}$$

The second term in this function, or $-25p_1$, tells us about increases or decreases in period 1 tripmaking which result from a price change in period 1. An increase in p_1 will decrease period 1 tripmaking and vice versa for a fall in p_1, everything else remaining constant (i.e., *given* that p_2, incomes, and all other relevant factors remain constant). The third term, or $+15p_2$, tells us about shifts to or from period 1 which result from changes in p_2. If the price in period 2 were to increase, then the amount of tripmaking in period 1 will increase because of shifts from period 2 to period 1; if the price in period 2 drops, then a shift in tripmaking from period 1 to period 2 will occur.

In particular, if p_1 is 15 and $p_2 = 12$, then $q_1 = 4000 - 25(15) + 15(12) = 3805$. The direct price elasticity is $\epsilon_{p_1}^1 = (-25)(15)/3805 = -0.1$ and the cross price elasticity is $\epsilon_{p_2}^1 = (15)(12)/3805 = 0.05$, the latter of which is positive and thereby indicates that an increase in p_2 will result in an increase in volume q_1.

3-3 DEMAND FUNCTIONS WITH RESPECT TO INDIVIDUAL PRICE COMPONENTS

Analysts often define demand functions with respect to individual user price components, such as travel time or monetary fares. While this

TABLE 3-1. Time-of-Day Demand Functions for a Transport Facility

h	Time-of-Day Period	Hourly Demand During Each Time-of-Day Period
1	6–7 AM	$q_1 = 4000 - 25p_1 + 15p_2$
2	7–9 AM	$q_2 = 7500 + 10p_1 - 21p_2 + 5p_3$
3	9–10 AM	$q_3 = 6500 \qquad\quad + 6p_2 - 18p_3$
4	10–2 PM	$q_4 = 6000 \qquad\qquad\qquad\quad + p_3 - 22p_4 + 2p_5$
5	2–3 PM	$q_5 = 6800 \qquad\qquad\qquad\qquad\qquad\qquad - 20p_5 + 4p_6$
6	3–6 PM	$q_6 = 8000 \qquad\qquad\qquad\qquad\qquad\qquad + 3p_5 - 20p_6 + 6p_7$
7	6–7 PM	$q_7 = 7000 \qquad\qquad\qquad\qquad\qquad\qquad\qquad\quad + 10p_6 - 24p_7$
8	7–6 AM	$q_8 = 3300 \qquad\qquad\qquad\qquad\qquad\qquad\qquad\qquad\qquad\qquad - 10p_8$

Note: q_h is the hourly quantity of trips to be demanded during the hth time-of-day period when the time-of-day prices are $p_1, p_2, \ldots, p_8$.

procedure adds complications and must be used with great care to insure that accurate forecasts are possible, it does have the advantages of focusing attention on the aspects of user cost which are of greatest interest (such as fare changes) and avoiding the explicit need to measure the user valuations of travel time and effort.

For example, it is possible (by means discussed in Chapter 11) to estimate demand curves with respect to fares, such as

$$q = \eta - \kappa f \tag{3-9}$$

This expression is similar in form to the demand function with respect to *price*, which includes all components of user cost as discussed earlier. The elasticity of demand with respect to fares or monetary charges would then be

$$\epsilon_f = \frac{\partial q/q}{\partial f/f} = \frac{\partial q}{\partial f}\frac{f}{q} \tag{3-10}$$

or, for the special case of the linear demand function of Equation (3-9):

$$\epsilon_f = \frac{-\kappa f}{q} \tag{3-11}$$

Alternatively, the elasticity of demand with respect to fare may also be calculated from the total user cost or price elasticity as

$$\epsilon_f = \epsilon_p \frac{f}{p} \tag{3-12}$$

so that the elasticity with respect to fares (or other components of user cost) is always *less* than the total price elasticity since fares f are only one component of total user cost or price p.

The elasticity of demand with respect to fare is quite useful in estimating the changes in volume and system revenues due to fare changes. Total revenues are defined as the volume using a particular service multiplied by the average fare or toll charge:

$$TR(q) = qf \tag{3-13}$$

or, using the inverted linear demand function of Equation (3-9) to get f,

$$TR(q) = qf = \frac{q\eta}{\kappa} - \frac{q^2}{\kappa} \tag{3-14}$$

Total revenue can be quite important to managers concerned with the *financial* situation of a particular service. An illustrative demand function with respect to fares and the associated system revenue functions are shown in Figure 3-4. Several important and general results may be derived:

1. The total revenues will be maximized when the quantity demanded is at the unit elastic point.

2. When the demand is *inelastic* before *and* after any price change, a fare increase will also raise the total revenues, while a fare decrease will reduce total revenues. In essence, when demand is inelastic, reductions in fare will induce more trips but the losses from a fare drop will outweigh the gains from the extra tripmaking; moreover, since a fare increase in case of inelastic demand would reduce trip-making, it also would reduce total costs, thus leading to an increase in total *net* revenues (or total revenues minus total costs) as well.

3. When the demand is *elastic* before *and* after any fare change, a fare reduction will increase total revenues while a fare hike will do the opposite; in this instance, however, little can be said about the effects on total *net* revenues since a fare drop would not only increase total revenues but also the amount of tripmaking and total costs.

4. When the demand is inelastic before a fare change and elastic after-wards (or vice versa), we do not know *a priori* whether the total revenues will increase, decrease, or remain the same; in this case it will be necessary to carry out the full set of calculations in order to know the result.

With regard to the change in total revenues, it is useful to introduce the marginal revenue curve. Marginal revenue is the change in total revenue resulting from a unit increase in volume and the accompanying change in fare:

$$mr(q) = \frac{\Delta TR(q)}{\Delta q}$$

$$= \frac{\partial TR(q)}{\partial q} \qquad (3\text{-}15)$$

Using Equation (3-13), marginal revenue can be further calculated as

$$mr(q) = \frac{\partial TR(q)}{\partial q} = f + q\frac{\partial f}{\partial q}$$

$$= f\left(1 + \frac{1}{\epsilon_f}\right) \qquad (3\text{-}16)$$

using differential calculus (as described in Appendix I).

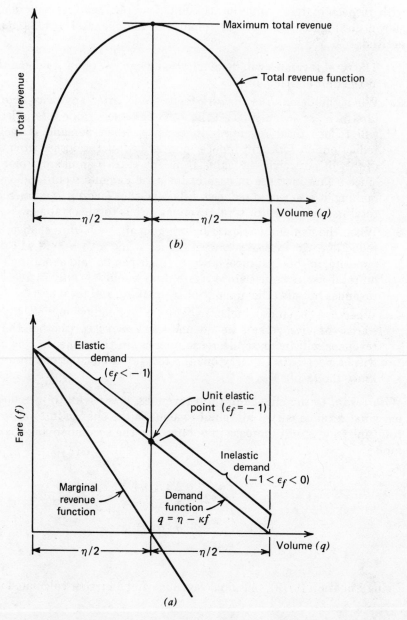

Figure 3-4. A demand function with respect to fare and the associated revenue functions.

38

With a linear demand curve such as Equation (3-9) and its total revenue curve [Eq. (3-14)], the marginal revenue curve is

$$mr(q) = \frac{\eta}{\kappa} - \frac{2q}{\kappa} \qquad (3\text{-}17)$$

which is linear and is shown in Figure 3-4. In the elastic demand range marginal revenues are positive and increased volumes (from reduced fares) *increase* revenue. In the inelastic demand range marginal revenues are negative and increased volumes (from reduced fares) *decrease* revenue.

Most of the above conclusions and principles apply with equal validity to both linear and nonlinear demand functions, the one practical exception occurring when the demand function is nonlinear *and* exhibits constant elasticity for all price levels.[1] That is, suppose the demand function were as follows:

$$q = \eta f^{-\kappa} \qquad (3\text{-}18)$$

in which η and κ are parameters. This is a hyperbolic function, and it can be shown that the elasticity with respect to fare, or ϵ_f, is equal to $-\kappa$ and is constant for all fare levels. In this instance it can be shown that all of the general conclusions stated before still hold *except* that the total revenues *for a given elasticity or value of* ϵ_f will not "increase to some maximum point and then fall until they reach zero when the fare becomes zero." Rather, if the demand is inelastic (i.e., ϵ_f is between 0 and -1), the total revenue will continually decrease with increases in volume or q. And if the demand is elastic (i.e., ϵ_f is less than -1), the total revenues will continually increase with increases in q until the fare is zero (at which point the total revenues fall to zero).

Before leaving this discussion of fare elasticity, we should note two common tendencies, one far too common with private firms and the latter increasingly coming into vogue with public ones. Private transport firms when faced with distressing financial conditions or rising costs almost always react to those conditions with a plea for higher monetary changes or fares, in spite of the fact that such action can (when the demand is elastic) result in a decrease in total revenues, as well as a drop in total net revenues. When demand *is* elastic, especially when there appears to be excess capacity and low costs associated with higher utilization of existing facilities, a good case would exist for at least considering the prospects stemming from a fare reduction. (The dramatic fare drops invoked by the airlines industry in 1978 serve as but one case in point. Similarly, one must wonder about the tendency in the taxicab business to always meet

---

[1]It is also possible to construct demand functions which have numerous elastic and inelastic portions, but such curves are generally inappropriate for travel demand.

rising costs with fare increases—even though the few available data indicate both elastic demand and low vehicle utilization.) By contrast, public transport agencies appear to have a primary concern with the extra patronage which can be achieved by lower fares, all in spite of the fact that (at current fare levels) demand is usually quite inelastic (often between -0.1 and -0.3) and that fare reduction will reduce both total and net revenues enormously.

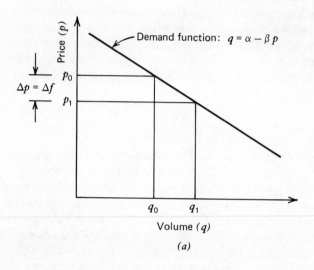

(a)

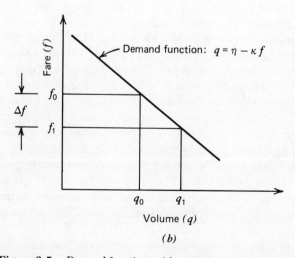

(b)

Figure 3-5.   Demand functions with respect to trip price and fare.

In addition to the use of demand functions defined with respect to fares, it is common to see demand functions which are defined only with respect to travel time; thus,

$$q = \omega - \lambda t \tag{3-19}$$

where ω and λ are parameters and t is travel time. As with fares, an analyst may calculate elasticities with respect to travel time using this model.

It is important to note the difficulty in estimating changes in usage by employing *components* of the price functions, such as those in Equations (3-9) or (3-19). To illustrate this difficulty, first consider a demand function with respect to price, such as

$$q = \alpha - \beta p \tag{3-20}$$

illustrated in Figure 3-5*a*. A naive analyst might be tempted to argue that a change in fare results in an equal change in price. Thus, he might expect a fare drop from f_0 to f_1 to result in an equal drop in price (from p_0 to p_1) and to change usage as indicated by the demand function in Equation (3-20) or Figure 3-5*a*. Figure 3-5*b* indicates the corresponding demand curve with respect to fares. Importantly, however, this "demand function" (and corresponding fare elasticity) can be used to estimate changes in volume *only if the other components of user cost (e.g., travel time) and socioeconomic conditions remain constant*. This is seldom the case as volumes change.

Figure 3-6*a* indicates the actual impact of a fare change on the equilibrium volume and price for the case in which travel time (and user cost) is dependent upon volume of tripmaking; this figure is similar to Figure 2-6, which was discussed earlier. Linear rather than nonlinear (and monotonically increasing) price–volume functions are illustrated for simplicity. A fare decrease results in a downward shift in the price–volume function as indicated in Figure 3-6*a*. Volume increases due to the reduction in user costs, just as in the case illustrated in Figure 3-5. However, the increase in volume causes congestion which, in turn, increases travel time and the user cost of travel. The net result is that equilibrium volume increases, but not as much of an increase as would occur without considering the change in travel time due to congestion. Similarly, the user cost of travel is reduced, but not by as much as the fare reduction would cause alone. The resulting equilibrium price and volume levels would be p_e and q_e, respectively. In the graph of fare versus volume (Fig. 3-6*b*), the change in travel time results in a *shift* in the demand curve with respect to fare, and this shift must be considered. By tracing out the equilibrium volumes, prices, and travel times at various fares, it is possible to construct a demand curve with respect to fares which incorporates congestion effects. However, this construction presupposes an equilibrium analysis such as that in Figure 3-6a.

With large computer models it is possible to account for simultaneous changes in the various components of user cost. However, manual analysis often omits the complications caused by user costs which are functions of volume, leading to inappropriate analysis and inaccurate results. A careful analyst should pay particular attention to the effects of volume changes

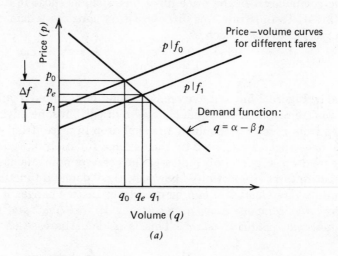

(a)

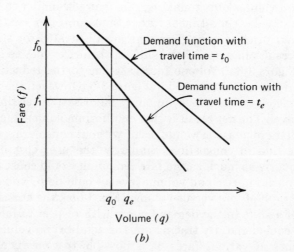

(b)

Figure 3-6.   Illustrative equilibrium changes in volumes due to fare changes.

on different components of travel price. In this book we shall generally restrict ourselves to demand functions defined with respect to trip price rather than a component of price such as fares. While demand functions with respect to fare or other cost components may be derived (as in Fig. 3-6b), exposition and graphical illustrations are greatly simplified by restricting our attention solely to price changes.

3-4   ANALYTICAL IDENTIFICATION OF EQUILIBRIUM IN THE TRAVEL MARKET

In Chapter 2 we discussed the equilibrium in the travel market as indicated by the demand and price–volume functions. Equilibrium trip volume and price may be identified by the intersection of these two functions, as in Figure 3-6a. By restricting our attention to two functions, identification of the equilibrium conditions was relatively straightforward and our exposition was greatly simplified. We should note, however, that it is possible to identify equilibrium directly from individual demand and performance functions, as well as to account for interactions among time periods, modes, and cost components.

In introducing demand functions, we noted that it is possible to estimate different demand functions for individuals or subgroups in the population. These *disaggregate* demand functions may be summed to determine the aggregate demand for travel in any particular case. Similarly, the price of travel may be calculated by summing the different components of user cost (money charges, time, and effort) multiplied by their respective values. In the previous section we noted that some components of trip price may be directly incorporated in the demand function so that demand might be expressed as a function of, say, travel time, fares, and socioeconomic conditions. It is possible to identify equilibrium travel conditions directly from these individual or group demand functions and appropriate performance curves.

Mathematically, the problem of identifying equilibrium with this approach is equivalent to identifying the volume and levels of the user cost components such that all the demand and performance functions are correct. A representative set of equations for linear demand and performance curves as well as the corresponding functional notation would include the following:

Individual demand functions:

$$q_i = q_i(t, f)$$
$$= \alpha_i - \beta_i t - \gamma_i f \qquad (3\text{-}21)$$

Aggregate demand summation:

$$q = \sum_{i=1}^{n} q_i = q_1 + q_2 + \cdots + q_n \tag{3-22}$$

Performance functions:

$$t = t(q)$$

$$= t_0 + \delta q \tag{3-23}$$

where q_i is individual demand; q is the aggregate volume; t is travel time; f is the fare level; $t(q)$ is a performance function; t_0 is the travel time at low levels of volume; and $\alpha_i, \beta_i, \gamma_i$, and δ are parameters. Functional notation, such as $q = q(t, f)$ simply indicates that the dependent variable q is in some manner determined by the explanatory variables t and f, as discussed in Appendix I. Linear functions are used in Equations (3-21) and (3-23) solely as illustrations; either nonlinear or linear functions could be used in practice.

It is possible to further disaggregate this set of equations by defining separate performance functions for different aspects of user cost, such as separate functions for time spent riding, walking, or waiting. Corresponding demand functions would be required, defined with respect to these various components of travel time. Even further, an additional equation might be added to relate the fare level f to the volume of travel. That is, we might expect operators to set fares with respect to the actual volume using their facilities. We shall discuss different fare setting and pricing policies later; so for the moment, we shall assume that fare is constant for all individuals and at all volume levels.

With only one demand and price function, we could represent the problem of identifying equilibrium on a single graph, as in Figure 3-6a. Unfortunately, the set of Equations (3-21) to (3-23) cannot be represented in a simple pictorial form. They can be solved on a computer, however, to find equilibrium volumes and user costs.

The usefulness of expressing the problem of identifying equilibrium in the form of equations such as Equations (3-21) to (3-23) is twofold. First, these equations may be easily represented for computer application. Second, it permits a generalization of the parameters involved in the demand and user cost functions. Note that we have defined different parameters or weights in the individual demand functions [Equation (3-21)] to reflect the values of different individuals. Each individual or group may be represented as having a *different* trade-off or value attached to the various components of user cost. It is also possible to make these parameter values dependent upon socioeconomic characteristics, so that, for example, wealthier individuals put less value on monetary payments and more on the time and effort incurred in travel.

TABLE 3-2.   Illustration of Equilibrium Volumes
and Prices with Time-of-Day Cross-Relationships

Period	Equilibrium Price	Equilibrium Volume
1	322	2748
2	453	2982
3	355	2825
4	211	2286
5	288	2648
6	400	2908
7	342	2797
8	156	1744

Note: Demand functions are shown in Table 3-1. The price function for period h is $p_h = 31 + 1750/(28 - 0.008q_h)$. Prices and volumes are rounded to the nearest integer.

In what follows we shall generally assume a single price function; that is, we assume that travelers are homogeneous with respect to the money and nonmoney parameters of the price function. This assumption is common in transportation studies, simplifies the presentation, and permits the use of graphical illustrations. Unless noted otherwise, our results may be generalized in any instance by identifying the appropriate individual or group price functions and solving for equilibrium with Equations (3-21) to (3-23).

Analytical identification of equilibrium is also useful when cross-elasticities are present. For example, in Section 3.2, we described eight time-of-day demand functions in which travel demand in any one period generally depended upon the price of travel in that period and in other periods (Table 3-1). Even with a single price function which relates the price of travel to the volume in a particular period, such as[2]

$$p_h = 31 + \frac{1750}{28 - 0.008q_h} \tag{3-24}$$

the problem of finding equilibrium volumes and prices cannot be accomplished graphically.

Equilibrium volumes and prices for this problem are shown in Table 3-2. These equilibrium values were obtained by means of a computer analy-

[2]This illustrative price function for roadway traffic was used in M. Wohl and B. Martin, *Traffic System Analysis*, McGraw-Hill Book Co., New York, 1967, Section 10.2.1.

sis program.[3] This analysis program found prices and volumes such that all the demand and price functions are satisfied simultaneously.

3-5 NETWORK EQUILIBRIUM ANALYSIS

One representation of transportation systems and its associated analytical problems deserves particular note since it has been found to be useful in numerous applications. Transportation systems can often be represented by a series of elements which are interconnected. For example, roadway systems consist of a set of individual streets, arterials, and roadways that are connected together. In a network model these individual components are called *links* or *arcs* and the entire system is collectively termed a *network*. The points at which links are connected are termed *network nodes*. Figure 3-7a illustrates a network of this type, which is typical for grid or rectangular street systems. The network consists of nine nodes (labeled A to I) and an arc between each node for travel in each direction. Thus, there are 24 links (indicated by the lines between each node); we define links such that flow can only take place in one direction on each link.

In a network such as the one in Figure 3-7a, each component or link is usually assumed to have its own cost and price functions which depend upon the volume of traffic flow on the link. Thus, costs and prices are defined over individual links. In contrast, travel demands are usually defined with respect to travel flows between nodes. For example, there may be a demand function that indicates the travel between node A and node C in Figure 3-7. Importantly, the price of travel between two nodes (such as A and C) is the sum of the user costs for each link traversed. Thus, in traveling between A and C, a vehicle might traverse the link between nodes A and B, thereby incurring travel time and other costs p_{AB}, and the link between nodes B and C, thereby incurring travel time and other costs of p_{BC}. In this case the total price or user cost for the trip would be the sum of the two link costs, $p_{AB} + p_{BC}$.

The use of a network representation such as the one in Figure 3-7a enables an analyst to account for a number of systematic effects. First, the choice of a route between two nodes can be examined. In many transportation systems there are alternative paths or routes to travel between two points. For example, a freight shipment might travel by two different rail

---

[3]The specific computer package used was MINOS (B. Murtaugh, "MINOS User's Manual," Stanford University, 1979). Solution was obtained by minimizing the sum of the squared differences between the price variables (p_h) and the price function [Eq. (3-24)] in each period, subject to the demand function relations in Table 3-1. By reducing this sum to very close to zero, the price functions as well as the demand functions are consistent with equilibrium prices and volumes.

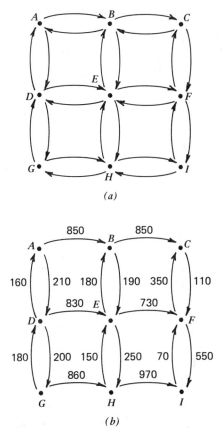

(a)

(b)

Figure 3-7. Equilibrium volumes for an illustrative network equilibrium problem. (a) Illustrative network and (b) equilibrium flows on the network. Note: equilibrium volumes are shown to the nearest 10 trips per hour.

carriers over different rail lines. Also, within urban areas, there are often numerous routes to travel between two points. A network can allow these different route choices to be modeled. A second advantage of a network representation is that the effects of traffic between numerous origins and destinations on individual transportation facilities or services can be examined. For example, the traffic on the link from node E to F in Figure 3-7a might originate in a variety of places and be destined for numerous other nodes. A network model permits the aggregation of these various origin–destination traffic flows on the link EF to be performed in an effective and efficient manner. The cost and price of travel on a link will generally be a function of the total traffic on the link, so calculation of this aggregate volume facilitates the examination of travel costs.

TABLE 3-3   Illustration of Equilibrium Volumes and Prices on a
Transportation Network

Nodal Pair	Demand Function	Equilibrium Volume	Equilibrium Price
A–C	$q_{AC} = 600 - 4.4p_{AC}$	400	46
A–I	$q_{AI} = 900 - 4.7p_{AI}$	500	86
D–C	$q_{DC} = 600 - 4.8p_{DC}$	300	62
D–I	$q_{DI} = 800 - 4.6p_{DI}$	500	66
G–C	$q_{GC} = 800 - 4.7p_{GC}$	400	85
G–I	$q_{GI} = 650 - 4.3p_{GI}$	450	46

Note: Prices are given to the nearest dollar and volumes to the nearest 10 trips.

To illustrate the use and results of equilibrium network analysis, suppose that six demand functions as shown in Table 3-3 exist for travel between various nodes in the network appearing in Figure 3-7a. For each link we assume that the user cost of travel is $p_i = 6.2 + 350/(28 - 0.008q_i)$. Finally, we make the assumption that individual travelers choose the route through the network which minimizes their own travel cost. Thus, our equilibrium problem consists of six demand functions, 24 price functions (one for each link), plus physical restrictions that the traffic entering a node must either continue on further links or be destined for that node.[4] The resulting equilibrium internodal volumes are shown in Table 3-3, while the equilibrium flows on each network link are shown in Figure 3-7b. As can be seen in Figure 3-7b, some of the flows between particular nodes take alternative routes through the network. Also, links between adjacent nodes are used in both directions of travel, as would occur in roadway networks.

In passing, we might note one common assumption which is made in analyzing the choice of routes on transportation networks. Suppose that all travelers between two nodes are identical with respect to the value that they place on different components of user travel costs. Moreover, suppose that each traveler chooses the route through the transportation network which minimizes his or her trip cost, which is the sum of the user costs incurred on each link of the chosen route. Together, these two assumptions lead to what is known as a "user equilibrium" which implies that each traveler attempts to minimize his or her own travel cost.[5]

---

[4]Solution of this equilibrium problem makes use of an iterative algorithm described in N. H. Gartner, "Optimal Traffic Assignment with Elastic Demands," *Trans. Sci.* **14**(2), 1980, and programmed by B. Janson of Carnegie-Mellon University.

[5]This assumption was advanced by A. C. Pigou, (*The Economics of Welfare*, MacMillan, New York, 1920) and J. G. Wardrop ["Some Theoretical Aspects of Road Traffic Research," *Proc. Inst. of Civil Engineers* **2**(1), 1952].

An interesting property of a user equilibrium is that each route between two nodes that is used by the travelers between those nodes must have equal travel cost. If one route had lower cost, then travelers would switch to that route and thereby reduce their travel cost. Routes that do not have any flow between the two nodes must have higher travel costs; otherwise, some traffic would divert to these routes. These properties are typically used in computer solution algorithms to identify desirable routes and the corresponding volumes and prices on the various links in a transportation network.

The examples so far in this section have used transportation networks and links as models of actual facilities spread over space, such as roadways or rail lines. We should also note that it is possible to represent services or other abstract phenomena as links in a network. For example, airline route maps are typically drawn as a network of links and nodes, even though there is no physical connection existing between nodes. In this case a "link" consists of a scheduled service of airline flights. Similarly, a link attached to a destination node might have an associated user cost which represents the cost of parking at the destination zone. In formulating network models it is only required that each link have its own cost and price functions and that the total user cost of traveling between nodes be equal to the sum of the prices incurred in traveling on each link of the route.

We might also note several disadvantages of using complicated network models for transportation analysis. First, these models are typically expensive to formulate. Developing appropriate cost and price functions for each link is particularly burdensome and, in practice, quite crude approximations are often made. Moreover, analysis of equilibrium travel flows usually requires computer analysis, which may be quite expensive. Avoiding additional computational costs often leads to rigid representations of demand and cost functions which may be poor representations of reality. Indeed, commonly available computer software cannot even include price-sensitive demand functions for internodal travel. Before introducing complicated network models, analysts should consider the usefulness of simpler conceptual models, which may preclude some systematic interactions but provide a richer representation of the various components of demand and cost, as described in the next chapters.

CHAPTER 4

COSTS OF TRAVEL AND TRANSPORT FACILITIES

Along with an estimate of system or facility usage, a second important concern of planners is the cost associated with facility construction and operation. To obtain an accurate estimate of costs requires specification of the human and material resources—or factors of production—required to produce a particular quantity and quality of transportation service. As will be seen, the required input of resources depends crucially upon investment decisions and system usage, among other factors.

As we originally discussed in Chapter 1, it is also important to be quite clear about the point of view which is adopted to specify costs of travel and transport facilities. Private operators typically consider only those costs which *they* experience, neglecting a wide range of costs incurred by users or society as a whole. Users of transport facilities consider only their own *private* costs, ignoring the costs incurred by other users, bystanders, and the taxpayers who may subsidize or be disadvantaged by a particular facility. In what follows we shall adopt the viewpoint of society as a whole, so that the total required amount of human and material resources is considered. As argued in Chapter 1, this viewpoint might be appropriate for facilities or services which involve federal funding. This definition of costs includes not only the labor and material inputs required to provide, operate, and maintain the vehicles and facilities or ways but also will include the personal travel time, effort, and hazard costs expended by the travelers for their tripmaking.[1] While such a viewpoint clearly has more applicability in the public than in the private sector of the economy, private cost functions can be developed from the corresponding social cost

---

[1]This framework is consistent with the formulation adopted previously by economists in dealing with transport matters. See, for example, M. Beckmann, C. B. McGuire, and C. B. Winsten, *Studies in the Economics of Transportation*, Yale University Press, New Haven, 1956, Chapters 2 and 4; W. Vickrey, "Pricing as a Tool in Coordination of Local Transportation," *Transportation Economics*, National Bureau of Economic Research, Columbia University Press, 1965; A. A. Walters, *The Economics of Road User Charges*, Johns Hopkins Press, Baltimore, 1968, Chapters II and III.

functions. For example, the "user cost" function of tripmakers described in Chapter 2 represents a private cost function which, as will be seen, forms one component of social costs. Private cost functions will be discussed more extensively in later chapters.

4-1 DESCRIPTION AND MAKEUP OF TRANSPORT COST FUNCTIONS

To determine costs, it is first necessary to describe the physical systems used and their operations. From this, the required factors of production may be specified, including labor and material inputs. Ideally, the relationships among the production or output (given by the level of facility usage or tripmaking) made possible by a technology, operating policy, and both the labor and material inputs will be stated in parametric or mathematical form. These relationships are usually called *production functions* and provide insight into the extra resource commitments required for increases in either the quantity or quality of output.

Although fully specified production functions would be very useful, they are usually not available. Instead, engineering studies provide a set of reasonable technological and physical options for particular types of facilities. For example, one option in a particular situation might consist of a four-lane divided freeway. However, even within a particular option, an engineer must make judgments concerning the best technology in particular cases (such as concrete or asphalt pavement type). In developing options, engineers attempt to select those technologies which will require the least resources and, in turn, have the lowest cost for a given quantity and quality of output.

Once production functions or technological options have been specified for the range of output levels deemed worthy of consideration, they must be transformed into cost functions or relationships which express the dependence of cost upon the quantity and quality of usage, given the specific technological features of the facilities used. Simply stated, these cost functions are developed by applying factor prices (i.e., the prices of the factors of production) to production functions or technological options. Thus, each of the labor and material resources required by the facility or system is multiplied by its price and the individual input costs are then summed to obtain the total social cost. Note that the development of cost functions requires both the specification of input factors (often thought to be the task of *engineers*) and the estimation of appropriate factor prices for present and future material and labor inputs (which is traditionally a problem for an *economist*). It is not idle to suggest that cost functions can best be developed by utilizing the joint efforts and talents of engineers and economists, working side by side.

Cost functions will generally include the following items:

Fixed (or nonseparable with respect to the volume of usage) facility and social dislocation costs.

Variable facility costs.

Fixed vehicle ownership costs.

Variable vehicle costs.

Variable user travel time, effort, and hazard costs.

Other costs (e.g., external air and noise pollution costs).

The term *fixed* and *variable* will be described more extensively in a later section; for the time being, though, fixed costs mean those which remain fixed and do not change with increased usage of a facility while variable costs are those which do vary or change with increased usage of a facility.

The last cost item, "other costs," is the first to warrant some explanation. Generally, it is meant to include *external costs* which are imposed on others (especially nonusers) as a result of transport movement by users.[2] Examples of such losses for transport situations are air pollution and noise costs for nontravelers. Clearly, these types of externalities are not unique to public situations but apply equally to both public and private sectors. (Consider, for example, the effects of noise, air, or stream pollution caused by either your neighbor or a private firm.) However, *private* decision makers generally ignore external costs. It should be recognized that to properly account for externalities in the public sector, but not in the private sector, is to establish a double standard for investment policy and thus to at least permit inefficient decisions to be made and an improper allocation of investments between the public and private sectors.

It is evident that, from a social perspective, externalities *should be* but usually are not accounted for in both the public and private sectors, as long as overall economic efficiency is a goal. This introduces the practical problem of analyzing both the relative *and* overall worth (to the public) of public investment projects. For determining the overall worth or economic feasibility of public investment, all externalities should be properly measured and accounted for when computing the total net benefit; clearly, those public projects with negative total net benefit after inclusion of external costs and benefits (but with a positive total before their inclusion) should be rejected, even if externalities are not treated for private investment and assuming that there are no significant feedback effects.

[2]The literature on this subject area is lengthy: two good references are; R. N. McKean, *Efficiency in Government Through Systems Analysis*, Wiley, New York, 1964, Chapter 8; J. Margolis, "Secondary Benefits, External Economies, and the Justification of Public Investment," *Review of Economics and Statistics* **39**, 284, (1957).

On the other hand, if externalities are included only for public projects, no clear-cut statement can be made regarding the relative worth or desirability of investment as between the public and private sectors. Thus, inconsistent treatment can distort resource allocation between the two sectors.

Second, there can be no doubt but that the measurement of external costs is extremely difficult and somewhat subjective, if at all possible. This difficulty is particularly acute in the absence of market mechanisms to provide even approximate indications of real losses.[3] However, as a means of estimating the external costs, one might argue that a reasonable proxy would be to determine the resource costs required to eliminate the nuisance or to reduce it to a "tolerable" level. In the first instance the likelihood of overstating the external cost is high, while in the second it can easily be overstated or understated—depending on one's judgment of "tolerable." (More will be said about this later.) And, finally, in matters of this sort, it is far too easy (if not common) to improperly label income transfers as external costs and thus to double-count[4] (i.e., one man or group loses, but another gains to an equal extent, thus resulting in no real loss or external cost to society).

An example may be useful in regard to such valuations of external costs. Suppose that retail sales of particular stores decline due to the traffic disruption caused by construction. Are these sales declines a real cost to society? The direct answer is, no, they are not. Presumably, sales lost in the vicinity of the construction will be made elsewhere, so the lost sales represent a transfer of income from nearby store owners to those further away. The only increase in real cost which may occur in this relocation of purchases is the increased travel cost and inconvenience of using other stores. Thus, lost retail sales are not generally a real cost of construction. Of course, decision makers may consider this redistribution of sales income *inequitable*, but this judgment is not directly an economic efficiency matter.

All in all, while the analyst should make every attempt to measure and include all external costs—and benefits—in the evaluation of public projects, he should remain apprised of the possible inconsistencies and inaccuracies which can result from failure to examine the circumstances for both public and private sectors from estimating the external effects.

Additional discussion is warranted with respect to some of the other transport cost items. First, these cost items generally apply to the cost functions for a particular facility (or plant size) at a specific point in time.

---

[3]For a summary of research and knowledge on the cost of air pollution, for example, see K. A. Small, "Estimating the Air Pollution Costs of Transport Modes," *Journal of Transport Economics and Policy* **11** (2), May 1977.

[4]For a good discussion of this point, see J. Hirshleifer, J. C. DeHaven, and J. W. Milliman, *Water Supply: Economics, Technology and Policy*, University of Chicago Press, Chicago, 1960, p. 128.

Second, though more will be said about this point, the costs should be thought of as those pertaining to a particular *pattern and mix* of flow or output which occurs during some particular year (or at some more specific point in time).

The fixed facility costs for a new or expanded facility will include the costs for construction, land acquisition, and social dislocation (i.e., the costs for moving displaced parties or firms as well as neighborhood disruption); in those instances where the market prices do not reflect the true costs or the marginal opportunity costs, the market prices should be changed accordingly.[5] Particular care must be taken in evaluating either the cost of land which is being acquired for new or expanded facilities or that of land being used for existing facilities and which continues to be used for transport facilities. Again, it is the marginal opportunity cost which is appropriate rather than the book value or a zero price (which is occasionally assumed if the land is already being used for an existing transport facility or if it is public property).

Marginal opportunity cost is the market value of a resource in a perfectly competitive market situation where all alternative uses are properly considered. For those structural facility items which wear out over time and which must be replaced in some later years (but during the analysis period), the analyst must be careful to use the factor prices and appropriate technologies for that later point in time rather than simply assume that the replacement costs will be equal to the initial ones. Factor prices are the opportunity costs of the material or labor inputs (and the material or labor inputs are often referred to as the factors of production). The use of marginal opportunity cost to value fixed resources again represents the use of *social* rather than *private* costs of resources.

For example, by continuing to use land for transport facilities, society as a whole foregoes the opportunity for alternative activities on this land; the net value of these foregone activities is represented by the opportunity cost of the land. It seems likely that the land acquisition costs employed in engineering cost studies are often below the proper opportunity cost. In a similar vein it is also likely that the vehicle ownership costs are overstated (i.e., higher than the marginal opportunity costs). More specifically, in the former case, one often finds that engineers evaluate the cost of land used for transport facilities (especially that for existing facilities or that which is converted from other public uses) below the value which it would have had in alternative private, commercial, or other public uses (such as use

[5]For discussion of this point, see A. Maass, M. M. Hufschmidt, R. Dorfman, H. A. Thomas, Jr., S. A. Marglin, and G. M. Fair, *Design of Water Resource Systems*, Harvard University Press, Cambridge, 1962, pp. 49 ff., and Hirshleifer, et al., op. cit., pp. 77 ff. Also, this remark on the differential between market prices and true costs applies to all cost items, not just fixed costs.

for zoos, recreational areas, or schools). In the case of evaluating vehicle ownership costs, it would seem that use of market prices paid for automobile purchases or cash flow payments for those autos purchased on installment plans would lead to an overstatement of the opportunity costs. Such a conclusion rests upon the fairly certain assumption that lack of perfect competition in the automobile industry has resulted in auto purchase prices being above marginal cost and that less than perfect information and knowledge about discounting practices and effective interest rates for many installment loan plans has led buyers to pay more than opportunity costs for autos.

Fixed vehicle costs present a reasonably difficult problem because of the complexities of establishing the relationship between vehicle ownership and tripmaking on specific facilities. For example, as a new facility is built or an existing facility expanded, does increased automobile ownership result which otherwise would not have occurred? Or do people merely make more frequent trips? How is ownership and usage related to the facility size? And so forth. In some situations the vehicle ownership costs could be regarded as variable rather than fixed costs (i.e., they would be regarded as separable with respect to changes in output), while in others it would be more appropriate to regard them as being fixed. For instance, that portion of vehicle ownership costs which does not depreciate with use (i.e., that portion which is not variable with tripmaking or mileage) could be regarded as fixed in those instances where output increases merely represent more frequent tripmaking by the same vehicle owners. By contrast, if increases in output are generated by new tripmakers and if they require additional vehicles to be put into use, the vehicle ownership costs might be regarded as variable with respect to output. The latter type of situation would be more appropriate for work-trip commuting, for example, and in those instances where a constant and repetitive day-to-day or week-to-week pattern is followed by the same group of travelers. Also, the relative ease and quickness with which travelers can switch over to other modes, or from driver to car poolers and can sell used cars probably induces drivers to take a longer-term view of their private variable costs rather than simply to account for the day-to-day out-of-pocket travel expenditures (in time, money, and effort).[6]

---

[6]While these are but very tentative hypotheses, some comfort might be taken from the fact that about 70% of new car buyers use installment loans to make their purchases and thus receive monthly reminders of the auto purchase and use costs (which are probably higher than the opportunity costs). (Motor Vehicle Manufacturer's Association, "Motor Vehicle Facts and Figures 1980.") On the other hand, the picture is complicated by resale considerations and related matters.

At any rate, for our purposes, it will be assumed that the vehicle ownership costs can be placed on a variable "per vehicle trip" basis, along with the vehicle operating and maintenance costs.[7]

Variable user travel time, effort, and hazard costs at different levels of tripmaking (or output) and with facilities of varying capacity are components of the "user costs" described in Chapter 2. At this stage we will not dwell on the difficulties of properly assessing these cost components other than to emphasize the importance of doing so and to note the extent to which the total costs hinge on their measurement. While research on the value of travel time is far from complete or even reliable, it appears reasonable to state that some analysts have concluded that commuter travel time savings are valued at about one-quarter of the individual's wage, and intercity trip time savings are even higher valued. In the former case the travel time cost component would represent *at least* 25% of the total door-to-door trip cost for downtown commuter trips (with full parking and vehicle ownership costs, as well as others, included) and an even larger proportion of total door-to-door trip costs for urban trips in general.

Note that fares are not included in this list of total costs. Fares simply represent a transfer of wealth from users to facility operators, not a net loss to society. Similarly, for all of these cost items, no taxes should be included other than to the extent that they are representative of and proxies for other resource costs (such as those for policing or administration). We exclude such transfer payments to simplify calculations. An alternative approach would be to include such transfer payments as a *cost* to users and a *benefit* to recipients (i.e., providers or governments). In examining the difference between benefits and costs in order to evaluate investments, these transfer payment benefits and costs would cancel out:

$$\text{(Benefits + transfer payments)} - \text{(costs + transfer payments)}$$
$$= \text{benefits} - \text{costs}$$

Thus, entirely omitting transfer payments simplifies the analysis.

4-2   THE FUNCTIONAL FORM OF COST RELATIONSHIPS

Beyond noting or assuming an approximate form for the cost functions to be employed, no major attempt will be made here to describe them accu-

---

[7]If the market purchase and resale prices were good signals of real costs, the ownership cost per trip—for this situation—could be computed as follows.

$$\text{Cost per vehicle trip} = [(P - L)(A \mid P, i, m) + (L)(i)]/N$$

where $(A \mid P, i, m)$ is the capital recovery factor as shown in Equation (4-2) below. P is the initial purchase price of the auto, L is the resale value of the auto at the end of m years, i is the discount rate, and N is the number of vehicle trips made annually. (This formulation implicitly assumes that the auto is replaced every m years, under virtually identical purchase conditions.)

rately or specifically (other than for the discussion of special topics).[8]
Needless to say, the formulation to be used will be an oversimplification
but, nonetheless, will still be sufficiently realistic to properly portray cost
functions for a wide range of circumstances. Chapter 12 discusses the
various methods which are used to formulate and to estimate cost functions.

As an initial point, the cost function is very much dependent upon the
technology and level of usage or output. By technology, we mean both the
nature and extent as well as the manner in which facilities and services
are operated. Advanced technology, more capacity, or more usage implies
the commitment of extra resources and thus of extra costs. Mathematically, one may speak of costs as a *function* of the technology, capacity, and
output or usage. Further, the cost function has a direct and important
relationship to the time dimension or, more specifically, to the time available for adjusting the technology and operations. For example, over a short
period of time or, if you will, *over the short run*, only relatively minor
adjustments or additions can be made to the technology (i.e., to the
existing facilities, rolling stock, type of operation, etc.), and thus increases
in output or usage will result mainly in extra costs for increased wear and
tear, energy consumption, congestion, and the like. *Over the long run* or
over a fairly long period of time, the technology can be substantially
altered (e.g., both the type of and usage of technology can be changed,
rights-of-way can be acquired or abandoned, rolling stock can be replaced,
and fleets can be increased or decreased, etc.), and thus cost changes can
stem from changes in either the technology or level of output or usage. As
a consequence, it will be necessary to make a distinction between short-
run and long-run cost functions.[9]

Another way of thinking about the distinction between short-run and
long-run cost functions would be as follows: A short-run cost function
describes the relationship between cost and output for a particular facility
and its operation and thus can be used for determining the actual day-to-
day operating conditions and costs; the long-run cost function by repre-

---

[8]Useful references of specific forms include J. R. Meyer, M. J. Peck, J. Stenason, and C. Zwick,
The Economics of Competition in the Transportation Industries, Harvard University Press,
Cambridge, 1959, Chapters II to V; J. Meyer, J. Kain, and M. Wohl, *The Urban Transportation
Problem*, Harvard University Press, Cambridge, 1965, Chapters 8 to 11; A. A. Walters, op. cit.,
Chapter VI; and J. H. Boyd, N. J. Asher, and E. S. Wetzler, "Evaluation of Rail Rapid Transit
and Express Bus Service in the Urban Commuter Market," Report by Institute for Defense
Analyses for U.S. Dept. of Trans., Washington, D.C., October 1973, Appendices A to G; T. E.
Keeler, L. A. Merewitz, and P. M. J. Fisher, "Full Costs of Urban Transport", Report #NSF-RA-
S-75 069A, The University of California, Berkeley, California, NTIS # PB-248 145-147, 1974.

[9]Some analysts prefer to employ cost functions applying to three time periods—that is, the short
run, intermediate run, and long run. For simplicity, we use only two. See R. Heflebower,
"Characteristics of Transport Modes," in *Transport Investment and Economic Development*, G.
Fromm (ed.), The Brookings Institution, Washington, D.C., 1965.

senting the relationship among costs, output, and facility size or capacity describes the costs to which one can adjust or adapt over a long time frame and thus aids importantly in the investment planning process. Accordingly, it is useful to think of the short-run cost function as an operating function and the long-run cost function as a planning function.

Put differently, long-run cost functions are used to help determine which technology should be employed, how large a facility to build, as well as to aid in the process of deciding whether any facility should be built and, if so, when it should be provided. By contrast, short-run cost functions describe the costs which will stem from operating a given facility at various volume levels and thus are used to help decide which level of output or volume is most appropriate for that specific facility and operation.

Some examples might be helpful in illustrating the differences. For an airport, changes in operating rules (e.g., takeoff and landing priorities, hours of operation, and ground traffic control) would be considered in a short-run cost function. Major runway or terminal investments would be considered in long-run cost functions. For transit services, changes in routes and schedules are short-run decisions, whereas capital construction projects (e.g., subway investments) are long run. Purchases or leasing of additional vehicles might or might not be included in a short-run cost function, depending upon the analysis purpose and the flexibility of such changes.

4-3 SHORT-RUN COST FUNCTIONS

Let us characterize the short run cost function for some given facility and technology as follows:

$$SRTC_{x,t}(q) = F_{x,t} + SRVC_{x,t}(q) \tag{4-1}$$

where $SRTC_{x,t}(q)$ = short-run total costs for a volume of q (in, say, trips per hour) using facility x during year t
$F_{x,t}$ = fixed costs for facility x during year t
$SRVC_{x,t}(q)$ = short-run total variable costs for a volume of q using facility x during year t

That is, given some facility, the short-run total costs during some year t will consist of fixed- and variable-cost components, or costs which are fixed or variable with respect to changes in output or volume q. For a given facility, some factors of production, such as rights-of-way, maintenance facilities, garages, and rolling stock, are fixed over the short-run, regardless of whether q is large or small. Other factors of production, such as fuel, tire wear and tear, and user travel time, will vary or change as q

rises or falls and thus are variable in the short run. Also, the fixed costs are common to and inseparable among all units and levels of output q.

One might ask: What is the appropriate value or cost to be used for the fixed factors of production? Should it be the book value? The undepreciated balance? The value of any outstanding bonds? The replacement cost? Simply, the appropriate value for the fixed costs (from the standpoint of resource costs to society, which is the viewpoint being considered here) is the value of the fixed factors of production in their best and highest alternative use; usually this is termed the *foregone opportunity costs* of the fixed factors of production and denotes the value of the opportunities which we must forego if we utilize the fixed factors of production for this particular facility.

However, appropriate assessment of the opportunity value of existing facilities requires consideration of the principle of *sunk* costs. Suppose, for example, a new fleet of buses was purchased for $2 million only one year ago with funds obtained from revenue bonds; assume further that only part of the revenue bonds has been paid off, the remainder being $1.9 million. Would the remaining $1.9 million in bonds need to be considered when we were estimating the opportunity value of the buses and considering the economic desirability of continuing to operate the bus fleet rather than (say) abandon bus service altogether? If our concern and point of view is the economic welfare of society as a whole, then consideration of any remaining revenue bonds (as an economic matter to the public at large, and aside from legal commitments) is irrelevant; the *original* resources which were committed when the vehicles were purchased are sunk or irrevocably expended. The only question *now* is what is their value in the best alternative opportunity, whether higher or lower than the book value or the value of the remaining bonds. Also, money payments made by users or others to pay off remaining revenue bonds only represent a money transfer (from those making payments to those holding the bonds) and do not represent any net economic gain or loss for society.

Another example of sunk cost may be helpful. Some years ago, a large Middle-Atlantic city carried out planning and engineering studies, as well as constructed an experimental facility, to test the feasibility of building a rubber-tired rapid transit line. Also, a busway was built which could then be incorporated into the rubber-tired rapid transit facility if, subsequently, it were to be built. Following this initial work, the public transit authority decided to reevaluate the rubber-tired rapid transit alternative and to compare its costs and benefits with those stemming from construction of a conventional rapid transit line, a light-rail transit line, or an express bus facility instead. In turn, the question arose: Should the costs *already incurred* (for planning, engineering, right-of-way acquisition, construction, etc.) be included within the benefit-cost analysis? The answer is: *NO*. The prior costs represent the value of resources which were irrevocably committed in earlier years, an act which cannot be altered. Thus, the prior dollar payments are sunk costs and inadmissible for our purposes. However, to the extent that the facilities which remain from those earlier-year expenditures do have value in alternative uses today, then such an opportunity value should be included as part of the costs. Also, if the earlier-year expenditures reduce the costs for completing another alternative, then that difference should be reflected. But, in any case, the specific dollar payments made in earlier years are irrelevant today and hereafter.

A final technical problem remains for discussion before any more detailed characterization of the cost functions is attempted. This problem regards specification of the *time interval for the output measure*. Costs can be correctly computed only by relating the output or flow levels for some specified (albeit arbitrary) time interval to the particular characteristics of that facility and by accounting for changes in factor inputs and their prices (or opportunity costs). In other words, given the output or flow pattern for (say) *each hour* over time (assuming that this is the most appropriate unit time interval for output as related to the facility and its performance characteristics), the costs for the pattern of flow, flow rate, and flow mix can be determined. Each different pattern of flow and flow rate may have a different total cost. As a consequence, cost functions of the sort to be used here are appropriate or accurate only for the implied flow pattern.

To be more specific, it is necessary to use flow or tripmaking volume *per hour* (or some fairly short time interval) as the output measure for transport situations because of hourly fluctuations in demand and because a larger unit time interval (such as volume *per day*) would not permit a realistic assessment of the actual travel and congestion conditions. For example, a volume of 50,000 vehicle trips per day on a four-lane highway will not permit determination of the congestion and travel time costs without first specifying the hourly pattern of flow. Spread uniformly throughout the day, 50,000 vehicle trips per day would cause little or no congestion and the daily travel time costs would be small, but if four hours a day had flows of 6000 vehicle trips per hour and the remaining 26,000 trips were spread uniformly, the total daily travel costs would be much larger. By use of this unit time interval for the output, it is thereby implied that the hourly flow remains constant over the short-run time period (say a year) for which the total costs are aggregated.

In turn, the simplest (though still arbitrary) procedure for placing the fixed costs on the same hourly output time interval basis as the variable costs is by making use of capital recovery factors, which are defined as follows:

$$(A|P, i, n) = crf_{i,n} = \frac{i(1 + i)^n}{(1 + i)^n - 1} \tag{4-2}$$

in which $(A|P, i, n)$ or $crf_{i,n}$ is the capital recovery factor for a n year analysis period and a discount rate of i (expressed as a decimal fraction).

Use of this factor implies that the discount rate remains constant over the n year analysis period. With varying discount rates, the analysis is more complicated, but one may still obtain a uniform allocation of fixed costs over time. Chapter 8 will discuss the selection of an appropriate interest rate for this purpose.

It should be recognized that the capital recovery factor is equivalent to a sinking fund factor plus interest; when multiplied times fixed costs, the product will be equal to the equivalent uniform annual fixed costs. Use of this procedure is tantamount to regarding the product of the capital recovery factor and fixed costs as the annual income stream which is foregone by virtue of using the fixed factors of production in the fashion described rather than using them in the "best other alternative use."

Finally, if the time interval for the output or volume of tripmaking is, say, an hour, the annual fixed costs can be converted to an hourly basis by dividing the equivalent annual payment by the number of hours in a year.

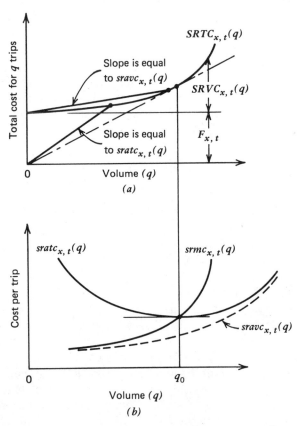

Figure 4-1. Basic short-run cost functions and relationships for facility x during year t.

That is,

$$F_{x,t} = \frac{EAFC_{x,t}}{8760} \tag{4-3}$$

where

$EAFC_{x,t}$ = equivalent fixed costs for facility x during year t or $(A|P, i, n)$
times the opportunity value of the fixed factors of production

Figure 4-1a illustrates the short-run total cost function shown by Equation (4-1), as well as its variable- and fixed-cost components. For most public transport facilities the short-run total costs will tend to increase with q at an increasing rate—as indicated in Figure 4-1a—if user time, effort, and inconvenience costs are included along with those for constructing, maintaining, and operating the physical guideway and rolling stock.

4-3-1 SHORT-RUN UNIT COST FUNCTIONS

Figure 4-1b illustrates various unit cost functions which can be derived from the short-run total cost function. The three unit cost functions are, respectively, $sratc_{x,t}(q)$, the short-run average total cost at flow q; $sravc_{x,t}(q)$, the short-run average variable cost at flow q; and $srmc_{x,t}(q)$, the short-run marginal cost at flow q. Mathematically, these unit cost functions can be represented as follows:

$$sratc_{x,t}(q) = \frac{SRTC_{x,t}(q)}{q} \tag{4-4}$$

$$sravc_{x,t}(q) = \frac{SRVC_{x,t}(q)}{q} \tag{4-5}$$

$$srmc_{x,t}(q) = \frac{\partial SRTC_{x,t}(q)}{\partial q} = \frac{\Delta SRTC_{x,t}(q)}{\Delta q} \tag{4-6}$$

$$= \frac{\partial SRVC_{x,t}(q)}{\partial q} = \frac{\Delta SRVC_{x,t}(q)}{\Delta q} \tag{4-7}$$

The derivatives in Equations (4-6) and (4-7) represent an approximation since, in actuality, q can only assume integer values and thus the cost function is discontinuous. Appendix I describes both the derivative and difference functions.

The short-run average total and average variable cost functions are straightforward, definitionally, and thus need little further explanation. Graphically, the former may be viewed as the slope of a line from the origin to the short-run total cost function, while the latter may be viewed as the slope of a line from the threshold on the vertical axis (or point

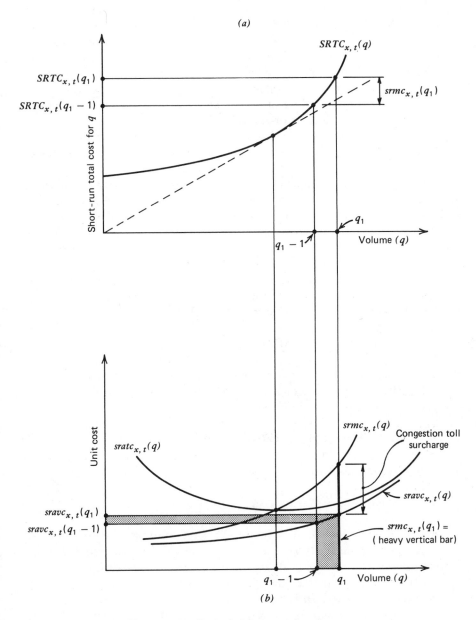

Figure 4-2. Basic short-run cost functions.

where the short-run total cost function intersects the vertical axis) to the short-run total cost function. Put differently, if travelers—whether using transit or private autos—generally experienced the same (average) time, discomfort, effort, and expense when making trips and generally made or perceived no money payment other than to cover maintenance and operating costs, then they would be subject to short-run average variable costs. If, however, fares for transit or tolls for highway facilities include a surcharge to exactly cover the fixed construction and facility costs as well as the variable operating costs, then private user costs would equal the short-run average total costs.

The short-run marginal cost function, however, is less straightforward and for this and other reasons deserves more attention. This function defines the short-run marginal cost at flow q, an amount which also is (approximately) equal to the slope of the short-run total cost function at flow q (i.e., its derivative). A better definition is that the *short-run marginal cost is equal to the increase in short-run total cost which occurs when the flow q is increased by one unit.* That is, $srmc_{x,t}(q)$ is equal to the increase in short-run total costs for facility x which occurs when the flow q increases from $q - 1$ to q. Algebraically, this is

$$srmc_{x,t}(q) = SRTC_{x,t}(q) - SRTC_{x,t}(q - 1) \qquad (4\text{-}8)$$

Since increases in short-run total cost can stem only from changes in variable costs (as the fixed costs, $F_{x,t}$, are indeed fixed or invariant with respect to q), it should be clear that

$$srmc_{x,t}(q) = SRVC_{x,t}(q) - SRVC_{x,t}(q - 1) \qquad (4\text{-}9)$$

and, using Equation (4-5),

$$srmc_{x,t}(q) = q\{sravc_{x,t}(q)\} - (q - 1)\{sravc_{x,t}(q - 1)\} \qquad (4\text{-}10)$$

Referring to Figure 4-2b, it is apparent that short-run marginal cost $srmc_{x,t}(q_1)$—as indicated by the heavy vertical bar—is equal to the increase in either the total costs or the total variable costs which resulted from a unit increase in the flow rate from $q_1 - 1$ to q_1, the latter being equal to the shaded area in Figure 4-2b.

Also, in this discussion of short-run costs, another identity should be mentioned, and that pertains to the relationship between short-run marginal costs and short-run variable costs. As pointed out, marginal costs represent the increase in total cost which stems from a unit increase in output or flow rate. But since only the variable costs can change *during the short run*, the marginal costs reflect only changes in the total variable costs or in $SRVC_x(q)$. As a result, short-run total variable costs with a flow rate of q_1 are simply the sum of short-run marginal costs experienced at all flow levels between 0 and q_1. Mathematically, this is

$$\sum_{q=1}^{q_1} srmc_x(q) = SRVC_x(q_1) = q_1\{sravc_x(q_1)\} \qquad (4\text{-}11)$$

and

$$SRVC_x(q_1) = SRTC_x(q_1) - SRTC_x(0) \qquad (4\text{-}12)$$

since, when q is zero, $SRTC_x(0)$ is equal to F_x (the fixed costs) and $SRVC_x(0)$ is equal to zero.

The identities shown in Equations (4-11) and (4-12) can also be illustrated by the simple example shown in Figure 4-3. If the flow rate were 4 vehicles per hour (say), then

$$SRVC_x(4) = \sum_{q=1}^{4} srmc_x(q)$$

$$= srmc_x(1) + srmc_x(2) + srmc_x(3) + srmc_x(4)$$

and

$$SRVC_x(4) = 4sravc_x(4)$$

the last of which follows from the definition of short-run average variable cost shown in Equation (4-5).

It is important to give meaning to the short-run marginal cost and the above relationships; indeed, they represent more than mere mathematical abstractions and underlie the reasoning and push for the replacement of existing facility pricing policies with marginal cost pricing.

First, most public highways presently use an approximation of short-run average variable cost pricing. That is, travelers when using highways are faced with user costs (including uniform fares, other money outlays, travel times, and discomfort levels) which, when combined, are approximately equal to short-run average variable costs. This situation is roughly equivalent to using a short-run average variable cost pricing policy as a means for governing the amount of use of highways. Of course, this observation is only approximately true. To some extent, highway construction costs are charged to users as part of gasoline taxes, thus pushing user cost above short-run average variable cost. But the opportunity cost of land is usually undervalued and pollution costs are not included. Users of *privately* operated, unsubsidized transport services generally incur short-run average total costs; otherwise the private firm would find that their own costs exceeded their revenue. Before the advent of extensive subsidization of operating expenses, transit systems also used an approximation of short-run average variable cost pricing.

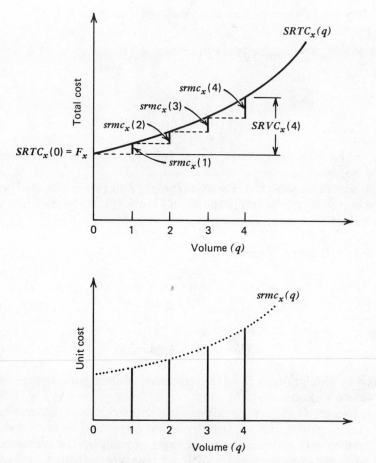

Figure 4-3. Short-run variable costs as the sum of short-run marginal costs.

Second, if we wanted to use short-run marginal cost pricing—that is, to have travelers face the short-run marginal costs rather than short-run average variable costs—then at a flow level of say q_1 a congestion toll or fare equal to $srmc_{x,t}(q_1) - sravc_{x,t}(q_1)$ would have to be imposed (see Figure 4-2b). Moreover, all of the q_1 travelers would *each* incur the marginal cost price, which is simply equal to the average time, effort, discomfort, and money expenses each face or perceive [or $sravc_{x,t}(q_1)$] *plus* the congestion toll surcharge, the total being their user cost.

At this point we might ask: Why should travelers pay a marginal cost price instead of the long-standing average variable cost price? And, why should each of the q_1 travelers and not just the q_1th traveler pay the same marginal cost price of $srmc_{x,t}(q_1)$? The rationale is as follows:

1.   If the flow rate (measured in, say, persons per hour) using a transit line or a highway is allowed to increase by one additional person per hour, then the users of the transit line or highway will all experience slightly higher delays, crowding, and discomfort than they otherwise would. The combined increase in travel time, crowding, and discomfort which is experienced collectively by all q_1 users (when the q_1th person is allowed to jump onto the bus or highway) is equal to the short-run marginal cost of $srmc_{x,t}(q_1)$. That is, the short-run marginal cost indicates the additional costs which accrue to everyone as a result of adding one additional passenger. If you will, they indicate the social costs stemming from the added rider, while the average variable costs simply represent the private costs, the latter of which would permit riders or drivers to ignore the costs imposed on others as well as themselves. (The difference between the social and private costs are equal to the extra congestion and other such costs, or the extra costs imposed on other travelers when additional travel is made.)

2.   When the q_1th rider or driver (per hour, say) is added to the transit line or highway, we are not simply adding another rider or driver *at the end of the hour* or *at the end of the line*; rather, we are increasing the flow *rate* and thus are "packing in" more riders or drivers per hour onto the same number of buses or lanes of highway. Thus, the extra congestion or crowding results from a higher flow rate (or, say, the number of people an hour) and not from adding another rider or driver at the end of the line. Congestion or crowding is a *group* phenomenon which results from the size of the group *collectively*. And no one member of the q_1 group of riders or drivers is any more or less responsible for the last increment of congestion—as measured by the short-run marginal cost or $srmc_{x,t}(q_1)$; this last increment of cost is caused by the collective action of all q_1 travelers. In short, it would *inappropriate* to charge the first rider on a bus (or first driver getting onto the highway) an amount equal to $srmc_{x,t}(1)$, the next one an amount equal to $srmc_{x,t}(2),\ldots$, the next to last one an amount equal to $srmc_{x,t}(q_1-1)$, and the last one an amount equal to $srmc_{x,t}(q_1)$.

4-3-2   AN EXAMPLE OF SHORT-RUN COSTS

A specific example may be helpful. For this purpose let us assume that the variable costs for vehicular traffic on city streets can be represented by the following linear short-run average variable cost function:

$$sravc(q) = \tau + vt(q) \qquad (4\text{-}13)$$

where $sravc(q)$ is the short-run average cost per mile at flow rate q, τ is the parameter value for operating costs (dollars per mile) which do not vary with the flow rate or speed, v is the parameter value for travel costs which vary with speed, and $t(q)$ is the travel time per mile for a flow rate of q. Throughout this example, the subscripts x and t (to represent the facility and year) will be dropped for convenience. Also, let

$$t(q) = \frac{1}{V_{max} - \delta q} \tag{4-14}$$

where V_{max} is the travel speed at very low volume levels and δ is a speed reduction parameter for city streets; this function is appropriate only for values of q less than V_{max}/δ.

This results in short-run average variable cost of[10]

$$sravc(q) = \tau + \frac{v}{V_{max} - \delta q} \quad \text{for } q < V_{max}/\delta \tag{4-15}$$

Since the total variable costs, or $SRVC(q)$, are equal to q times $sravc(q)$, and given the definition for short-run marginal costs as shown in Equation (4-7), we get

$$srmc(q) = \frac{\partial SRVC(q)}{\partial q} \tag{4-16}$$

$$= \frac{\partial[q\ sravc(q)]}{\partial q} \tag{4-17}$$

$$= sravc(q) + \frac{v\delta q}{(V_{max} - \delta q)^2} \tag{4-18}$$

For illustrative purposes let us use parameter values which were estimated by Thomson and Dawson for Central London roadways, as follows:[11]

$$sravc(q) = 6.2 + \frac{350}{(28 - 0.008q)} \tag{4-19}$$

and

$$srmc(q) = sravc(q) + \frac{2.8q}{(28 - 0.008q)^2} \tag{4-20}$$

in which both are measured in cents per vehicle-mile. Also,

$$t(q) = \frac{1}{28 - 0.008q} \quad \text{in veh-hr/veh-mi} \tag{4-21}$$

[10]For a more detailed discussion of this type of cost model, see Walters, op. cit., pp. 172 ff.

[11]For details, see M. Wohl and B. V. Martin, *Traffic System Analysis*, McGraw-Hill Book Co., New York, 1967, Section 10.2.1.

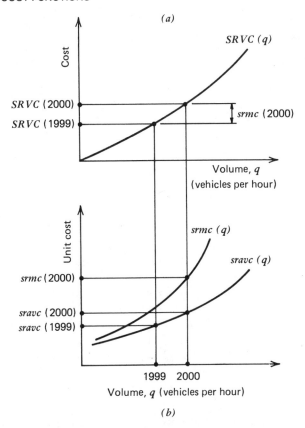

Figure 4-4. Illustrative short-run variable cost and marginal costs for a roadway.

The two unit cost functions, $sravc(q)$ and $srmc(q)$, are plotted in Figure 4-4b and the total variable cost function, $SRVC(q)$, is shown above in Figure 4-4a.

Suppose that in this particular situation, the flow rate was to increase marginally (or by one unit) from 1999 vehicles per hour to 2000 vehicles per hour. How would this marginal increase change the various costs? What would the unit costs be, and how should they be interpreted?

First, using Equations (4-19), (4-20), and (4-21), the unit costs and associated trip times for the two volume rates would be as shown in Table 4-1. As a consequence, to add one more vehicle per hour onto the roadway—and thus to slightly increase congestion on it—would increase the average travel time per mile $t(q)$ by a tiny increment, or from 299.8 to 300 seconds per mile. Thus, each person would suffer a slight increase in his delay and discomfort portion of the average trip cost, an increase which is reflected by the increase in average trip cost or $sravc(q)$ from 35.35 to 35.37 cents per mile.

TABLE 4-1.   Illustration of Short-Run Average Variable Cost, Marginal Cost, and Travel Time on a Roadway

	Hourly Flow Rate (q)	
	1999	2000
Short-run average variable cost, $sravc(q)$, in cents/vehicle-mile	35.35	35.37
Short-run marginal cost, $srmc(q)$, in cents/vehicle-mile	74.16	74.26
Travel time, $t(q)$, in seconds/mile	299.8	300.0

However, even though each individual vehicle experiences only a 0.2-second increase in average travel time, *in total* the extra time for all 2000 vehicles amounted to an extra 0.2 seconds for each of the first 1999 vehicles (or a total of 399.8 seconds) and 300 seconds for the 2000th, or 699.8 seconds in all. The extra vehicle which entered the flow is unaware that an extra 399.8 seconds in delay to the other 1999 travelers has resulted from his entry—since he feels only 300 seconds or the average travel time; thus, time added to others can be regarded as *external* to individual users.

Second, what gives rise to the marginal cost of 74.26 cents per mile for the flow rate of 2000 vehicles? And what does it mean? Recall that the marginal cost is equal to the increase in short-run total cost (or, equivalently, to the increase in the short-run total variable cost) which occurs when the flow rate is increased by just one unit. Thus, when the flow rate is increased from 1999 to 2000 vehicles per hour, the additional cost to all q vehicles—or extra total cost—will be about 74.26 cents. This is the accumulated extra cost which is experienced, collectively, by all 2000 vehicles and represents the combined user cost of the extra 0.2 seconds which is added onto each of the first 1999 vehicles plus the cost of the 5-min trip to the 2000th tripmaker. The disutility experienced by the first 1999 vehicles—or the difference between $srmc(2000)$ and $sravc(2000)$—is of course not felt by the 2000th vehicle; it is an external cost and in the absence of a congestion toll will be ignored by any individual vehicle in the flow.

One might ask: Who is responsible for the marginal cost? Using our same example, we noted that the marginal cost associated with a flow rate of 2000 was 74.26 cents. Since it is the extra total cost which was added when the 2000th vehicle entered the flow, we *might* be tempted to say that the last vehicle arrival, or 2000th vehicle to enter the flow, caused this extra cost and thus was responsible for the additional cost. *However, this would not be correct*. This marginal cost stemmed from a unit increase in flow rate. Specifically, in this case, it is the extra cost which occurred when 2000 rather than 1999 vehicles jammed onto a highway facility during an hour, without regard for when during the hour "the" extra vehicle arrived. In short, neither the position in line nor which vehicles were there first is pertinent. The extra cost stemmed from the extra congestion occurring when 2000 rather than 1999 vehicles used the facility. Also, if the first 1999 vehicles had not been there, the "last" vehicle would not have "caused" the congestion (in total) to increase as indicated by the marginal cost. Each and every one of the 2000 vehicles contribute equally to the occurrence of the congestion and to the value of the marginal cost at the margin.

4-4 LONG-RUN COST FUNCTIONS

The "fixed capacity" cost relations discussed in the previous section should be regard as *short-run cost functions* since it is assumed that the fixed capacity (i.e., amount of guideways, rolling stock, etc.) can not be altered so as to change the overall travel cost function during the time interval represented by the short run. Thus, in the short run only the congestion and other such variable costs will vary with changes in usage or flow levels. *Over the long-run*, however, the facility capacity and cost relationships can be altered (both upward and downward), thus changing the short-run total cost function. Occasionally, long-run cost functions may be called *planning cost functions* since they incorporate planned changes in facilities and operations. A long-run cost function represents the minimum cost of serving a particular volume q. That is, among the various technological options available, we assume that—as a planning matter—we can choose the technological alternative to serve a desired volume at least cost. We emphasize that in the long run facilities can be completely altered and rebuilt. The long-run or planning curves will be designated by the prefix *lr* and short-run or operating ones by the prefix *sr*; capitals will be used for the *total* cost curves and lowercase for the *unit* cost curves.

Let us consider the long-run cost relationships (or planning cost functions) in two steps; first, while analyzing the cost functions for facilities of just three facility capacity levels and, second, while considering the entire range of capacity possibilities. The first of these conditions is shown in Figure 4-5 in which facility (0) is assumed to represent the cost conditions for the smallest possible facility.

Several comments are in order regarding these three facility sizes (or plant sizes, in the jargon of the economist). First, the fixed cost (F_0) for the *smallest* facility does not represent the initial capital outlays (or book value or outstanding bond value) for that facility but is the opportunity value of the facility land and other fixed factors of production; simply, F_0

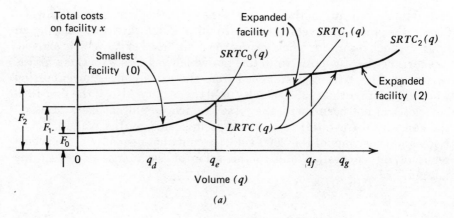

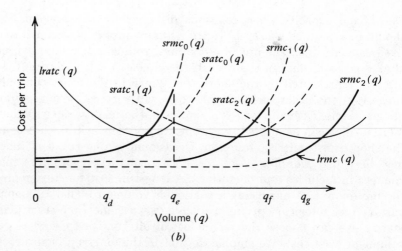

Figure 4-5. Cost functions for three facility sizes. (*a*) Total cost functions. (*b*) Marginal and average total cost functions.

represents the value of the required fixed facilities and land in their highest other use and thus the opportunity value which must be foregone if they are retained in transport service. Second, for these three cases it would be less costly to expand the smallest facility to the level of facility 1 if the flow q were expected to be between q_e and q_f *and* if the smallest facility were not rejected. In short, here we are merely examining which alternative is less costly at specified levels of output; none are examined in terms of overall feasibility. Similarly, among the three cases, facility 2 is the less costly for expected flows above q_f.

Summarizing these comments, the heavy line in Figure 4-5a, or $LRTC(q)$, defines the *long-run total cost function* which is applicable for facility expansion and planning purposes. That is, over the long run we can expand capacity such that the total costs for flow q are defined by the heavy line; thus, the long-run function informs us about the trade-off between fixed and variable costs or, if you will, between capacity and congestion costs. Of more significance, the slope of this heavy total cost line—or, the derivative of the long-run total cost function with respect to flow q—can be defined as the *long-run marginal cost* curve or $lrmc(q)$ and is shown as a "sawtoothed" heavy solid line in Figure 4-5b. The dashed portion of any of the marginal cost curves together with its solid line portion defines the short-run marginal cost for the particular facility to which it refers. For example, suppose that the existing facility were expanded to the level of facility 1 because of long-run demand expectations as related to long-run total cost conditions. Once the facility has been expanded to that level, though, only its short-run marginal cost curve, or $srmc_1(q)$, is relevant for determining the day-to-day cost changes associated with changes in flow q.

Definitionally, the long-run and short-run marginal cost curves are somewhat similar. The long-run marginal cost is equal to the increase in total cost which stems from a unit increase in flow rate, over the long run. Thus, it tells one about cost increases stemming from changes in capacity or congestion (as they jointly interact). As flow, and thus congestion, builds up on a low-capacity facility, it increasingly becomes cost-effective to increase the capacity; then, just after an increase in capacity, the congestion and long-run marginal cost is low until once again the flow builds up.

Analytically, we get

$$lratc(q) = \frac{LRTC(q)}{q} \qquad (4\text{-}22)$$

$$lrmc(q) = \frac{\Delta LRTC(q)}{\Delta q} = \frac{\partial LRTC(q)}{\partial q} \qquad (4\text{-}23)$$

and

$$lrmc(q) = LRTC(q) - LRTC(q-1) \qquad (4\text{-}23)$$

where $LRTC(q)$ = long-run total cost for a volume of q
    $lrmc(q)$ = long-run marginal cost for a volume of q
    $lratc(q)$ = long-run average total cost for a volume of q

The discontinuities for the $lrmc(q)$ function, which occur for flows of q_e and q_f in Figure 4-5b deserve explanation. If the flow rate were expected to be exactly q_e, then $LRTC(q_e)$, $SRTC_0(q_e)$, and $SRTC_1(q_e)$

would all be equal. Thus, in terms of short- or long-run total costs, the planner would be indifferent between facility 0 and facility 1. However, at flow q_e, the short- and long-run marginal cost would be equal to $srmc_0(q_e) = lrmc(q_e)$ if facility 0 was in place, but would be equal to $srmc_1(q_e) = lrmc(q_e)$ if facility 1 were built instead.

For the situation shown in Figure 4-5, the long-run *incremental* costs of expanding facility capacity and output beyond some nonzero output level can be determined simply by summing the long-run marginal costs between the before and after output levels. Whereas marginal costs represent the extra total costs which are incurred when the output is increased by *one* unit, incremental costs represent the extra total costs which are incurred when the output is increased by *more than one* unit. As an example, let us determine the incremental costs (i.e., the additional costs) which result from expanding the output level from q_d to q_g (where $0 < q_d < q_e$ and $q_g > q_f$). The long-run incremental costs for the extra flow, or $LRIC_{dg}$, will be as follows:

$$LRIC_{dg} = LRTC(q_g) - LRTC(q_d) = \sum_{q=q_d}^{q_g} lrmc(q) \qquad (4\text{-}25)$$

Also, it can be shown that $LRTC(q_g)$ is

$$LRTC(q_g) = LRTC(q_f) + \sum_{q=q_f}^{q_g} srmc_2(q) \qquad (4\text{-}26)$$

By a similar substitution for $LRTC(q_f)$ in Equation (4-26),

$$LRTC(q_g) = LRTC(q_e) + \sum_{q=q_e}^{q_f} srmc_1(q) + \sum_{q=q_f}^{q_g} srmc_2(q) \qquad (4\text{-}27)$$

Also, it can be seen that

$$LRTC(q_e) = LRTC(q_d) + \sum_{q=q_d}^{q_e} srmc_0(q) \qquad (4\text{-}28)$$

After substituting Equation (4-28) into equation (4-27) and substituting the sum into (4-25), the incremental costs incurred when the output is increased from q_d to q_g are

$$LRIC_{dg} = \sum_{q=q_d}^{q_e} srmc_0(q) + \sum_{q=q_e}^{q_f} srmc_1(q) + \sum_{q=q_f}^{q_g} srmc_2(q) \qquad (4\text{-}29)$$

Thus, with the above formulation, only variable costs are involved in adjusting facility capacity and expanding the output level beyond some nonzero output level (over the long run). However, this is not to say that consideration of the fixed costs associated with different levels of output is unimportant or that they are not involved. Rather, the fixed costs are directly related to a determination of the lowest cost technology, of the appropriate cost function for various levels of output, and, therefore, of both the long-run and short-run marginal cost curves. Furthermore, the fixed costs are involved importantly in matters of both economic and financial feasibility, in matters of pricing policy, and in matters of facility abandonment; these problems will receive detailed treatment in later chapters. Also, while the formulation in Equation (4-29) did not explicitly include the fixed costs, or changes in fixed costs, it must be emphasized that they *are* incorporated, albeit implicitly. First, it must be recalled that long-run cost functions do not make any distinction between fixed and variable costs since both can be varied over the long run. Second, and referring to Equation (4-25), we can rewrite that expression if we substitute for $LRTC(q_g)$ and $LRTC(q_d)$ as follows:

$$LRIC_{dg} = [F_2 + \sum_{q=1}^{q_g} srmc_2(q)] - [F_0 + \sum_{q=1}^{q_d} srmc_0(q)] \qquad (4\text{-}30)$$

where the short-run marginal cost functions are summed from $q = 1$.

Thus, it is apparent that the long-run cost functions do account for changes in both variable costs and fixed costs. The quandry revolves around the fact that the formulation shown by Equation (4-29) includes only *long-run* marginal costs—since the short- and long-run marginal costs are equivalent for the volume ranges indicated—while in Equation (4-30) the ranges include both short- and long-run marginal costs and thus necessitate the inclusion of fixed costs.

The cost functions characterized thus far, and shown in Figure 4-5, were those for highly *indivisible* technologies for which the expansion possibilities were greatly restricted and "lumpy." In simpler terms it was implied that capacity and service (which are joint products) can be expanded only in large increments or in large jumps. More realistically, though, if one considers the entire range of design and operational features which *can* be altered by the engineer and which affect either capacity or travel conditions (speeds, accidents, etc.), in addition to the variability with respect to number of vehicles or passengers using the facilities, it seems more reasonable to regard transport technologies as being highly divisible and as being capable of expansion in small if not virtually continuous increments. For *perfectly divisible* technological situations, in which a virtual infinity of options are available, the inclusion of the cost functions for all cases would result in the long-run marginal cost (or long-run total cost) curve being changed from the sawtooth (or scalloped) character shown in Figure 4-5 to the smooth curves of Figure 4-6. Importantly, the short-run marginal cost and short-run average total cost curves would remain (shapewise or in form) much the same as before,

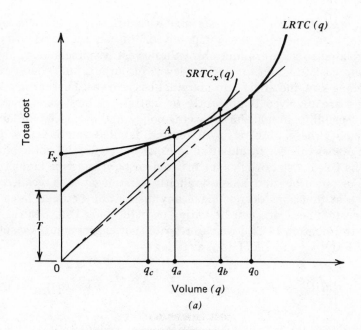

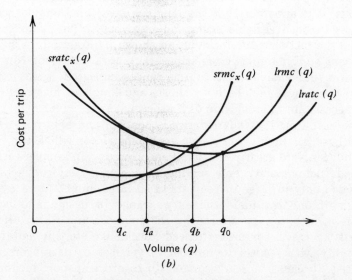

Figure 4-6. Long-run cost functions with nonconstant returns to scale. (*a*) Total cost functions: T = threshold cost; $SRTC_x(q)$ and $LRTC(q)$ are tangent at point A. (*b*) Unit cost functions.

except of course there are more of them; the short-run curves are also shown in Figure 4-6 for some facility x.

For the general long-run cost situation illustrated in Figure 4-6, increasing returns to scale (or economies of scale) are exhibited for output levels below q_0, and decreasing returns to scale (or diseconomies of scale) are exhibited for output above q_0. In the former case the long-run average total costs are falling as output increases and in the latter they are rising. Also, in situations such as this, the long-run average total costs will continue to fall until they reach a minimum—at output level q_0—then will begin to increase. At the point when the long-run average total costs are at a minimum, they will be equal to the long-run marginal cost. [They are equal since the slope of the long-run total cost function at q_0 is exactly equal to the slope of a line from the origin to $LRTC(q)$ at volume equal to q_0. Recall that the slope of the $LRTC(q)$ function is equal to the long-run marginal cost and that the slope of a line from the origin to the $LRTC(q)$ function is equal to the long-run average total cost.] No particular significance should be attached to this minimum average total cost point, however. While it is the point at which the unit costs will be lowest, it should not be regarded as the "optimum" situation or as the most cost-effective point—*unless* the expected demand and output will be at level of q_0 and constant. We shall consider this point more fully below.

To reemphasize, the long-run cost function is developed by determining the total cost of *the* lowest cost alternative at each and every output level. Thus, it represents the costs to which we can adjust or adapt over the long run. For instance, at an output of q_a there are numerous technologies and operations available for producing an output of level q_a. One of these alternatives will have the lowest total cost for producing an output of q_a and *its* cost is equal to $LRTC(q_a)$. In this case, as shown in Figure 4-6, facility x is the facility having lowest total cost at an output of q_a; thus, *if* we were to expect an output of level q_a, then facility x would be the most cost-effective facility. For this situation the following conditions would hold:

$$LRTC(q_a) = SRTC_x(q_a)$$
$$lratc(q_a) = sratc_x(q_a)$$
$$lrmc(q_a) = srmc_x(q_a)$$

and

$$srmc_x(q_b) = sratc_x(q_b) \qquad (4\text{-}31)$$

The first condition holds because the two cost points are coincident: facility x is the facility having the lowest total cost at output q_a. The second condition holds since the average total cost is simply the total cost divided by the output q_a; or, put differently, the slope of a line from the origin to either $SRTC_x(q_a)$ or $LRTC(q_a)$ is coincident. The third condition holds true since the $SRTC_x(q)$ function is tangent to the $LRTC(q)$ function at output q_a and since, therefore, the slope of two functions will be identical at that point. Finally, the last condition holds since the short-run marginal cost is always equal to the short-run average total cost at the minimum cost point for the latter.

For the situation depicted in Figure 4-6, it should be noted that the long-run marginal cost decreases until output reaches a level of q_c and increases thereafter. That is, $lrmc(q)$ is at a minimum at an output of q_c. Graphically, this means that the slope of the $LRTC(q)$ function gradually decreases as we move from an output of 1 unit to q_c units (which is the inflection point) and then begins to increase. Or, analytically, the first derivative of the $LRTC(q)$ function with respect to q decreases until the output is q_c, at which point it begins to increase [i.e., the second derivative of $LRTC(q)$ with respect to q changes its sign at an output of q_c].

As mentioned before, some analysts often take a particular interest in the output level which affords the minimum average total cost, incorrectly believing that this necessarily represents the most cost-effective situation. Suppose, for instance, that output were expected to be at a level of q_a (and to remain constant). In this case facility x would be preferred since it would permit the total costs—during *both* the long and short run—to be minimized. Once facility x was adopted and built, however, one often is tempted to maintain that it *should* be operated at *its* minimum average total cost level, which in this case would be output level q_b. *But this higher output level for facility x would represent a misuse of resources.* That is, if the long-run demand were such that output level of q_b rather than q_a were to be accommodated, then lower total costs for that level of output could be achieved by expanding the facility capacity rather than by operating facility x at its short-run minimum average total cost output level. This can be seen simply by comparing $sratc_x(q_b)$ with $lratc(q_b)$ and noting that the latter is smaller, thereby indicating that total cost savings would accrue to the q_b tripmakers if the facility were expanded still further (instead of operating facility x at a higher output level than q_a).

The problem of determining the long-run total cost function, as shown by $LRTC(q)$ in Figure 4-6a, is simply one of determining the most cost-effective (or least-cost) technology for each level of output to which one can adjust over the long run. It is of course comparable to the usual engineering design problem in which the least annual cost design solution is sought by comparing various pavement types or thicknesses, and so forth, and by making trade-offs between technologies, between materials and labor, or among facility, vehicle operating, and user travel costs until the least costly design is determined. While most engineers make these sorts of calculations within the context of benefit-cost analysis, here it will be assumed that the long-run cost functions represent the minimum cost possibilities for the specified levels of output and thus that no other (profitable) engineering design changes can be made for the specified output and time period conditions.

The difficulties and complexities of converting the required input of material and labor resources into costs will not be subject for discussion here except to mention two aspects: (1) it will be necessary to account for absolute or relative changes in the cost of labor or material inputs that occur over time and (2) it will be necessary to distinguish between market prices and opportunity costs where they differ. Regarding the latter aspect, on occasion market prices may overstate or understate the value which the forfeited resources have or would have in alternative opportunities or uses; in these instances market prices will be replaced by "shadow prices" or prices which are more appropriate measures of the real opportunity cost to society of the inputs.[12] Chapter 12 discusses the various methodologies which are available to estimate cost functions.

---

[12]For a good discussion of this point, see Maass et al., op. cit., pp. 49 ff, and 198 ff. Also, the opportunity costs of inputs may be defined as the revenues from other alternative investments which must be foregone in order to acquire the input.

CHAPTER 5

BENEFITS OF TRANSPORTATION

In addition to the costs associated with travel, there are benefits resulting from tripmaking. Indeed, a major task of transportation planners is to insure that the benefits of tripmaking exceed the costs of travel and the associated facilities. As will be seen, the assessment of travel benefits is intimately related to the specification and measurement of demand functions. As noted in Chapter 2, our knowledge about demand is meager and our accuracy in predicting demand changes is poor, especially over a long time period. To make any progress in the investment planning and pricing process, however, we need to understand the sources of travel benefits.

5-1 DEMAND AND USER BENEFIT FUNCTIONS

In Chapter 2, we noted that a demand function expresses the dependent relationship between the quantity of tripmaking desired and the *price* of travel, where the trip price includes all the private time, effort, and money expenses incurred by travelers. A demand function may also be interpreted and used to indicate the willingness of tripmakers to pay for travel. This willingness to pay is the primary measure of the (individual) value or benefit derived from a particular trip.

The use of "willingness to pay" as a measure of user benefit requires some discussion. First, we must distinguish between what tripmakers actually *do* "pay" and what they *would be willing to* "pay." For example, and referring to Figure 5-1, if the price or user cost were p_B and if q_B trips were demanded, the value of the trip *for the tripmaker at the "margin"* (i.e., the q_Bth traveler) can be determined; that is, the marginal tripmaker or person having the lowest trip value among those traveling just broke even, paying exactly as much as the trip was worth to him. If the price increased, the q_Bth traveler would forego his trip, as might others because the value or "willingness to pay" for the trip is less than its cost. Obviously, this same value also serves as a measure of the amount which each of the other (or $q_B - 1$) travelers *does* pay, as distinct from the total amount that they would be *willing* to pay. No more than q_B trips would be demanded because the fixed price (p_B) is higher to those not making the trip than its value would be to them; thus, for price p_B, those not making the trip would find that their position on the demand function is to the right of and below point C. Thus, user cost serves as a lower bound on the amount that tripmakers will pay.

For all those actually making trips, other than the one at the "margin," it is reasonable to expect that they would accrue some value or benefit *over and above* the price they must pay. In the terms of the economist all tripmakers or consumers, except for the traveler at the margin, would accrue a surplus.

The *additional* value or benefit over and above the price paid is termed *consumer surplus* by the economist. That is, an individual will *usually* be willing to pay a little more than he was actually charged or than his payments in time, effort, and money; consequently, he usually will receive a little *extra* value, an amount equal to his consumer surplus. The total consumers' surpluses accruing to the q_B users when the price is p_B (from Figure 5-1) would be equal to the area HBC. Note, further, that if the price were lowered to p_A, the consumers' surpluses would be increased to the level of area HAD; the extra consumers' surpluses resulting from the price change would be equal to the difference between the two areas, or $BADC$.

At this point it is important to distinguish more precisely between the term *benefit* (and "user cost") as commonly defined by many transportation planners and engineers and as used here. These distinctions are essential to a full understanding of all that follows.

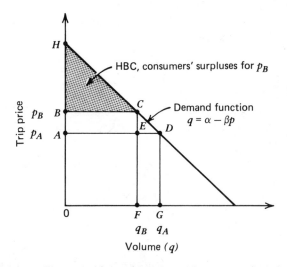

Figure 5-1. Illustrative demand function with consumers' surplus shaded.

First, the economist (usually) defines user *benefit* as being equivalent to the value which travelers expect to receive from making trips, as measured by the gross amount which travelers would be willing to pay for those trips. Referring to Figure 5-1, for a price of p_B, travelers would be willing to pay amounts as indicated by the area under the demand curve to the left of point C. More specifically, if the price were p_B, the total benefit or value accruing to the q_B tripmakers would be equal to area $HOFC$ or the entire area under the demand curve and to the left of point C. If the price were lowered to p_A more trips would be demanded and the total benefit or value accruing to q_A tripmakers would be equal to area $HOGD$.

The transportation engineer's definition of "benefit" usually does not correspond to the economist's definition presented above but is defined as the reduction in user cost which accompanies a price change (where price is construed broadly in terms of the time, effort, and money expense of travel). In this example, if the price were at a level of p_B, then the "cost" *to each user*[1] would be the same as the price he pays or p_B. (Of course, all but the tripmaker at the margin would be willing to pay more than that amount.) If the price were dropped to p_A, then the "user cost" would drop accordingly. The difference in "user cost," or reduction from p_B to p_A, is what the planner usually defines as the "benefit" per trip. Thus, the total amount of "user cost reduction" or total amount of "benefit" associated with a price reduction from p_B to p_A—as usually defined by the transportation planner—would be equal to the area $BADC$. This "benefit" measure is equivalent to the change in total net user benefit (where net user benefit is defined as being equal to users' value minus users' "cost") which stems from a price change (or change in user "cost"); further, it is identical to the change in consumers' surpluses which results from a price change. While this definitional matter may be subtle, the fact remains that it is crucially important when evaluating the benefits and worthwhileness of *a specific facility* as opposed to evaluating the benefits and worthwhileness of a change to some facility. The above point can be demonstrated as follows:

1. **Engineer's Analysis.**
    a) Travel "benefits" from price reduction = reduction in total user "costs" (from price change) = $BADC$ = change in consumers' surpluses.

2. **Economist's Analysis.**
    Net User Benefits (NUB) Before the Change in Price
    a) Travel benefits at price p_B = value derived from q_B trips = $HOFC$.

---

[1]As noted in Chapter 3, there is no strict relationship between (real) cost to society and "cost" to the user; so no confusion will develop, the latter is placed within quotation marks.

b) User "costs" at price p_B = user payments for q_B trips = $BOFC$.

c) Net user benefits at price p_B = HBC = consumers' surpluses at price p_B = NUB_B.

Net User Benefits After the Change in Price

a) Travel benefits at price p_A = value derived from q_A trips = $HOGD$.

b) User "costs" at price p_A = user payments for q_A trips = $AOGD$.

c) Net user benefits at price p_A = HAD = consumers surpluses at price p_A = NUB_A.

Change in Net User Benefits (ΔNUB) from the Change in Price

a) Change in net user benefits from price reduction = $BADC$ = change in consumers' surpluses = $NUB_A - NUB_B$.

As a numerical example, suppose we wish to measure the change in net user benefits accompanying an increase in the frequency of service on a transit route. Increased frequency of service can result in reduced waiting times and crowding, so that average user cost declines. Suppose further that equilibrium volume and price were 1000 trips per hour at an average price of \$2.10 before the change and 1150 trips per hour at an average price of \$1.70 after the change. These two situations correspond to points C and D in Figure 5-1. If we assume that the demand function is approximately linear between these points, then the change in net user benefits (equal to area $BADC$ in Figure 5-1) is

$$\Delta NUB = \text{area } ABCE + \text{area } CED$$

$$= 1000(2.10 - 1.70) + 1/2(1150 - 1000)(2.10 - 1.70)$$

$$= \$430 \qquad\qquad (5\text{-}1)$$

Importantly, so long as the analyst is *only* interested in determining the *extra* benefits accompanying some price reduction (or service improvement), then either definition will provide the same ultimate result. That is, either definition will lead to a determination of the additional consumers' surpluses resulting from the change. In turn, these extra consumers' surpluses can be compared with the extra resource outlays which are required to bring about that change. Thus, one can determine whether the extra costs required to improve some facility from level B to level A are less than the extra benefits stemming from the improvement. If, on the other hand, the analyst wants to consider *as well* the desirability of the facility itself—before or after improvement—rather than simply analyze the desirability of the extra resource outlays, then the engineer's definition will not suffice. It provides *no* indication of the overall benefits and costs of the facility, before or after improvement—in contrast to the economist's definition. Specifically, with the economist's definition, we can see that the net user benefits at price p_B (before improvement), for example, are HBC; in turn, we can ask whether these net user travel benefits are at least as large as the resource costs (exclusive of those included in the user payments) required to provide and maintain the facility at a volume of q_B. And so forth. In what follows, we shall use the economist's definition of benefits.

In this discussion of net user benefits we should emphasize that examination of changes in net user benefits may be insufficient to reveal the desirability of different investments when they are considered in isolation. In particular, problems of interpretation and analysis arise in two situations. First, if the price change discussed above is accomplished by changes in the monetary charge for travel, then the change in net *user* benefit is equivalent to the change in net *social* benefit only if the reduction in the monetary revenue is accompanied by an equivalent change in the real cost of providing the service. A second circumstance in which exclusive attention to changes in net user benefit is inadvisable is when changes in external benefits occur. For these more general cases the best method of analysis is to examine the difference between total benefits and total costs, or for the changes in these quantities, to evaluate a change. This more general analysis is described below.

Returning to the main discussion, the essence can be summarized as follows. The demand function can be regarded as a schedule which indicates *in descending order* the value of the trip to those choosing to pay the indicated price of the trip. Since the qth tripmaker will be willing to pay (at a maximum) a price of $p(q)$ to make the trip, the value of the trip to him is just equal to $p(q)$. If we start with a simple linear demand function,

$$q = \alpha - \beta p \tag{5-2}$$

and invert it to find price as a function of volume, we get

$$p(q) = \frac{\alpha}{\beta} - \frac{q}{\beta} \tag{5-3}$$

in which $p(q)$ is the price which the qth tripmaker will be willing to pay (at a maximum); thus, this is his trip value. This linear demand function is often used as an approximation to more general functions for the purpose of net benefit evaluation.

The trip value—that is $p(q)$—is equivalent to the *marginal benefit*, or $mb(q)$, where marginal benefit is defined as the increase in total benefit which is accrued when the flow rate is increased by one unit (from $q - 1$ to q trips per hour). Or, stated differently,

$$mb(q) = TB(q) - TB(q - 1) \tag{5-4}$$

where $TB(q)$ is the total benefit accruing from a flow of q trips per hour. Accordingly,

$$mb(q) = \frac{\partial TB(q)}{\partial q} = \frac{\Delta TB(q)}{\Delta q} \tag{5-5}$$

Also, it can be seen that

$$TB(q) = \sum_{x=1}^{q} mb(x) \tag{5-6}$$

For the linear demand function shown in Equation (5-2), the marginal benefits are

$$mb(q) = p(q) = \frac{\alpha}{\beta} - \frac{q}{\beta} \tag{5-7}$$

and

$$TB(q) = \sum_{x=1}^{q} mb(x)$$

$$= \frac{q\alpha}{\beta} - \sum_{x=1}^{q} \frac{x}{\beta}$$

$$= \frac{q\alpha}{\beta} - \frac{q^2 + q}{2\beta} \tag{5-8}$$

Total user payments for a volume of q, or $TUP(q)$, can be calculated more directly, as price times the quantity of tripmaking:

$$TUP(q) = pq \tag{5-9}$$

or, for the linear demand function,

$$TUP(q) = \frac{q\alpha}{\beta} - \frac{q^2}{\beta} \tag{5-10}$$

Total user payments and benefits associated with a linear demand function at various flow levels are shown in Figure 5-2. In any particular situation or application, of course, the flow level which would actually be observed is the equilibrium flow determined by the interaction of the demand and price functions.

As a numerical example, suppose that $q = 100 - 10p$ or $mb(q) = 10 - q/10$. At a volume of $q = 80$, total benefits are $TB(80) = (80)(100)$

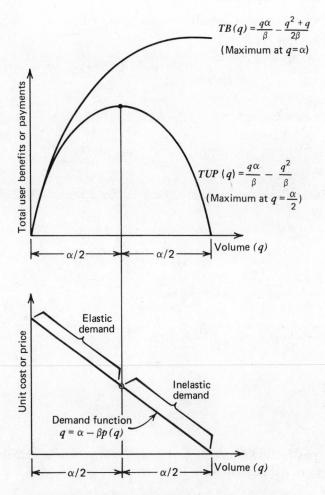

$$TB(q) = \frac{q\alpha}{\beta} - \frac{q^2 + q}{2\beta}$$

(Maximum at $q = \alpha$)

$$TUP(q) = \frac{q\alpha}{\beta} - \frac{q^2}{\beta}$$

(Maximum at $q = \frac{\alpha}{2}$)

Figure 5-2. Total benefit and user payment functions.

$/10 - (80^2 + 80)/2 \cdot 10 = 476$. Price with $q = 80$ is $p = 100/10 - 80/10 = 10 - 8 = 2$. Net user benefits at a volume of $q = 80$ are $NUB(80) = TB(80) - TUP(80) = 476 - (80)(2) = 316$. With a price reduction from $p = 2$ to $p = 1$, volume increases to $q = 100 - 10 \cdot 1 = 90$, total user benefits are $TB(90) = 491$ and net user benefits are $NUB(90) = 401$. The change in net user benefits is $\Delta NUB = NUB(90) - NUB(80) = 401 - 316 = 85$, whereas the change in total user benefits is $\Delta TB = TB(90) - TB(80) = 491 - 476 = 15$.

One final observation with respect to the willingness to pay for travel and individual incomes should be made. In general, individuals who have higher disposable incomes or greater wealth would be willing to pay more for their trips than would individuals with lower incomes. If the *full value* (in contrast to cost) of trips was extracted from each user (via some form of variable toll), the individual's disposable income would be reduced and his remaining trips would be valued lower than they otherwise would be. Consequently, the individual willingness to pay for trips depends—to some extent—on the price charged for travel and the resulting effect on disposable income. Fortunately, this effect can generally be ignored in transportation since most demand functions represent only one or a few trips per individual and the cost of all travel is very low relative to an individual's income; thus, overall income effects for any particular individual due to travel price changes are minor. Moreover, these income effects are likely to be *much* smaller than the uncertainty associated with estimating demand functions.[2] In what follows we shall ignore this secondary income effect.

5-2   TOTAL BENEFITS

The guiding principle in assessing the economic benefits (or costs) of new investments is to sum or aggregate the individual changes in welfare of all affected individuals. These changes in welfare can be measured as the value—in money terms—placed on them by the affected individuals. For travelers the value of this welfare is indicated by the total area under the demand curve, defined above as total user costs plus consumer surplus. Included in this total are benefits to users on competing modes, as discussed below.

While the benefits accruing directly to users form most of the economic benefits of facilities, several other categories of benefits have been suggested. First, the producer's surplus or profit associated with extra sales or rent resulting from increased travel has been included in some studies. These changes are extremely difficult to meaningfully measure. Moreover, it is likely that any such increased sales or land values would have occurred without improvements in the transportation system (although the sales and land values may have occurred somewhere else in the urban area or nation). That is, transportation improvements often concentrate economic activity which would otherwise have occurred anyway. No net social benefit can be attached to this transfer of activity since other areas lose to the same extent that a particular area may gain.[3]

---

[2]For a rigorous discussion of income effects, consumer surplus and measurement errors, see R. Willig, "Consumer's Surplus Without Apology," *American Economic Review* **66**(4), 1976.

[3]See Real Estate Research Corporation, *The Costs of Sprawl*, U.S. GPO, 1974; M. D. Cheslow and M. L. Olsson, "Transportation and Metropolitan Development," Urban Institute, Paper 5049-07, 1975; or the references cited in Chapter 1.

A second external benefit which is often claimed for transportation systems is that they possess an insurance value. For example, a transit system may be valued as a back-up mode of travel in case of an auto breakdown, even though an individual might never actually use the system. Again, this "insurance" value is extremely difficult to measure. The "insurance" value accruing to very occasional users of a system is reflected in the demand function, of course. It seems reasonable to assume that individuals who would never use a system over a long period of time receive no real benefit from it (especially since taxis or other forms of transportation provide pervasive and widely available alternatives for travel).

As a final note, investments in transportation facilities may serve social objectives other than increasing net economic benefit. In particular, investments may be used to affect a redistribution of income from wealthier to poorer individuals. A planner may consider this objective by weighting travel benefits accruing to poorer individuals higher than the benefits or value to wealthier members of society. We shall consider objectives of this sort and the related analysis in Chapter 10. In what follows we shall consider only the objective of maximizing net social welfare, to whomsoever the benefits and costs accrue. This objective seems quite reasonable, insures economic efficiency in using available capital funds, and should be a basic concern of any public agency.[4] Moreover, the analysis methodology used for pursuing this objective may be extended to other objectives.

5-3 BENEFITS ASSOCIATED WITH DIFFERENT FACILITY SIZES

To illustrate the change in equilibrium flow and the associated benefits that accompany changes in facility capacity (or service capability), the relationships shown in Figure 5-3 will be helpful. This figure corresponds to approximately the same situation which exists today for public highways or transit facilities (though less so for the latter because of operating cost subsidies), assuming that the price–volume function and average variable cost function are equivalent and that all payments by travelers are perceived in the course of their tripmaking. (For this case it should be easy to convince one that highway or transit improvements will virtually always lower the price–volume function or translate it horizontally and to the right.) As such, improvement of facility A to the level of B will drop the equilibrium travel price from p_A to p_B and will induce more tripmaking; that is, the quantity of travel demanded will increase from a volume of

---

[4]This objective has received a Congressional mandate in the field of federally funded water resource projects. See p. 2964 of *United States Code*, "Flood Control Act of 1936," 33 U.S.C. 701a (1980).

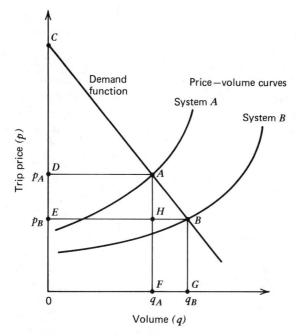

Figure 5-3. Equilibrium conditions for different facilities. Note: System A, existing facility *before* improvement; system B, existing facility *after* improvement.

q_A to q_B. It may be helpful to point out that the volume q_A which formerly used facility A and now uses facility B may be regarded as the "diverted volume" and that the volume increase may be termed the "induced" or "generated" volume. Note that the change or increase in flow or volume of movement is not called an increase in demand (the latter of which implies a shift in the demand function); a drop in the price which induces an increase in the quantity demanded or equilibrium flow is just that—and not an increase in demand!

As for the travel benefits associated with these two facilities, and the implied pricing policy, they can be determined in the fashion suggested earlier. For facility A, and its equilibrium flow and price levels of q_A and p_A, respectively, the total travel benefit (for q_A trips) would be equal to area $AFOC$, while that for facility B (and q_B trips) would be equal to area $BGOC$. The additional or extra benefit accruing to travelers from the improvement would be equal to the difference between the total benefit for B and that for A, or would be equal to area $ABGF$. Also, the net user benefit (or difference between total user benefits and user payments) before improvement would be equal to area ADC and after improvement would be area BEC. The difference between these two totals, or the change in net user travel benefit, would be equal to area $ABED$; as noted before, it is equal to the change in consumers' surpluses. As described earlier, this change in net travel benefit from an improvement is what transport engineers generally define as the "benefit" from improvement.

Also, it is well to note that the diverted travelers accrue a larger increment in net benefit than do the new or induced travelers. Specifically, each traveler among the volume q_A will experience a net benefit increase of $p_A - p_B$ from the improvement and as a group will find their net benefit increased by $AHED$; by contrast, the first additional or new traveler will receive an increase in net benefit (from improvement) that is slightly less than $p_A - p_B$ and the last additional traveler (i.e., the q_Bth traveler) or traveler at the margin will receive no increase in net benefit. The induced travelers ($q_B - q_A$) will each receive an increase in net benefit that averages $\frac{1}{2}(p_A - p_B)$, assuming that the demand curve is linear or nearly linear in this range. As a group, their increase in net benefit will be equal to the triangle AHB.

The above point is emphasized as transport planners often attribute the entire unit increase in net benefit (or, $p_A - p_B$) to both the former and induced travelers, a practice which is incorrect and which will overstate the increase unless the demand happens to be perfectly inelastic. The case of perfectly inelastic demand is illustrated in Figure 5-4. Such a case appears to be unrealistic but nevertheless is commonly implicit in many economic analyses conducted for public transport alternatives. While

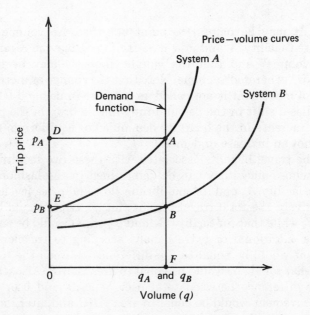

Figure 5-4. Equilibrium conditions for perfectly inelastic demand.

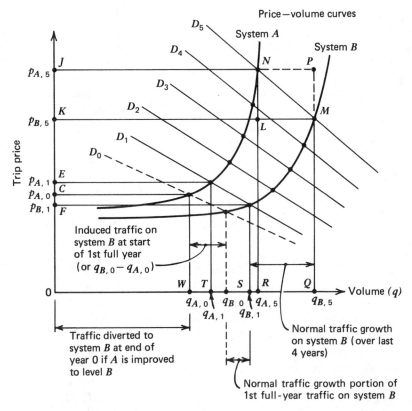

Figure 5-5. Equilibrium conditions (by year) for unimproved and improved system or facility. Note: D_t is the demand curve for the tth year and $q_{x,t}$ is the equilibrium flow for facility x during year t.

analysts do not explicitly assume that the demand is perfectly inelastic, it is the practical result of assuming that the equilibrium flow or actual volume after improvement will be identical to the volume before improvement.

Turning now to the longer-term effects of shifts in demand, as related to changes in facility capacity or service, these can be determined from the curves in Figure 5-5. (In this situation the comparative relationships are shown from the end of year 0 through the end of year 5. We will ignore the circumstances while facility A would be in the process of being improved to the level of facility B.) The year-by-year equilibrium conditions can be determined for the two alternatives, as well as the benefit and net benefit circumstances. Also, the functions shown in Figure 5-5 can be used to describe the increases in tripmaking or traffic flow and to relate these increases to the more usual terminology of the transportation engineer.

Specifically, if facility A were improved to the level of B and opened for usage at the end of year 0, the volume which would have used facility A (had it not been improved) or $q_{A,0}$ is diverted to facility B; this volume or $q_{A,0}$ would be the so-called diverted traffic.[5] An additional volume of traffic will be induced to travel because of the improved service conditions (as measured by the drop in equilibrium price); this increment of volume will be equal to $q_{B,0} - q_{A,0}$ and is equivalent to the so-called induced volume. The additional increases in traffic flow from year to year (i.e. following the end of year 0) can be regarded as the normal traffic growth for facility B; during the first full year, the normal traffic growth for B would be $q_{B,1} - q_{B,0}$ while the increased flow from the end of the year 0 to the end of year 5 or $q_{B,5} - q_{B,0}$ is the normal traffic growth during the first five years of facility B.

Suppose that we wanted to measure the change in net user benefits (i.e., the increase in consumers' surpluses) which stemmed from the improvement of facility A to the level of facility B. In such an instance we should measure these changes year by year and then accumulate them over the planning horizon (which in this case is 5 years). Also, the year-by-year amounts should be discounted to their present value to account for the time value of money, a point which will be ignored for the moment but discussed fully in Chapter 8. Some analysts incorrectly suggest—by implication—that one should measure the change only during the design year (or last year of the planning horizon) and then treat this as occurring during all years. For example, it is obvious (at least in this instance) that the increase in consumers' surpluses in year 5—or area $JKMN$—is hardly equal to that occurring during any other year. Also, do not make the mistake (as some do) of treating area $JKMP$ as being equal to the change in net user travel benefits which would be accrued, rather than area $JKMN$.

5-4 DEMAND AND BENEFIT MEASUREMENT IN CHOICE SITUATIONS

In Chapter 3 demand functions were formulated to represent the conditions for choice situations in which the decision to use one mode or another, as but one example, is dependent upon the price of the mode in question as well as that of the competing mode. In turn, it is useful to indicate how to estimate the change in benefits and consumer surpluses

---

[5]Strictly speaking, it may be more appropriate to describe this component of volume (or $q_{A,0}$) as "base" or "current" traffic. However, if facility or system B represents a replacement for system A (the latter of which is then abandoned) and if facility B is on a new location but between the same pair of origin and destination points, then one might describe this component as diverted traffic. Since these definitional distinctions are not crucial to this exposition, the latter usage will be adopted for convenience.

when choice situations exist. Such situations are common with competing carriers, modes, or routes.

Let us assume that travelers are choosing between two competing alternatives (say, between two modes or two times of day) and that they consider the price of both alternatives when deciding whether or not to travel as well as which alternative to select. Then, an appropriate set of linear demand functions for alternatives x and y would be as follows:

$$q_x = \alpha_x + \beta_x p_x + \gamma_x p_y \qquad (5\text{-}11)$$

$$q_y = \alpha_y + \beta_y p_x + \gamma_y p_y \qquad (5\text{-}12)$$

where q_x and q_y represent the hourly quantity of trips to be demanded for choices x and y, respectively, when the price of choice x is p_x and price of choice y is p_y. The coefficients $\alpha_x, \beta_x, \gamma_x, \alpha_y, \beta_y,$ and γ_y are the demand parameters of the demand functions. For analytical convenience and simplicity in illustration, we have used a linear demand model and a binary choice situation.

The above demand functions can also be used to determine the travel benefits and net user benefits which are associated with different price levels. To illustrate this application, however, let us restate the demand function shown in Equation (5-11) as follows:

$$q_x|p_y = \alpha_x'|p_y + \beta_x p_x \qquad (5\text{-}13)$$

in which $q_x|p_y$ is the quantity of mode x trips to be demanded at price p_x, given that the price for mode y is p_y. Also, $\alpha_x'|p_y$ is the transformed value of the intercept, given the mode y price of p_y. As such, the cross-effects of the competing mode price are included. In effect, then, $\alpha_x'|p_y$ is equal to $\alpha_x + \gamma_x p_y$. (Referring to Figure 3-3, a graphical representation of the above function would be the trace which results if a plane perpendicular to the p_y axis were passed through the surface shown.) This form of the demand function is plotted in Figure 5-6 in two-dimensional form for two different levels of price p_y, as well as the corresponding one for $q_y|p_x$, or the quantity of mode y trips to be demanded at price p_y given that the mode x price was p_x. It can be seen that increases in p_y lead to demand increases for mode x due to shifts in tripmaking from mode y to mode x. By the same token, it can be shown that an increase in p_x would lead to an increase in the demand for mode y (and vice versa with respect to price reductions).

First, can these demand functions—when there are competing choices—be used to determine total benefits, total revenues, consumers' surpluses, and total costs? Simply, they would be used exactly as described previously. For instance, if the (equilibrium) prices for modes x and y, respectively, were 12 and 10 cents per trip, then the applicable demand functions

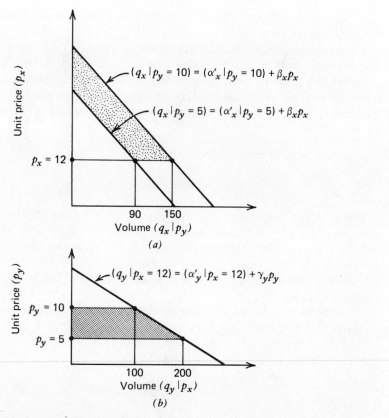

Figure 5-6. Demand functions and changes in consumer surplus in a choice situation.

for the two modes would be $q_x|p_y = 10$ and $q_y|p_x = 12$. The equilibrium volumes for modes x and y would be 150 and 100 trips per hour. In turn, the total benefits, total revenues, and so forth, could be calculated by separately computing these totals for each mode, one mode at a time. For instance, the consumers' surpluses for mode x would be equal to the area under the demand curve $(q_x|p_y = 10)$ but above the line where p_x is equal to 12. Those for mode y would be equal to the area under the demand curve $(q_y|p_x = 12)$ but above the line where p_y is equal to 10. And so forth.

Second, how we can use these functions to determine the consequences (such as the change in benefits or consumers' surpluses, etc.) which stem from a price change for one (or more) of the competing choices?[6]

---

[6]For a fuller discussion of the points to follow, see E. J. Mishan, *Cost-Benefit Analysis*, Praeger Publishers, New York, 1976, Chapters 7 to 9.

To begin the discussion on this point, let us again make use of the choice situation illustrated in Figure 5-6. Initially, assume that mode x has a price p_x which is equal to 12 cents per trip and that the price for mode y is equal to 10. Then, let the price p_y of mode y drop 5 cents per trip. As a result of this price reduction, the demand function for competing mode x will shift downward and to the left, as indicated, and become $q_x|p_y = 5$. (Of considerable importance for this initial example, we assume that the reduction of flow rate for q_x from 150 to 90 trips per hour will have no effect on the trip price of 12 cents per trip.) The demand function for mode y will remain as before ($q_y|p_x = 12$) since the price of its competing mode x remains unchanged.

As a result of the drop of p_y, more trips will be made on mode y and thus more total benefits will be accrued. Moreover, the increase in consumers' surpluses for mode y users will be equal to the shaded area in Figure 5-6b. This area—the increase in consumers' surpluses for mode y users—represents the total change in consumers' surpluses resulting from the price reduction since the mode y demand function embodies the effect of mode y price changes on both entirely new tripmakers and those shifting from mode x (given, of course, that the price of mode x remains fixed at price p_x of 12 cents per trip). That is, the dotted area in Figure 5-6a does *not* represent a loss or decrease in consumers' surpluses for mode x users since some of those former mode x users chose to shift over to mode y and thus to better themselves once the price of mode y was dropped. The remaining mode x users are no better and no worse off after the price drop for mode y than before; and their consumer surpluses remain unchanged.

The foregoing example (illustrated in Figure 5-6) can and often will represent an oversimplification of the "real world" and of the difficulties of measuring the full-scale effects of price changes (or service improvements) for many competing mode situations. To illustrate, we will consider a more complex situation, as illustrated in Figure 5-7. In this case recognition is made of the fact that in some competing mode situations changes in the equilibrium flow rates (or actual amounts of tripmaking) will lead to price changes for all of the competing modes and thus to shifts in the demand functions for all of competing modes (in contrast to the previous example in which the demand function or price changed for only one of the competing modes).

Again, the price functions shown in Figure 5-7 embody the total time, effort, and money expenses for tripmaking. Thus, the price varies with changes in the flow rate, thereby indicating changes in crowding, discomfort, and delay. And, since a price change for one mode will change the usage level of the competing mode—because of the demand cross-relations—it will lead to both a shift in the demand function and change in price for the competing mode, and vice versa. If, in this instance, the price function for mode x is lowered (either as a result of a fare or toll drop or as

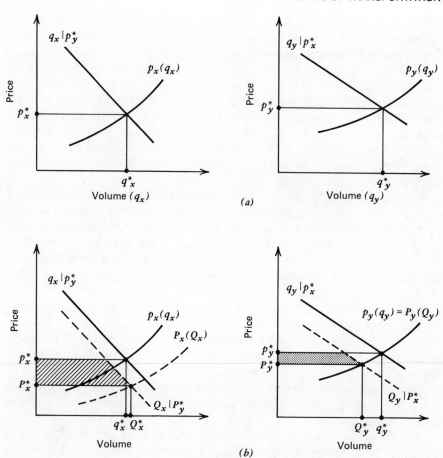

Figure 5-7. Illustrative changes in equilibrium consumer surplus in a choice situation. (a) Before improvement of mode x. (b) After improvement of mode x.

a result of some service improvement which lowers the travel time and thus trip price)—from $p_x(q_x)$ to $P_x(Q_x)$—the demand function for mode x will shift downward from $q_x|p_y^*$ to $Q_x|P_y^*$ and that for mode y will shift downward from $q_y|p_x^*$ to $Q_y|P_x^*$. However, the demand function for mode x shifted downward *not* because of the price drop in its own price but in response to the price drop for its competing mode y. Also, p_x^* and q_x^*—in lowercase—represent the equilibrium price and volume levels for mode x prior to the price change, while P_x^* and Q_x^*—in uppercase—represent the equilibrium values after the price change; a similar type of notation applies to the equilibrium values for mode y. Accordingly, we can see that a price reduction can easily lead to multiple effects, especially for transport facilities (and whether highway or public transit ones). We suspect that the illustration in Figure 5-7 would be typical in that price reductions to one of two competing modes would tend to reduce trip prices for both modes and thus to change consumer's surpluses for both modes.

Specifically, all former users of modes x and y, as well as some entirely new tripmakers who were induced to travel because of the price reductions, will be better off after the price reduction (or service improvement) to mode x, which in turn leads to a drop in the equilibrium price for mode y as well. However, it is not entirely clear how much each user will gain from the price reductions. For instance, as the price for mode x goes from p_x^* to P_x^* and that for mode y goes from p_y^* to P_y^*, some portion of mode y's former users—an indeterminate amount—will continue to use mode y and each of these will gain (or accrue extra consumer surplus) by an amount equal to $p_y^* - P_y^*$; the other users of mode y (or remainder of Q_y^*) consist of former mode x users and entirely new tripmakers, each of whom gain less than that amount. (They obviously gain something; otherwise, they would not have changed their travel patterns after the price drop.) It would appear that the increase in consumers' surpluses to the mode y users would be equal to the shaded area in Figure 5-7b. The situation for mode x is similar. Again, the mode x users—which in total are Q_x^*—are made up of three groups: former users of mode x who remain on mode x after the price drop; some users who shifted from mode y to mode x; and entirely new users who were induced to travel by the price drop. Each of the first group (i.e., the former mode x users) gain by the amount of the price drop, or $p_x^* - P_x^*$, while each user in the other two groups gains by less than that amount. Again, the specific number in each group is indeterminate, but even so we might estimate that the aggregate increase in consumers' surpluses for the mode x users would be equal to the crosshatched area in Figure 5-7b.

In practice, analytical rather than graphical solutions for equilibrium volumes and changes in consumers' surpluses are likely to be required in such complicated situations. Section 3-4 introduced some relevant techniques; Section 11-2 also discusses analytical techniques that are applicable.

CHAPTER 6

PRICING AND ECONOMIC EFFICIENCY IN THE SHORT RUN

In this chapter we consider the economic effects of different pricing and operating policies for specified transport facilities which, during the short run, can be regarded as fixed with respect to the amount of rolling stock, guideways, and so forth. The short run represents the period of time in which changes in facilities cannot be accomplished due to the delays of construction or purchasing. The managerial problem in the short run is how to manage and price the existing resources and facilities in the most advantageous manner. More particularly, a manager should ask how will different pricing policies affect the usage of a particular facility or operation, and, in turn, its benefits, costs, and revenues? Subsequently, which policy will lead to maximizing the net economic benefit to society and what are the implications of implementing such a policy (e.g., subsidy requirements, incidence of the benefits and costs among users, or the financial situation of the operating agency)? Or, for private providers, which policy will lead to increased profits?

Throughout this *initial* discussion of pricing and efficient utilization measures, the *costs of implementing* different pricing or control schemes will NOT be included or considered; "costless" pricing and control mechanisms will be assumed, thus ignoring any delays or inconveniences to riders or drivers that may result from collecting fares, instituting toll gates or installing control devices, and neglecting any capital or operating expenditures for the fare, toll collection, or control devices. In Chapter 13 this assumption will be relaxed and the consequences or costs of instituting and implementing different sorts of pricing or control schemes will be explored.

Three basic assumptions underlie the entire discussion and should be emphasized: (1) goods and services throughout the economy are priced at marginal cost; (2) the commitment of resources to the transport sector will not affect prices for the remainder of the economy or have feedback effects upon either the transport demands or the costs of providing transport services; and (3) the marginal utility of income is equal for all travelers and is constant over time (i.e., an extra dollar is worth the same to everybody and for all price levels). In addition, it will be assumed that travelers are homogeneous with respect to their travel time, effort, and money expenditures. As noted in Chapter 2, the last is not a necessary assumption, but it does simplify the discussion. In application, a heterogeneous traveling population may be assumed (as in Chapter 13).

Also, the economic efficiency objective function is presumed to be a maximization of total net social benefits in this chapter. Obviously, this objective function in no way involves the consideration of conflicting or overriding social or political criteria which call for a different income redistribution and the like. Nor does this objective consider the financial implications of the various short-run pricing and operating policies which are discussed. Certainly, these other considerations are of concern to operators. For simplicity, we have chosen to initially discuss the various situations encountered in making short-run decisions from the viewpoint of economic efficiency alone. Other objectives will be discussed in Chapters 9 and 10, and the practical difficulties of different short-run pricing strategies will be considered in Chapter 13.

To structure the discussion, we shall concentrate upon three prototypical situations. The first, which is common for high-density situations, is that in which average *total* travel costs are increasing with output increases; we term this case one of (relatively) *high demand*. In the *low-demand* case average total travel costs are falling with higher volumes. A specialized case is also considered, that of a backward-bending cost curve which may occur with very high volumes and an uncontrolled transport facility, such as an unsignalized roadway, which undergoes capacity *reductions* at high volumes. Also, we assume user costs equal $sravc_x(q)$, aside from surcharges.

6-1 BASIC ECONOMIC PRINCIPLES FOR PRICING AND OPERATING TRANSPORT FACILITIES IN THE SHORT RUN

For constant-demand situations both intratemporally (e.g., hour to hour) and intertemporally (e.g., year to year), the incremental benefit–cost principle is of primary importance in this short-run analysis and may be stated as follows: extra tripmaking should be encouraged so long as the marginal benefit associated with extra tripmaking is equal to or greater than the marginal cost incurred for extra tripmaking; or more simply, one should continue to increase transport output until the marginal benefit is just equal to the marginal cost. In analyzing the extra benefits, it is necessary to note that the demand function (or, alternatively, the quantity demanded vs. "willingness to pay" curve) in its inverse form approximates the marginal benefit curve; that is, it describes the increase in total benefit which results from increasing the hourly flow rate q by one tripmaker. Marginal benefit is *not* equivalent to the marginal revenue (or marginal payment) which results from uniform prices; the distinction will be made more precisely later within this section. As noted in Chapter 5, for a *linear* demand function, as shown in Equation (5-2), the marginal benefit for the qth tripmaker or $mb(q)$ is

$$mb(q) = p(q) = \frac{\alpha}{\beta} - \frac{q}{\beta} \qquad (6\text{-}1)$$

where $p(q)$ is the price which the qth traveler is willing to pay and α and β are parameters based upon income, population, and so forth. As shown in Equation (6-1), the price which the qth traveler is willing to pay is equal to the marginal benefit or $mb(q)$—that is, it is the benefit added by increasing the output q by one more trip. In Figure 6-1 the equality of marginal benefit and marginal cost occur at a volume of q_A.

Also, it should be reemphasized that our essential concern is not focused simply on the extra *facility* costs which must be incurred to expand or increase output, but on all extra costs associated with increases in output (to include increments in cost for facilities or vehicles and those for personal travel time and effort). Thus, our marginal benefit and marginal cost functions encompass all benefits and costs as described in the previous two chapters.

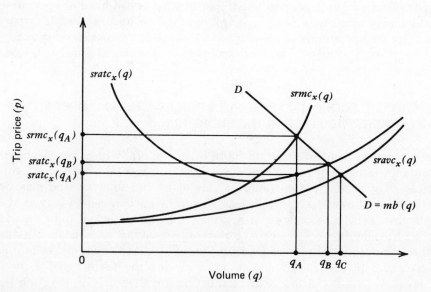

Figure 6-1. Short-run cost and demand relationships for a particular fixed facility and high demand (relative to cost). $mb(q)$ = marginal benefit or demand curve; $sratc_x(q)$ = short-run average total cost curve; $sravc_x(q)$ = short-run average variable cost curve; $srmc_x(q)$ = short-run marginal cost curve.

While the principle of setting marginal benefit equal to marginal cost was stated above in the context of providers concerned with maximizing net social benefit, it is important to note that this result can be achieved with private, profit-seeking firms acting in an environment of keen competition and in the absence of market imperfections such as external benefits or costs. This conclusion is one of the most important results of classical microeconomic theory and is the basis of Adam Smith's assertion of an "invisible hand" which directs individuals through the marketplace for the advantage of all.[1]

To develop this result, suppose that four firms are interested in providing a market with virtually identical services (Figure 6-2). In this case the volume served by each of the four potential providers must be summed to indicate the market or total volume q^*, so that $q^* = q_1^* + q_2^* + q_3^* + q_4^*$. For a market with perfect competition and identical services, the various providers would be forced to offer the same price to travelers. If one provider charged more, then travelers would move to its competitors. Likewise, a lower price would attract travelers from competitors. Moreover, each provider would charge a price such that the price equaled their short-run marginal cost at the volume each served. In Figure 6-2, for example, firm 1 serves q_1^* trips at a price p^* with $p^* = srmc_1(q_1^*)$.

The result that the equilibrium price equals short-run marginal cost for each provider occurs due to the firm's attempts to maximize profits. If the equilibrium price exceeded a firm's short-run marginal cost, then the firm could reduce its price, attract additional volume, and still have the incremental revenue exceed its incremental costs. Profits would then increase. Conversely, if the equilibrium price was less than a firm's short-run marginal cost, then a firm should try to reduce its volume since it would be losing money on the marginal travelers. Indeed, firm 4 should not offer *any* service at the equilibrium price p^* since costs would exceed payments at any volume level. Thus, in Figure 6-2, firm 2 serves q_2^* trips, firm 3 serves q_3^* trips, and firm 4 has no volume. Note, by the way, that firm 3 only covers its short-run variable cost [since $p^*q_3^* = q_3^* \cdot sravc_3(q_3^*)$], whereas firms 1 and 2 have payments exceeding variable costs.

It is the competition among firms for patronage in the situation depicted in Figure 6-2 which leads inexorably to the condition in which marginal costs equal marginal benefits (or p^*) for each firm. Since this is socially desirable in the sense that net benefits are maximized, it is a powerful argument in favor of free competition. Moreover, there are equally strong incentives to insure that least-cost operation policies are chosen (which is implicit in our definition of short-run variable costs) and that efficient investment occurs. Unfortunately, there are various imperfections in markets which tend to reduce the efficiency of free competitive

---

[1] A. Smith, *An Inquiry into the Nature and Causes of the Wealth of Nations*, W. Straham, London, 1776.

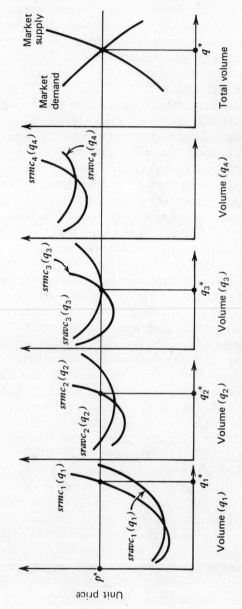

Figure 6-2. An illustration of competitive equilibrium and market supply.

markets. Notable in the case of transportation services is the effect of increasing returns to scale. In this case equilibrium prices equal to short-run marginal costs will result in deficits to individual providers; this case is discussed below.

6-2 PRICING AND OPERATION IN HIGH-DEMAND SITUATIONS

Turning first to the short-run situation for a particular facility x, typical cost and benefit functions might be as shown in Figure 6-1. The demand and short-run average total cost functions intersect to the right of the minimum average total cost point, so this is termed the *high-demand* case. In the short run the fixed costs will remain the same at high- or at low-volume levels; clearly, in the short run and over a time period too short to abandon, contract, or expand the facility, they should not affect the level of output if one is concerned with maximizing the total net benefit from use of the facility (i.e., without regard for matters of cost and benefit incidence and income distribution).

The only costs that are affected by the output level in the short run are the variable costs; the marginal cost curve or $srmc_x(q)$ measures the increase in total costs with increases in output. Up to an output level q_A (i.e., from $q = 1$ to $q = q_A$), and for the cost and demand (or marginal benefit) conditions of Figure 6-1, each additional trip or successive increase in the output level will add more to total benefits than it will add to total costs; that is, $mb(q) \geq srmc_x(q)$ for $q \leq q_A$. Thus, total net benefits will continue to increase up to level q_A and will be equal to[2]

$$TNB_x(q_A) = \sum_{q=1}^{q_A} mb(q) - \sum_{q=1}^{q_A} srmc_x(q) - F_x \tag{6-2}$$

where $TNB_x(q_A)$ are the (hourly) total net benefits for facility x when the output level is q_A. However, for an output above q_A, the marginal costs or $srmc_x(q)$ will always exceed the marginal benefit $mb(q)$, thus decreasing the total net benefit. Thus, while each added traveler (above q_A but below q_C) would *privately* gain from making the trip, the amount *he or she* would gain would be less than the increment in costs imposed on society and would reduce the total net benefit. That is, left to his own devices, each new traveler would consider only the short-run average variable cost and would ignore the extent to which he added congestion to others. The marginal cost represents the accumulated value of the delays to others as well as himself if an additional trip is made.

---

[2]In practice, since the fixed costs, or F_x, cannot be affected in the short run, our problem is simply to maximize the following difference between the sums of marginal benefits and short-run marginal costs: $\Sigma mb(q) - \Sigma srmc_x(q)$. Mathematically, this difference, and thus $TNB_x(q)$, will be maximized when the output is such that $mb(q)$ equals $srmc_x(q)$.

While, *in the short run*, total net benefits when maximized need not be positive in order for maximum efficiency to be achieved, they will be positive in cases of high demand if the facility is operated efficiently [i.e., maximize volume such that $mb(q) \geqslant srmc_x(q)$]. Also, for this high-demand case, the total net benefits will always be positive for flows equal to or less than q_B (since the marginal benefit will be equal to or greater than the short-run average total cost). They may still be positive at even higher flows—because of the consumers' surpluses—but the actual result will depend on the exact nature of the demand and cost functions.

Other aspects are important. If the output level were increased beyond q_A to q_B, the total costs for q_B would still be less than the total benefits for q_B, and would be

$$TNB_x(q_B) = \left[\sum_{q=1}^{q_B} mb(q) \right] - SRVC_x(q_B) - F_x \qquad (6\text{-}3)$$

$$= \sum_{q=1}^{q_B} mb(q) - \sum_{q=1}^{q_B} srmc_x(q) - F_x \qquad (6\text{-}4)$$

The total benefits would exceed the total costs to the extent of the consumers' surpluses.

While for the cost and demand relationships in Figure 6-1 output at q_B would cause no apparent loss to society (i.e., total net benefit would still be positive), there would be a loss for society relative to the cost and benefit situation for output at q_A. In this case the net loss from increasing output from q_A to q_B or incremental total net benefit ($ITNB_{x,AB}$) would be

$$ITNB_{x,AB} = TNB_x(q_B) - TNB_x(q_A) \qquad (6\text{-}5)$$

and substituting from Equations (6-2) and (6-4),

$$ITNB_{x,AB} = \sum_{q=q_A}^{q_B} mb(q) - \sum_{q=q_A}^{q_B} srmc_x(q) \qquad (6\text{-}6)$$

Since $mb(q) < srmc_x(q)$ for $q > q_A$, it should be clear that the incremental total net benefit is negative.

The losses occurring when output exceeds the flow rate at which the marginal cost is equal to the marginal benefit can also be illustrated graphically, as shown in Figure 6-3. For each and every additional unit of output above q_A, the extra cost is somewhat larger than the extra benefit. As a consequence, if the output were to increase to q_C, the loss in total net benefit—as compared with that which would be obtained with an output of q_A and $mb(q) \geq srmc_x(q)$ for all units of output—would be equal to the hatched area in Figure 6-3. Algebraically, this area is calculated as the difference in marginal benefits and marginal costs summed at each intermediate volume level:

$$ITNB_{x,AC} = TNB_x(q_C) - TNB_x(q_A) \qquad (6\text{-}7)$$

$$= \sum_{q=q_A}^{q_C} mb(q) - \sum_{q=q_A}^{q_C} srmc_x(q) \qquad (6\text{-}8)$$

If travelers are allowed to consider only their private travel costs—which we assume here to be equal to the short-run average variable costs or $sravc_x(q)$—then the flow will stabilize at q_C with a price equal to $sravc_x(q_C)$. As a consequence, if we are to maximize net benefits, some device or mechanism must be used to insure that output is limited to q_A and to insure that travelers are "segregated" in the fashion indicated by the demand curve. Specifically, to induce the most economically efficient result, we must insure that travelers having trip value or benefit below the benefit or trip value *at the margin* do not travel in place of others who have values which place them above the level at the margin. Referring again to Figure 6-3 and Equation (6-2), the total net benefit would be maximized only if the output were q_A and if restricted to travelers having values equal to or higher than $p(q_A)$ or $mb(q_A) = srmc_x(q_A)$.

At least theoretically, a price mechanism—such as special tolls or fares—would appear to be the most suitable instrument for effectuating this type of control; in fact, not to use such a device would be to admit, if not

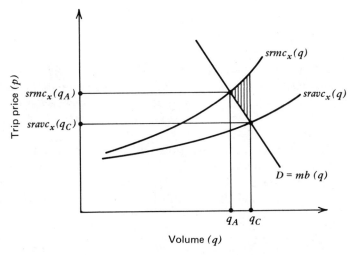

Figure 6-3. Social losses from a flow exceeding the economically efficient output.

guarantee, that the facilities would not actually produce the maximum total net benefits. Furthermore, it should be clear that more than the economically efficient output level is involved here; it is assuring, in addition, that the expected or anticipated benefits do occur.[3] In other words simple volume controllers could limit the flow using a facility to its "correct" output level, but could (and probably would) result in the actual total net benefits being lower than expected or potential total net benefits because the "wrong" (i.e., lower valued) trips could get there first and preempt the space. Until later chapters, the problems, costs, and interactions of effective price mechanisms will be ignored; they are hardly trivial or "costless." Also, this is not to suggest that the use of prices does not aid in other important economic planning matters, particularly of a financial nature.

Some elaboration on the above points will be helpful. Again, if travelers consider only their privately perceived payments, or $sravc_x(q)$, then the price function will be $sravc_x(q)$ and "supply" and demand will interact to bring about equilibrium flow and price levels of q_C and $p(q_C) = sravc_x(q_C)$, respectively. Thus, a variable cost pricing policy will cause facilities to be overutilized and total net benefits to be less than their maximum value in this high-demand case. Contrarily, a marginal cost pricing policy—in which the price function will be $srmc_x(q)$—would cause the equilibrium flow and price levels to be q_A and $p(q_A) = srmc_x(q_A)$, respectively. However, if travelers are to be faced with a price equal to $srmc_x(q_A)$, then a surcharge or congestion toll will have to be imposed—since without a toll and with a flow of q_A each user will individually "feel" a travel cost of only $sravc_x(q_A)$. Thus, the congestion toll for marginal cost pricing would be as shown in Figure 6-4, or algebraically as

$$\text{Congestion toll} = srmc_x(q_A) - sravc_x(q_A) \qquad (6\text{-}9)$$

in which q_A is the output level at which the marginal benefit equals the marginal cost. Remember that the toll is only one component of the trip price, the other being $sravc_x(q_A)$ which is perceived by each traveler as travel time, effort, and cost, aside from the toll. Note that a congestion toll would insure that only those travelers having a trip value (or marginal benefit) at least as high as the marginal cost, $srmc_x(q_A)$, would choose to travel, thus insuring that total net benefits would be maximized.

Referring to Figure 6-4, it might seem, at first glance, that a simpler and better way of insuring that output did not exceed q_A would be to use

---

[3]This is not to be confused with the "compensation principle" and related aspects of economic theory, which are wholly different matters.

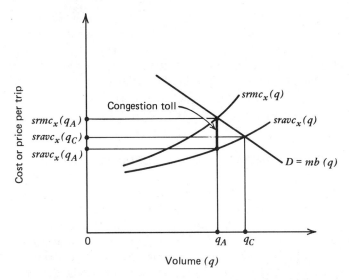

Figure 6-4.   Illustration of an economically efficient congestion toll.

physical control devices of one sort or another, instead of congestion tolls. That is, simply restrict the volume entry rate to q_A vehicles per hour. The problem with such a solution is that some travelers with trip values [$mb(q)$ values] lower than $srmc_x(q_A)$ could gain entry to the facility and thus force off some travelers with higher travel values. As a consequence, total net benefit would not be maximized. (Obviously, one can argue for a physical control and "first-come-first-served" type of policy on the basis that it "seems to be fairer"; but the fact remains that, as an economic efficiency matter, it would be less desirable.)

While the price mechanism serves other important purposes in economic planning, it does occupy a central role in assuring that facilities are utilized most efficiently (in economic terms); secondarily (perhaps), its usage impinges on matters of "simple justice" and of insuring (as a matter of fairness) that wherever possible the costs incurred to provide transport services are paid for by those using and enjoying the benefits of such service. (This secondary rule is *not* an economic efficiency matter, though hardly unimportant as a practical matter.) However, an important pricing rule is that only a single uniform price should be charged for the same or identical services, thus disallowing the use of discriminatory pricing (i.e., "charging what the traffic will bear" or charging different prices for the same service according to the value of the service). In brief, this pricing rule insures that output is continually increased until the marginal cost and benefit are equal for the last trip and that transport facilities and services are efficiently utilized.[4] Clearly, there are exceptions with respect to discriminatory pricing, some having the full sanction of state and federal regulatory agencies. Governmental agencies permit if not "force" discriminatory pricing in certain instances to insure that particular services (which are deemed to be "publicly desirable" or "in the public interest") continue to be provided even though they may be unprofitable. Discriminatory pricing is discussed further in Chapter 9.

6-3 PRICING AND OPERATION IN LOW-DEMAND SITUATIONS

For the low-demand case in Figure 6-5 the best output level from the standpoint of maximizing total net benefit—during the short run—would be that corresponding to an equality between marginal benefit (as represented by the demand curve $D'D'$) and short-run marginal costs, or $mb(q) = srmc_x(q)$, and thus output equal to q_H. Since the fixed costs cannot be altered *in the short run*, they do not affect decisions in the short run with respect to the proper level of output. At the same time, though, it should be evident that private firms could not long endure a short-run marginal cost pricing solution in cost and demand situations of this sort; that is, from the standpoint of financial feasibility, marginal cost pricing with a uniform price of $srmc(q_H)$ would produce total revenues that are less than the total costs (including normal return on capital). That is, $srmc(q_H)$ is less than $sratc_x(q_H)$. Specifically, the total net payment loss at an output level of q_H and price equal to $srmc_x(q_H)$ would be

$$\text{Losses} = q_H[sratc_x(q_H) - srmc_x(q_H)] \tag{6-10}$$

Of course, if either government agencies or private firms held a monopoly position and desired to maximize total net payments, then output could be adjusted to the level at which marginal payment was just equal to marginal cost, or q_F, by charging a price of $ap(q_F)$. In the latter instance total net benefit would not be maximized (in the short run), but financial feasibility would be assured as total payments would exceed the short-run total costs (with normal return on capital included). Alternatively, financial security (though less than maximum total net payments or benefits) could be maintained by adopting average cost pricing and adjusting output to level q_G by charging a price of $ap(q_G) = sratc_x(q_G)$. While it is obvious that in either of these cases total net benefits would not be maximized and that the economy would suffer (to the extent of the loss or decrease in

[4]An excellent and thorough discussion of the rationale underlying the requirements of equal prices to all tripmakers may be found in J. Hirshleifer, J. C. De Haven, and J. W. Milliman, *Water Supply Economics, Technology and Policy*, The University of Chicago Press, Chicago, 1960, pp. 37–40 and Chapter V.

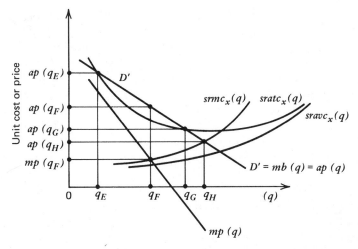

Figure 6-5. Short-run cost and demand relations for a fixed facility and low demand (relative to cost). Note: $ap(q) = \alpha'/\beta' - q/\beta'$; $ap(q_E) = sratc_x(q_E)$; $ap(q_F) = mb(q_F)$; $ap(q_G) = sratc_x(q_G)$; $ap(q_H) = srmc_x(q_H)$; $mp(q_F) = srmc_x(q_F)$.

total net benefits, relative to the maximum which could be obtained), no subsidy would be required and no threat of financial infeasibility would result. It is obvious that in the absence of competition a price anywhere between $ap(q_E)$ and $ap(q_G)$ would result in financial feasibility and thus provide no long-run financial problem for a private or public firm.

Four other aspects arise and should be considered.[5] One, is this short-run picture shown in Figure 6-5 typical of the long-run expectations? Two, should one consider the use of subsidies to make up the difference between total costs and total payments at an output of q_H and with a price of $ap(q_H)$? Three, should some sort of discriminatory pricing or perhaps a multipart tariff be employed such that payments and costs will be balanced? Four, can important inconsistencies develop between the private and public sectors of the economy?

To properly answer these questions requires us to first consider whether the public transport facilities are operated under competitive or noncompetitive (e.g., monopolistic) conditions. For the latter, which was discussed previously, firms or agencies *could* operate the facilities and price the services so as to be financially feasible—though less than desirable from the point of view of maximizing total net benefits. Moreover, and referring to Figure 6-5, it is evident that without subsidies from one level of govern-

[5]For a straightforward and more thorough treatment of this subject, see Hirshleifer et al., op. cit., pp. 90 ff.

ment or another, no transport facility could afford (financially) to operate at an output level above q_G and survive over the long run. As a consequence, no private firm could or would provide transport services in such a situation unless it could price so as to maintain output below q_G or unless it was assured of sufficient subsidies to cover the expected losses.

However, under competitive conditions, the low-demand case is even more difficult. Briefly, in this instance, it can be shown that private or public firms would be "forced"—in the short run—to provide service at the level of output q_H and at a price $ap(q_H) = srmc_x(q_H)$. As a consequence a disastrous long-run financial situation would develop since the total payments would be below total costs. Thus, when competition can be anticipated, private firms would never allow themselves to enter such a market in the first place—or if they entered it unwittingly, they would abandon the firm as soon as possible. Essentially, this is what happened with many transit firms throughout the country over the last three to four decades, as demand dropped from the high- to low-demand case.

However, if the demand and cost conditions are such that short-run and temporary financially infeasible conditions will be overcome over the long run, then short-run marginal cost pricing should be pursued for maximum economic efficiency, and no conflict will exist between economic efficiency and financial security. However, assuming this is not the case, the other aspects are open for consideration. In general, from the standpoint of economic efficiency, the "correct" solution is to price at marginal cost and subsidize the facility or venture, *whether it be a public or private project*. Thus, one might be led to conclude that subsidization of the losses is preferable and warranted (aside from distributional matters). However, such a position overlooks the inconsistencies with respect to private and public sectors that do exist and without doubt will continue to exist.

As a practical matter private industry does not, upon finding itself in a decreasing return-to-scale situation (such as shown in Figure 6-5) and being faced with competition, usually or even often undertake the program because the overall net benefits to society are enhanced, nor does it try to obtain the necessary subsidy from local, state, or federal sources. As a consequence, to consistently subsidize just public programs, aside from other social or political criteria, would in all likelihood bring about a double standard with respect to economic planning and produce unknown consequences with respect to overall economic efficiency. Also, and in contrast to the situation for externalities, it seems reasonable to argue (somewhat heuristically) that a policy which endorsed the subsidy of all public and only some private programs having increasing returns to scale would virtually assure overinvestment in the public sector and less than optimum allocation of resources. These qualifications make it difficult to reach any general conclusions regarding the desirability of always subsidizing public projects having increasing returns to scale and emphasize the necessity of a more comprehensive analysis than can be undertaken here.

The other means to be used for overcoming financial infeasibility in falling cost situations (such as that shown in Figure 6-5) are discriminatory prices or multipart tariffs. While a variety of these practices can be and often are used successfully to eliminate financial deficits, it should be recognized that their usage forces abandonment of the "equal-price-to-all" rule and, as a consequence, makes it impossible to conclude in general that the resultant project will or will not produce optimal efficiency.[6]

Finally, for the low-demand case (in which the demand function *does* intersect the short-run average total cost function, though to the left of the minimum average cost point) depicted graphically in Figure 6-5, it can be shown that short-run marginal cost pricing will bring about positive total net benefits even though total net payments will be negative for the most efficient pricing case, or when the price is $ap(q_H) = srmc_x(q_H)$. Simply, at a flow of q_G the total net benefits would be positive and equal to the consumers' surpluses since, at that point, the average payment or $ap(q_G)$ would be equal to the average cost or $sratc_x(q_G)$; also, since $mb(q) \geq srmc_x(q)$ for q from q_G to q_H, the total net benefit would increase and thus still be positive.

However, if the demand were so low that the demand function *at all points* lies below and thus does not intersect the short-run average cost function, then no *a priori* statements can be made about whether the total net benefits are positive or negative, even though they would be maximized by marginal cost pricing. Figure 6-6 illustrates this very low-demand case.[7] It can be seen that even with no competition and a price which maximized total net payments the facility would still prove to be financially infeasible. That is, with output at q_I—at which point $mp(q_I) = srmc_x(q_I)$—and a market clearing price at $p(q_I) = ap(q_I)$, the total net payments would be maximized but would still be below the total costs, indicating financial losses over the long run. Thus, there is no uniform price that would permit a firm or agency (without competition) to cover their costs. Given that we had such a facility (at least for the time being), we know that a price $p(q_J) = srmc_x(q_J)$ would maximize total net benefits

---

[6]This conclusion follows from the so-called General Theory of Second Best; for a short and simplified discussion, see J. R. Meyer, J. F. Kain, and M. Wohl, *The Urban Transportation Problem*, Harvard University Press, Cambridge, 1965, Chapter 13. For a more complete discussion, see R. G. Lipsey and R. K. Lancaster, "The General Theory of Second Best," *Review of Economic Studies* **34**, 11–32, (1956–1957).

[7]It is hard to pinpoint many documented examples of this case. One appears to be the Hopkins Airport Extension to Cleveland's rail transit system. See M. Wohl, "An Analysis and Evaluation of the Rapid Transit Extension to Cleveland Airport," Urban Institute Working Paper 708-43, January 1972. (A short version of this report appeared in *Highway Research Record No. 417*.)

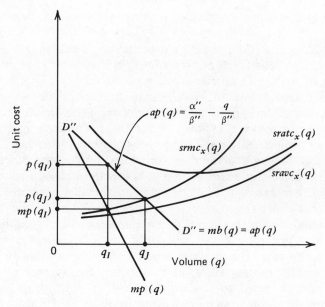

Figure 6-6. Short-run cost and demand relations for a fixed facility and very low demand (relative to cost). Note: $p(q_I) = ap(q_I)$; $p(q_J) = ap(q_J) = srmc_x(q_J)$; $mp(q_I) = srmc_x(q_I)$.

during the short run, even though sustaining financial losses. The question is, then, during the short run, would the total net benefits be positive, thus indicating economic feasibility for this facility? (If not, the facility can be regarded as both economically and financially infeasible, indicating that abandonment is desirable as an economic matter.) The answer to this question is ambiguous. In brief, without knowing the exact cost and demand functions, we do not know *a priori* whether the following difference representing total net benefits is positive or not:

$$\sum_{q=1}^{q_J} mb(q) - \sum_{q=1}^{q_J} srmc_x(q) - F_x \geq 0 \qquad (6\text{-}11)$$

6-4 SOME DILEMMAS CONFRONTING MARGINAL COST PRICING

An earlier section showed that the total net benefits—or, if you will, the "size of the economic pie"—would be maximized if a marginal cost pricing policy were adopted. That is, greater economic welfare would exist, without regard for who receives the benefits or who pays the costs. As a theoretical matter, and given all the assumptions noted previously, this conclusion is correct. But even so, there are some disturbing features which accompany this policy, both of a practical and of a theoretical nature.

First, since many if not most transport facilities now and for years on end have operated with average variable or average total cost pricing, a sudden switch to marginal cost pricing would cause prices to increase (sometimes sharply) *when there is high demand* (i.e., when demand is sufficiently high that the demand function intersects the average total cost function to the right of its minimum average total cost point). In turn, these price increases could have disastrous economic consequences for firms which earlier made location or expansion decisions in the face of an expected continuance of the former pricing policy.[8] Thus, one should ask: Do regulatory agencies have an obligation to protect the general public against ruinous or financially harmful pricing policy changes when the public at large had little reason to expect a change in what had become a long-standing pricing policy?

Second, some analysts have noted that a switch from average variable cost to marginal cost pricing would increase prices and thus tend to work to the disadvantage of low-income classes; this would be especially true in situations where there is high demand. While this observation is correct, it should also be pointed out that marginal cost pricing would produce more total net benefits than would average variable cost pricing and thus potentially could help both the well-to-do and less well-to-do more than would otherwise occur, depending, of course, on the distribution of the extra total net benefits. (This last point will be discussed again under the fourth point to follow.)

Third, a particularly disturbing feature of the imposition of marginal cost pricing would arise in circumstances when high demand exists and (for whatever reasons) the capacity is regarded as fixed both during the short *and* long run. For instance, in the central cores of large cities, many, if not most, analysts regard its highway and street system as "impossible to expand," regardless of cost or benefit. This would be the case (other than for minor additions) in downtown Philadelphia, Chicago, Boston, and San Francisco, to name but a few pertinent examples. In cases such as these, it is reasonable to assume that the high-demand case is common and that the marginal costs—at current and expected future levels of demand—would be considerably higher than average total costs, as illustrated in Figure 6-1. Accordingly, to invoke marginal cost pricing would result in large profits over and above total costs, a profit which could be exploited year after year, especially if demand increases in response to growth in income and population. While this solution may be desirable *during the short run*, the fact remains that public transportation agencies could exploit their monopoly position (with respect to the control of both

[8]See the related discussion in J. R. Meyer, M. J. Peck, J. Stenason, and C. Zwick, *The Economics of Competition in the Transportation Industries*, Harvard University Press, Cambridge, 1959, pp. 122-123.

pricing policy and expansion of capacity) and continue to reap the profits of applying a short-run policy over the long run with capacity being fixed, regardless of the desirability of expanding over the long run. As we will see in the next chapter, serious distortions could result from such an action.

Fourth, an interesting paradox arises from the imposition of marginal cost pricing in place of average variable cost pricing, especially as applied to both highway and transit facilities. The paradox applies to high- or low-demand situations and holds so long as the average variable cost is monotonically increasing. For this discussion let us make use of the situation depicted in Figure 6-7.

As the hourly flow rate on a highway or on a bus line (each having a fixed number of lanes or scheduled buses, respectively) increases, then the average travel time, discomfort, and effort will gradually increase due to congestion [indicated by the average variable cost function or $sravc_x(q)$]. That is, each additional bus rider or each additional highway vehicle, when added to the previous flow (during the same hour), will cause all the previous riders or vehicles to be delayed and crowded just slightly more than they previously were delayed and crowded. The difference between the marginal cost and average variable cost curves, or $srmc_x(q) - sravc_x(q)$, reflects the extra delay imposed on the former users or patrons by the one additional user.

Let us assume that either the highway or bus line is *now* operated with average variable cost pricing. Thus, the equilibrium flow and price would be q_C and $sravc_x(q_C)$. That is, each person in the total flow of q_C would

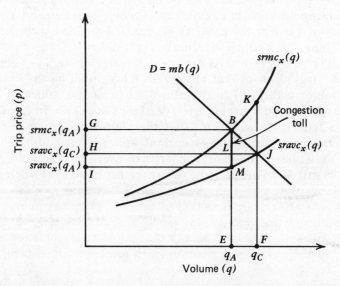

Figure 6-7.   Short-run cost function and congestion toll for demand as shown.

experience the same average travel time, discomfort, and so forth, equal to $sravc_x(q_C)$. Subsequently, it is argued that marginal cost pricing should be used instead on the grounds that total net benefits would be increased. Earlier, it was shown that the increase in total net benefits to be accrued (i.e., the loss in total net benefits to be avoided) would be equal to area KBJ on Figure 6-7, or

$$ITNB_{x,AC} = \sum_{q=q_A}^{q_C} srmc_x(q) - \sum_{q=q_A}^{q_C} mb(q) \qquad (6\text{-}12)$$

Paradoxically, though, it can easily be shown that with marginal cost pricing *all users* will be worse off than they would be with average variable cost pricing. Consider three groups: the tolled, the tolled off, and the untolled.[9]

1.   *The Tolled.*   If marginal cost pricing is imposed, a congestion toll equal to $srmc_x(q_A) - sravc_x(q_A)$ will be charged, bringing the total price, $p(q_A)$, to $srmc_x(q_A)$ and resulting in a reduced flow rate of q_A. While all of the q_A users having a trip value which is at least as high as $p(q_A) = srmc_x(q_A)$ will be willing to pay that price—rather than forego the trip—the fact remains that each of the q_A users are worse off than they were with average variable cost pricing. Simply, their trip price is now $p(q_A) = srmc_x(q_A)$ rather than the lower price $p(q_C) = sravc_x(q_C)$ they paid with the former pricing policy. Another way to look at this is as follows: The price increase has resulted in reducing the consumers' surpluses for the q_A users by an amount equal to area $GHLB$ in Figure 6-7. While some people argue that those paying the toll really would be better off after the pricing switch, because of the reduction in congestion, you will find that such an argument is fallacious. Specifically, congestion did drop after imposing the congestion toll, but only by an amount equal to the drop in average variable cost or $sravc_x(q_C) - sravc_x(q_A)$—an amount which is considerably less than the extra congestion toll required to bring about that reduction in congestion. Put differently, the tolled group of q_A users had to pay tolls amounting to area $GIMB$ in order to reduce their congestion by an amount equal only to area $HIML$. In short, the tolled users are worse off after marginal cost pricing.

2.   *The Tolled Off.*   The users who were tolled off (i.e., those who formerly traveled but who are unwilling to pay the congestion toll and higher overall price)—or $q_C - q_A$ users—are clearly worse off after the change in pricing policy. They were "forced" to move from a preferred

---

[9]These terms were coined by R. M. Zettel and R. R. Carll, "The Basic Theory of Efficiency Tolls: The Tolled, The Tolled-Off and the Untolled," *High. Res. Record* **47**, Washington, D.C., 1964.

situation into one which is clearly less preferable (otherwise they would not have been traveling on this facility prior to the price change). The extent of their losses (by having been tolled off) is indeterminate without knowing about their choices after being tolled off, but it can be said that they will lose, though no more than an amount equal to their consumers' surplus losses or area BLJ.

3. *The Untolled*. Even untolled users of transport facilities are made worse off by the shift to marginal cost pricing. (Untolled users are those travelers on travel facilities to which some tolled-off users divert after the change to marginal cost pricing.) That is, when the tolled-off users switch to second-best travel modes or routes after the price change, congestion and crowding is increased for both the untolled and tolled off, relative to the situation which existed prior to the price change.

Consequently, all groups of users—the tolled, the tolled off, and the untolled—are worse off after the imposition of marginal cost pricing. With *all users* preferring average variable to marginal cost pricing, how can we claim that marginal cost pricing will increase total net benefits *to society*? The answer to the riddle involves the congestion toll revenues which were collected from the toll users. That is, the congestion toll revenues—in total equal to area $GIMB$—represent benefits stemming from the price change, and they can be distributed to society in whatever fashion is desired. Moreover, it can be proved that the congestion toll revenues are larger than the combined consumers' surplus losses to both the tolled and tolled off. That is, it can be proved that area $GIMB$ is larger than the sum of area $GHLB$ (the consumers' surplus losses for the tolled) *and* area BLJ (the maximum consumers' surplus losses for the tolled off).[10]

As a final note, there may be adverse systematic effects which occur due to the imposition of efficient pricing on a *single facility*. These systematic effects may severely reduce the net benefit of the shift to efficient pricing. In particular, the losses to the *untolled*, the users of alternative services which become more congested, may exceed the net benefits (equal to the area $GIMB$ less $GHLB$ and BLJ). For example, improving the traffic signal timing at one intersection may result in increased congestion elsewhere.[11] While such systematic effects may be small in practice, shifting to marginal cost pricing on a single facility rather than for all facilities should be undertaken only with due care.

[10]For a more detailed discussion of these matters, see Zettel, ibid.; and M. Wohl, "The Short-Run Congestion Cost and Pricing Dilemma," *Traffic Quarterly*, January 1966. Briefly, it can be shown that $GIMB - (GHLB + BLJ) = BJK$.

[11]This effect accounts for "Braess' paradox" in which a roadway improvement can result in deteriorated level of service on a network, a phenomenon observed by Braess. See D. Braess, "Uber ein Paradoxen der Verkehrsplannung," *Unternehmensforchung* **12**, 258–268 (1968); or J. D. Murchlund, "Braess' Paradox of Traffic Flow," *Transportation Research* **4**, 391–394 (1970).

6-5   PRICING IN BACKWARD-BENDING OR CAPACITY-REDUCING SITUATIONS

Throughout the discussion in this chapter, as well as that in Chapters 2 and 3 on cost and price functions, it has been assumed that both the travel time and average variable cost functions for transport facilities are well behaved and that both travel time and average variable cost increase without limit as the volume using them increases.[12] One representation of such a non-backward-bending function would be as follows:[13]

$$sravc_x(q) = \tau_{\min} + v\delta_x q^\rho \tag{6-13}$$

where $\tau_{\min}$ is the travel cost per mile at low or near-zero volume levels, v is a value of time parameter, ρ is a speed reduction parameter which is assumed to be greater than 1, and δ_x is a constant for facility x. Figure 6-8 depicts such a non-backward-bending function.

Non-backward-bending situations would appear to be typical (in form) for those transport facilities whose capacity or output is not reduced when

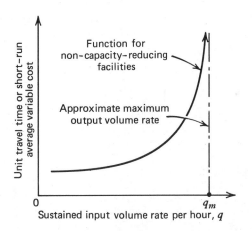

Figure 6-8. Approximate relationships for travel time and average variable cost for non-backward-bending or non-capacity-reducing facilities.

---

[12]This case has been described in some detail by A. A. Walters, "The Theory and Measurement of Private and Social Cost of Highway Congestion," *Econometrica*, October 1961, pp. 678–681; see also B. Johnson, "On the Economics of Road Congestion," *Econometrica*, January–April 1964, pp. 137–150.

[13]See, for example, W. S. Vickrey, "Pricing as a Tool in Coordination of Local Transportation," *Transportation Economics*, National Bureau of Economic Research, Columbia University Press, New York, 1965, p. 285.

the input flow rate approaches or exceeds the capacity or maximum output rate. For example, as the passenger input flow rate (or arrivals per hour) for scheduled buses, trains, or planes exceeds the maximum capacity, queues and delays build up continuously—so long as the arrival rate is sustained. The situation is similar at signalized traffic intersections. Importantly, though, the output rate or capacity of such facilities is not affected or reduced by the input rate.

By contrast, some transport facilities—notably nonsignalized and uncontrolled highways and expressways—have design characteristics which permit backward-bending or capacity-reducing situations to develop; that is, once the entering or input traffic volumes reach or approach some critical level, intervehicle behavior is such that shock waves and stop-and-go traffic flow result. This intervehicle behavior often reduces the effective traffic-carrying capacity of the roadways. Capacity reduction can continue so long as the input rate is sustained at or above some critical level. Facilities without input–output controls (or uncontrolled facilities) will be described as backward-bending or capacity-reducing types and those with input–output controls as non-capacity-reducing types. While intervehicle flow dynamics are not fully understood, the above remarks and the general diagram in Figure 6-9 probably characterize the phenomenon appropriately. Referring to Figure 6-9, the dashed position of the curve illustrates flow and capacity reduction behavior for capacity-reducing types of facilities *only after* input volumes have approached or exceeded the maximum or critical flow rate q_m and caused

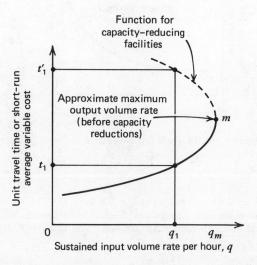

Figure 6-9. Approximate relationships for travel time and average variable cost for capacity-reducing facilities.

shock wave action. Shock waves occur when vehicles jam up momentarily. As the entering or input volume approaches the facility's critical output rate, shock waves build up, causing the average travel time to increase *and* the output rate to decrease. Whereas a flow rate of q_1 vehicles per hour (referring to Figure 6-9) could be handled with an average travel time of t_1 *if* shock waves could be prevented, it is evident that once the waves do build up, the facility's output capacity would be reduced and the travel time would increase to t_1'. Certainly, this extra delay is inefficient, and thus it is important to use devices of one sort or another to prevent shock wave action and avoid capacity-reducing situations. The objective would simply be to prevent the input volume rate from approaching "too closely" the capacity volume rate at the bottleneck section. One simple device for insuring that the input rate is properly controlled would be to install volume entry controllers (such as stop lights) which could insure that the entering volume was reasonably uniform and did not exceed (or approach too closely) the output capacity, the point at which shock waves build up. Another device which could be used would be tolls, as is sometimes suggested by economists.

First, though, it is important to note that for *some* (if not most) capacity-reducing facilities backward-bending situations do not arise and thus inefficiencies of the sort discussed in the previous paragraph are avoided. Suppose, for example, we had *low demand* such as shown in Figure 6-10. In this case the equilibrium price is sufficiently high enough to prevent a volume rate which approaches or exceeds the critical or maximum output rate of q_m. Thus, shock waves would not build up and the upper half or dashed portion of the backward-bending average variable cost function would never be approached. And, as a consequence, all of

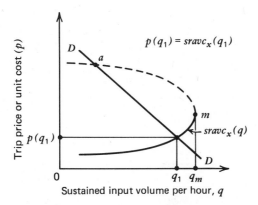

Figure 6-10.   Short-run variable cost and low-demand conditions for capacity-reducing facilities. Case 1: Low-demand and short-run average variable cost pricing.

the usual economic efficiency arguments (which were discussed earlier) can be used to identify the best pricing or entry control policy.

By contrast, *high demand* can lead to problems and result in pure inefficiencies of the sort discussed earlier. Figure 6-11 illustrates such a case in which the demand is sufficiently high to induce flow rates above the critical or maximum output rate q_m. (That is, when the demand function is DD, a price of $sravc_x(q_m)$ or below would cause the quantity of tripmaking to be demanded to be considerably greater than q_m.) Thus, shock waves would exist and cause the backward-bending average variable cost function to occur. Also, the equilibrium price of $p(q_1)$ and flow of q_1 is only approximate in that the dynamics of the situation would lead to large fluctuations in the flow rate, travel times, and costs. Even so, the approximate equilibrium point at B is useful for estimating the consequences of various pricing and control policies.

In this case—that is, with an equilibrium at point B in the absence of any tolls or controls—it is obvious that pure inefficiencies would occur. *Extra* delay and cost per trip, which otherwise could be avoided, would be Δt_1. However, this extra cost could be avoided *either* by restricting the entry rate to q_1 (or less) *or* by charging a toll equal to Δt_1. The economic efficiency arguments made above suggest the toll would be preferred (aside from considering the costs of implementing toll collection devices), while the users (including the tolled, tolled off, and untolled) would prefer the use of entry controllers. Simply, the users would prefer to benefit by having controllers lead to the reduction in trip price, rather than by having to pay a toll of Δt_1 and have the revenue from the toll be transferred to the general public. Moreover, it can be shown that the users—collectively—would find a toll of Δt_m more desirable than one at Δt_1. Briefly, their consumers' surpluses would be larger with a toll of Δt_m than with a toll of Δt_1, resulting in a flow of q_m rather than q_1.

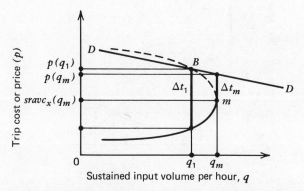

Figure 6-11. Short-run variable cost and high-demand conditions for capacity-reducing facilities. Case 2: High demand.

Next, it is appropriate to consider the costs and benefits from a broader public point of view (i.e., in terms of overall economic efficiency). The average variable cost curve for flow levels below the critical flow (i.e., for flow levels below the point where backward-bending cost situations are created) would be that indicated by the solid line curve below point m in Figure 6-12; also, if the flow were controlled (e.g., by entry controllers and/or tolls) such that shock waves and backward-bending cost situations could not occur, the average variable cost curve for *higher* levels of *input* flow (i.e., for input volumes greater than q_m) would be that of the solid line portion above point m. Here, of course, it is necessary to make a distinction between input and output and to note that input volumes greater than q_m would imply that queues, delays, and costs would be increasing indefinitely; thus, while a volume of q_m would be the constant *output*, the cost would be indefinitely high—at least so long as the input volume were sustained at levels equal to or greater than q_m.

The associated marginal cost function for this case would be roughly as shown in Figure 6-12. It is of importance to note that the marginal costs would become indefinitely high as the flow rate approaches q_m.[14] Further, since the marginal cost would become infinitely large as the flow

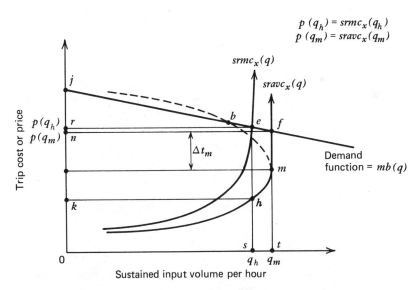

Figure 6-12. Short-run cost and demand conditions for backward-bending situations. Note: e and f are approximate equilibrium points.

[14]This can be shown mathematically by assuming any form of backward-bending function (such as a parabola) and then deriving the marginal cost function from the lower half of that function. See, also: Walters, op. cit. and Johnson, op. cit.

approached q_m, marginal cost pricing would guarantee that the input flow rate would never approach (too closely) or exceed the critical rate q_m.

For the circumstances depicted in Figure 6-12, with marginal cost pricing, an equilibrium flow of q_h and a price of $p(q_h) = srmc_x(q_h)$ would result and the total net benefits would be

$$TNB(q_h) = \sum_{q=1}^{q_h} mb(q) - \sum_{q=1}^{q_h} srmc_x(q) - F_x \qquad (6\text{-}14)$$

$$= \sum_{q=1}^{q_h} mb(q) - (q_h)[sravc_x(q_h)] - F_x \qquad (6\text{-}15)$$

The total net benefits for marginal cost pricing, shown in equation (6-15), can be shown to be equal to area *jkhe* in Figure 6-12; the net gains to *users* would be equal to area *jre*.

Since for flows greater than q_h the marginal costs are greater than the marginal benefits (the latter as measured by the demand function), any policy to increase the flow beyond q_h results in a reduction in the total net benefits and economic inefficiency, even if tolls are used. As a consequence, the earlier solution of average variable cost plus a toll of Δt_m would not represent the pricing policy of highest overall economic efficiency, and a loss to society would result. The extent of the economic loss would be as follows:

$$\text{Loss} = \sum_{q=q_h}^{q_m} mb(q) - \sum_{q=q_h}^{q_m} srmc_x(q) \qquad (6\text{-}16)$$

In summary, because of the relationship between marginal costs and marginal benefits for flow levels between q_h and q_m, we can conclude that $TNB(q_h) > TNB(q_m)$ and that marginal cost pricing will lead to the most economically efficient solution even in backward-bending situations. Moreover, this solution would prevent backward-bending situations from occurring on all uncontrolled facilities.

6-6 SUMMARY REMARKS ABOUT PRICING IN THE SHORT RUN

First, pricing *is* a short-run matter even though it does affect the long-run economics of facility expansion or abandonment. Simply, the fixed costs cannot be affected during the short-run; they can be changed or avoided (whichever is most desirable, economically) only over the long run as we decide to expand, contract, or abandon facilities. Thus, from day to day we need not consider the fixed costs since we cannot change or affect them during the short run. Only variable costs and thus marginal costs need to be considered, along with marginal revenues and marginal benefits, as we examine the wisdom of adopting one short-run pricing policy or another.

While the long-run decisions about the proper facility size clearly do affect the long-run economics and finances, once we have made this long-run decision, we then should proceed to price as wisely as possible day to day and to maximize either net benefits or net revenues, day to day, *given* that prior planning decision. The prior decision (in a sense) is "spilt milk"; thus, if we maximize in terms of profitability or economic welfare each day thereafter, then we will maximize and do our best over the long run as well (again, so long as we continue to operate a given facility).

Second, even in those difficult low-demand situations when agencies or firms are faced with competition, we should not lose our perspective when examining the economics of adopting marginal cost pricing and then of ending up with a price or average revenue below the average total cost. Why so, we should ask. Typically, for most public transport facilities (especially urban ones), the marginal cost curve will always lie above the *average* variable cost curve—much as shown in Figures 6-1 and 6-5. As a consequence, to invoke marginal cost pricing means that the marginal cost price or average revenue will exceed the average variable cost and thus contribute *something* to overhead as well. That is, our day-to-day revenues will more than cover our day-to-day out-of-pocket (or variable) costs and at least help cover some of the overhead or fixed costs as well. In turn, if our long-run planning shows that this situation will continue to repeat itself, day after day and year after year, then we have a clear signal (as a financial feasibility matter) to resort to abandonment or government subsidy for long-run survival.

CHAPTER 7

INVESTMENT AND OPERATIONS PLANNING FOR ECONOMIC EFFICIENCY IN THE LONG RUN

Economic planning is generally concerned with alternative investments and operating policies (such as planning system extensions and scheduling the service frequency for transit systems). It is undertaken to answer two questions:

1. Is *any* facility or service economically desirable and if so,
2. Which facility, vehicle fleet, or operating policy is the *most* desirable?

In this chapter we shall discuss the relevant principles for answering these questions from an economic perspective. As in the last chapter, the single criterion for judging the desirability of particular alternatives will be their net social benefits. For example, we shall conclude that investments which do not have positive net social benefits are not justifiable and should not be undertaken. Generally, the principles we shall discuss are aimed at insuring that the net social benefits from any action are both as large as possible and nonnegative.

In evaluating alternative plans, it is necessary to assume a particular pricing policy in order to determine the resulting benefits and costs. As discussed in the previous chapter, different pricing policies can have important effects on travel volumes and the level of net social benefits derived from the operation of a facility or service. Consequently, we shall presume a pricing policy in order to evaluate alternative plans in this chapter. By pricing policy we do not imply a particular price level but rather a policy such as setting price equal to the short-run marginal cost of a facility or service.

Throughout the chapter we shall mention some financial implications of the investment policies resulting from our concern with economic efficiency. Those enterprises which pursue investment, pricing, and operating policies so as to maximize net social benefit may find that they accumulate excess profits or incur financial losses. In addition to presenting the financial implications of such policies, this discussion is intended to provide some perspective for the discussion of multiobjective or multiattribute planning in Chapter 10, in which the financial situation of public enterprises, as well as the net social benefits, will be considered for planning decisions. Also, Chapter 9 deals with financial implications in more detail.

The discussion in this chapter will generally proceed from simpler to more complicated situations. Initially, we shall assume that demand for a particular service is constant and represented by a single aggregate demand function (see Chapters 2 and 3). With this assumption the case in which facility size or service is highly flexible is considered; for example, this case may arise when service frequency decisions are considered. Situations in which facility size is highly indivisible are then discussed. This is a more common case for roadway and other infrastructure investment decisions. Following this, we relax the assumption of a constant demand function and consider cases in which demand fluctuates (as with peak and off-peak demands) or changes over time (as with annual growth or shrinkage in the demand level). In each of these situations we shall draw a distinction between cases in which competition for a provider does or does not exist. Both of these cases are relevant for different types and environments of transportation providers. The following chapter will consider the problem of evaluation for discrete projects in more detail.

7-1 ECONOMIC PRINCIPLES FOR PLANNING TO ACHIEVE ECONOMIC EFFICIENCY

The two major principles to be employed in economic planning are as follows:

1. Any acceptable service or facility must have net social benefits which are positive; that is, total benefits from the alternative must exceed total costs.
2. An existing or planned service should be improved or expanded so long as the extra or incremental social benefits resulting from the improvement exceed the extra costs, subject to satisfying the foregoing conditions in 1.

These two principles should be applied to any planning situation in which changes in facilities or operations are considered. For example, a transit agency might possess a fixed fleet of vehicles and undertake a planning study to determine what frequency of service to offer during off-peak periods; in this case service should be offered as long as the net benefits are positive, and the frequency should be increased as long as the *incremental* benefits exceed the *incremental* costs. In a larger context the transit agency might use these principles to determine the appropriate fleet size to operate, that is, the extent to which investments in vehicle purchases should be undertaken.

In the literature of economics, investment or planning decisions of this type are referred to as long-run decisions, in the sense that changes to infrastructure or operating policies are expected to require a significant period of time to effect. However, the planning horizon can vary greatly in different situations. For schedule or frequency-of-service decisions, changes may be accomplished in a few weeks. For *de novo* construction of railways or roadways, a decade or more may be required to implement a desired change. What is important is that, in the long run, some infrastructure construction or operating decisions may be implemented so as to change, if only in part, the system costs and operation. In contrast, the short run is restricted—for the most part—to situations in which only *pricing* decisions may be altered.

As discussed in the previous chapter, pricing decisions for a transportation system are generally based upon *variable* costs and benefits during the short run, which is the period in which a facility or service cannot be altered. Economic planning is more broadly concerned with both variable and fixed costs. Clearly, pricing decisions do affect investment decisions since, for instance, higher prices decrease system usage, total costs, and benefits. However, investment planning must also consider the total net benefits so as to insure that system operation and construction is beneficial. It is also the case that investment decisions will profoundly affect the nature of the short-run cost functions and thereby alter the appropriate price levels. Planning studies must *a priori* assume a particular pricing strategy in order to evaluate alternative investments or policies. And, the incremental benefits and costs of expanding a facility are estimated with the assumption of a particular pricing policy (or, alternatively, the assumption of complete insensitivity of demand to price). Once a particular facility is constructed, the assumptions on which the planning study were made may change and the pricing policy for the facility may be different than that originally envisioned. Principles for such changes in pricing policies were discussed in Chapter 6.

7-2   PLANNING WITH FLEXIBLE POLICIES OR HIGHLY DIVISIBLE FACILITY SIZES AND INCREASING RETURNS TO SCALE

With flexible operating policies or facility sizes, we assume that a wide range of technological alternatives are available for consideration and implementation. As discussed in Chapter 4, there is a total cost curve associated with each alternative in which costs generally vary with volume. The total cost curve associated with any one facility or service option is called a short-run cost function, since we have defined the short run as the period in which facility or service changes are prohibited. When a planner considers a wide range of technological options over a fairly lengthy period of time (so that any necessary changes may be accomplished), we can define a *long-run* total cost curve which represents the

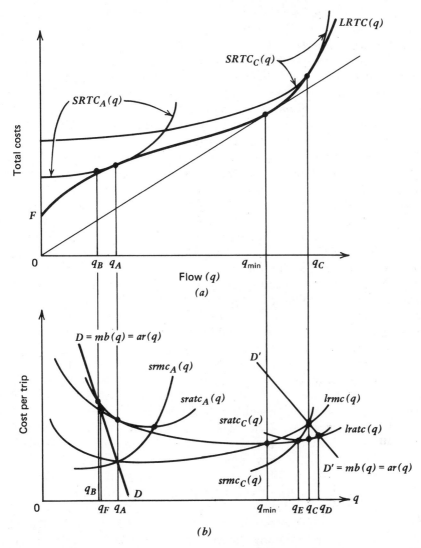

Figure 7-1. Illustrative long-run cost and demand relationships with nonconstant returns to scale and high divisibility. Note: $sratc_A(q_A) = lratc(q_A)$; $sratc_C(q_C) = lratc(q_C)$; $sratc_C(q_D) \neq lratc(q_D)$; $sratc_C(q_E) = srmc_C(q_E) \neq lratc(q_E)$.

minimum cost incurred to serve any given volume q, or by $LRTC(q)$ in Figure 7-1a. This long-run total cost curve represents the envelope of the various short-run cost curves associated with each alternative, and each point on the long-run curve represents a particular facility size or service alternative. Clearly, no short-run total cost curve may lie below the long-run curve (else we could change the facility to reach the situation of lower costs). (Other long-run cost functions are defined in Section 4-4.)

It is neither necessary nor generally correct to assume that the long-run total cost function exhibits constant returns to scale. Constant returns to scale would be illustrated by a horizontal average cost curve and a straight (constant-slope) total cost function which passes through the origin. In Figure 7-1b we illustrate the case in which economies of scale exist between volume levels 0 to q_{min}, while diseconomies of scale exist for higher volumes. "Economies of scale" refer to the slope of the average total cost curve, which, as shown in Figure 7-1b, is falling in the region of scale economies (i.e., increasing returns to scale) and rising in the range of scale diseconomies (i.e., decreasing returns to scale). With economies of scale long-run average total cost becomes *lower* as volume increases.

For this initial discussion it will be assumed that the demand function will remain constant (represented by *either DD or D'D'*), both from hour to hour and from year to year. While analysis for both demand cases will be discussed, it is clear that this assumption of constant demand is unrealistic. Nonetheless, the guiding principles remain valid, whether or not demand is constant. We shall discuss demand changes in later sections. Also, to clarify the linkages between short-run and long-run analysis, the appropriate short-run cost functions for (just) two facility sizes—A and C—are included in Figure 7-1. Facility A is the facility of least total cost for an output of q_A and facility C is the facility of least cost for an output of q_C. As such, these two facilities make up two points on the *long-run* cost functions, while the short-run cost functions for A and C represent the day-to-day costs which would result *if* one or the other were actually built and operated at various output levels.

For the cost functions shown in Figure 7-1a, we should first note that some minimum level of nonseparable costs (equal to F) must be incurred before even one unit of flow is possible. These nonseparable threshold costs represent costs which do not vary with output but are required to acquire land and vehicles or construct a guideway and thus provide the minimum level of facilities required to permit any level of movement. While these threshold costs are fixed with respect to the output level q (and are nonseparable among them), they are not fixed over time, since they can be avoided over the long run simply by abandoning the entire facility and providing no service. Recall that these are the opportunity costs, and where they apply to an *existing* facility, they are not equivalent to the original capital outlays—or to the opportunity costs of resources foregone at *the time of construction*—but are equal to the *current* alternative opportunity value. The original outlays are "sunk" and irrecoverable; at this stage the only thing that matters is what other uses can be made of the existing facility, land, structures, and so on. As a consequence, not to abandon the facility entirely would be to forfeit these alternative opportunities and thus to incur these costs.

Since the threshold costs of F vary over the long run (that is, they can be avoided over the long run), they must be considered in matters of long-run economic efficiency, as well as in those involving financial feasibility. As we shall see, the threshold costs are not directly involved in a determination of the proper price but only in ascertaining the overall or aggregative economic and financial feasibility.

More simply, over the long run the sum of both the long-run marginal costs *and* threshold costs must be exceeded by the total benefits accruing from usage if the investment is to be regarded as economically feasible or desirable from a public point of view.

For a single optimum facility size or service and for most efficient usage of it, the necessary relationships and conditions between costs and benefits are as follows:

$$LRTC(q_0) = \sum_{q=1}^{q_0} lrmc(q) + F \qquad (7\text{-}1)$$

in which

$$lrmc(q) = LRTC(q) - LRTC(q-1) = \frac{\partial LRTC(q)}{\partial q} \qquad (7\text{-}2)$$

and q_0 is the optimum output level. For the time being, we ignore problems of discounting costs and benefits to present-day values in this equation; this subject will be covered in Chapter 8. For economic efficiency in the long run, we require that the equilibrium output or flow be such that the marginal benefit equals the long-run marginal cost:

$$mb(q_0) = lrmc(q_0) \qquad (7\text{-}3)$$

This condition insures that additional facility expansion or service improvement will not have extra costs larger than extra benefits. In rare cases more than one volume level will result in the equality of marginal benefits and long-run marginal costs. In these cases all the planning options for which this is true may be compared in the same manner as discrete planning options, as discussed in Section 7-5. Similarly, facility contraction or service degradation should be undertaken whenever the losses in user benefits are less than cost savings. In addition to this condition, we require that total benefits exceed total costs:

$$\sum_{q=1}^{q_0} mb(q) \geq \sum_{q=1}^{q_0} lrmc(q) + F$$

$$\geq LRTC(q_0) \qquad (7\text{-}4)$$

It can be concluded that the *most* economically efficient (nonzero) level of output will be that at which the marginal benefit (as defined by the demand curve) is just equal to the long-run marginal cost. The use of the word *nonzero* is crucial as will be explained in succeeding paragraphs. Also, it is important to note that this full statement with no further qualification applies to well-behaved functions; otherwise multiple equalities and ambiguous answers can occur.

Turning first to the low-demand case (in which increasing returns to scale exist), which occurs with the demand function DD in Figure 7-1, one would conclude that the most efficient (*nonzero*) output level would be q_A and that the proper facility would be A, that is, the facility with lowest total cost for an output of q_A. This follows since each increase in output from $q = 1$ up to level q_A has marginal benefits which are at least as large as the long-run marginal costs. The next key question (from an overall economic feasibility standpoint) is: Do the marginal benefits *in total* at the optimum nonzero output level exceed the long-run total costs? In this case, as shown in Figure 7-1 with demand curve DD, it is clear that the total benefits do exceed the total long-run costs since at the lower output level q_F the demand curve intersects the long-run average cost curve. In other words for output level q_F we know that total benefits would exceed total costs (by an amount equal to the total consumers' surpluses for q_F), and from output level q_F to q_A, the total net benefits increase still further since the marginal benefits exceed or equal the long-run marginal costs for each unit increase in output between q_F and q_A. However, if the demand curve had fallen below the long-run average cost curve at all output levels (i.e., for very low demand), then without actually summing the benefits and costs, it would not be possible to tell whether the total net benefits were positive or negative.

Importantly, if the demand function *were* below the long-run average total cost curve at all points, and if the resulting total net benefits were negative, then for that demand case no facility would be economically feasible and thus no facility should be built, assuming that no *external* benefits accrue due to construction or operation of the facility (as discussed in Chapter 1). Similarly, any existing facility which has negative total net benefits should be abandoned as soon as is practicable, again from a long-run economic point of view. That is, while fixed costs for an existing facility can be ignored *in the short-run* and only variable costs need to be covered by short-run prices, as a long-run proposition they should not be ignored, at least not as long as the maximization of economic welfare is the criterion for investment planning and operations.

As for matters of pricing and financial feasibility, the principles are identical to those outlined for the short-run case. First, both pricing and financial feasibility pertain only to the circumstances for a specific facility and do not involve the long-run cost functions, once the facility or service has been chosen. Second, with a single uniform price and with short-run marginal cost pricing, the best price for facility A (and demand DD) from the standpoint of economic efficiency would be $p(q_A) = srmc_A(q_A) = mb(q_A)$. This price, or the average revenue at flow q_A, clearly falls below $sratc_A(q_A)$, the short-run average total cost for a volume of q_A, and thus would result in a financial deficit or total net revenue loss of q_A times the difference between $sratc_A(q_A)$ and $srmc_A(q_A)$. In this case the financial problem is that discussed in Chapter 6: Should the project be subsidized? Should multipart prices be used to make up deficits? And so forth. As before, one *might* conclude (in the absence of more comprehensive analyses) that, unless *all* private and public projects falling into this category are subsidized to the extent of the deficits, no public project should be subsidized on these grounds (again, aside from other criteria and distributional matters).

One difficulty with this "simpleminded" view, of course, is that less-than-competitive private industries faced with this particular increasing returns to scale and demand situation could find such a project (as facility A) financially feasible even when using uniform prices; that is, they could undertake project A, restrict output or flow to a level of q_B or below, and set the price at $p(q_B) \geq sratc_A(q_B)$, thus cover all costs and maintain financial feasibility. (Other financially feasible options exist as well, i.e., financing other facilities of least cost for output levels below approximately q_F). However, if this were done, then society would "lose" potential gains in two senses. One, for an output level of q_B or lower, facility A would not represent the lowest cost facility since facility A has higher *long-run* total costs than do other facilities for a flow level of other than q_A. Two, if facility A were built and operated at a flow of q_B, then extra total net benefits equal to the following:

$$\text{Total net benefit losses} = \sum_{q=q_B}^{q_A} mb(q) - \sum_{q=q_B}^{q_A} srmc_A(q) \qquad (7\text{-}5)$$

would be forfeited relative to those which could be gained with short-run marginal cost pricing.

The circumstances described in the foregoing paragraph sometimes give rise to the plea for multipart prices or some form of price discrimination. The private firm would also prefer to produce at an even lower output level than q_B since profits would be increased still further. Further, one can argue that private firms in many instances use product differentiation and "subtle" mark-ups for products in the higher-quality portion of the range as a means of price discrimination and a way of covering deficits which would occur with a uniform price (at marginal cost) for each different product. Also, since a (noncompetitive) industry certainly would tend to undertake the project (and gain profits from so doing and producing at level q_B or below), two obvious questions arise:

1. Why don't governments *always* subsidize such situations?
2. Should not public investments of the same sort (i.e., increasing returns and sufficiently high demand to be sure that total benefits exceed total costs) always be undertaken?

As for the first question, some would argue that most of the projects or situations of this sort fall (only) within the public sector or are taken over by the government, thus permitting them to be consistently subsidized. However, it is difficult to argue the validity of this view; further, it is hardly possible to argue that government policy follows a consistent and "proper" marginal cost pricing policy even for publicly owned facilities. As for the second question, and when faced with the fact that private industry sometimes will undertake projects of this sort (and that they seldom will price at marginal cost and be subsidized to the extent of the long-run losses), it is difficult to gauge whether the adoption of such public investments and use of marginal cost pricing will enhance economic efficiency. Again, we are confronted with second-best considerations and can reach no general conclusions.[1]

A final point to raise with regard to competition is that of the attractiveness of the market for competing providers. Will new firms attempt to provide competing services in the presence of increasing returns to scale? As we discussed in Chapter 6, competition and profit seeking act to reduce competitive prices to the level of short-run marginal costs. In this case private firms would hesitate to enter a market with increasing returns to scale since marginal costs are less than average costs. Even if a monopolist or single provider raised prices well above the level of short-run marginal cost, a new firm might hesitate to enter the market for fear that subsequent price reductions would result in unprofitable service.

7-3   PLANNING WITH HIGHLY DIVISIBLE FACILITY SIZES AND DECREASING RETURNS TO SCALE

For the high-demand case illustrated by curve $D'D'$ in Figure 7-1, we should consider two situations. First, what is the economically efficient facility, volume, and price for a single provider? Second, what would be the result of multiple providers and competition in such a market?

For a single provider attempting to maximize net social benefits, the conclusions for the increasing returns-to-scale case (discussed in the previous section) hold. Charging a price $p(q)$ equal to $srmc_c(q_c)$ and $lrmc(q_c)$ will maximize the difference between benefits and costs. Since the unit price or average revenue is greater than the short-run average total cost (which includes an allowance for normal profits on capital) "excess profits" and revenues to the extent of the difference will accrue. But these excess profits would hardly induce expansion beyond this point for economic efficiency or financial reasons, either in the short run or long run; in both instances the marginal costs exceed the marginal benefits and marginal revenues from higher output, thus reducing total net benefits to

---

[1]See the references concerning second-best considerations which appeared in Chapter 6: Meyer et al. (1965) and Lipsey and Lancaster (1956–57).

society and total net revenues. This suggests that neither public agencies nor profit-maximizing private firms should expand further.

With competition between providers, each firm selects a facility and service alternative, incurs costs, and charges a price for service. The total volume is equal to the sum of the volumes served by each provider. In this competitive case we can directly examine the complete market for service. With the high-demand situation in Figure 7-1 (demand function $D'D'$), there may be potential benefits from having more than one provider enter the market so as to have two (or more) providers operating at lower long-run average total costs than $lratc(q_C)$ (such as at the volume q_{min}). Since new entrants might have lower costs, they could charge a lower price than $lrmc(q_C)$. Unfortunately, for the situation illustrated in Figure 7-1 there is insufficient volume to have two providers both serve q_{min} trips. A detailed analysis of the market shares and costs of multiple providers—similar to that of the divisible case described below—would be required to determine if net social benefits increase or decrease with more than one provider. For the low-demand case (DD in Figure 7-1) the larger provider would have lower costs and thereby be able to drive competitors out of the market and discourage new competitors from entering the market.

The conclusions in this and the previous section can be summarized by stating the necessary conditions for economic efficiency *and* feasibility:

1. Total benefits must equal or exceed costs:

$$\sum_{q=1}^{q^*} mb(q) \geq \sum_{q=1}^{q^*} srmc_0(q) + F_0 \qquad (7\text{-}6)$$

where F_0 is equal to the fixed costs for the optimum facility, and q^* is the equilibrium flow as specified in condition 2 below, *or*

$$\sum_{q=1}^{q^*} mb(q) \geq \sum_{q=1}^{q^*} lrmc(q) + F \qquad (7\text{-}7)$$

where F is equal to the threshold costs for the smallest facility.

2. Efficient utilization at equilibrium flow:

$$p(q^*) = ar(q^*) = srmc_0(q^*) = lrmc(q^*) = mb(q^*) \qquad (7\text{-}8)$$

where $ar(q^*)$ is the average revenue at q^*.

Generally, if $mb(q) > lrmc(q)$ it is desirable to expand the facility size. While these conditions will hold for the optimum facility, it is of no little importance to emphasize that it is assumed that the demand is constant over time and that short-run marginal cost pricing is utilized.

Let us suppose, however, that because of revenue or other restrictions, some policy other than marginal cost pricing is applied. First, such a policy would prohibit achievement of maximum net social benefits (aside from considering the implications of implementation costs and benefit trade-offs, a matter which will be discussed in Chapter 11). Second, with other than short-run marginal cost pricing, the conditions stated in Equations (7-6), (7-7), and (7-8) would not necessarily hold true when selecting the optimum facility (that is, the optimum given the actual pricing policy to be invoked). Rather, a more complex procedure would be required in order to determine the facility affording maximum net social benefits, given the pricing policy adopted. Such a procedure is described in a later chapter.

7-4   ECONOMIC PLANNING FOR HIGHLY INDIVISIBLE CASES

In the case of highly indivisible alternatives we assume that capacity cannot be expanded in extremely small amounts, but only in fairly large increments which lead to abrupt changes in the long-run cost functions. Assume (for simplicity) that only two technological options are available or possible and that the appropriate cost functions for these two capacity levels are those in Figure 7-2. Such cases might include alternative roadway sizes or port operations technology. While the basic principles remain much the same as before, some ambiguities arise because of the "sawtoothed" and "scalloped" nature of the long-run marginal and average total cost functions, requiring analysis of incremental rather than marginal benefits, revenues, and costs.

The overriding economic efficiency principle is as follows: Expand facility size or improve service so long as the marginal or incremental benefits (whichever apply) associated with expansion are at least as large as the long-run marginal or incremental costs (whichever apply), provided that the long-run total net benefits are nonnegative. In competitive situations this rule also holds as long as the demand function is estimated for the individual provider.

Consider the above principle as applied to the lower-demand case (with curve DD) and to the higher-demand case (with curve $D'D'$) in Figure 7-2. For the *latter* the situation is quite straightforward and clear-cut at least in terms of economic efficiency. Each unit increase in output for $q = 1$ up to $q = q_e$ has a marginal benefit which is at least as large as the long-run marginal cost; that is, for $q = 1$ to $q = q_e$, the $mb(q)$ exceeds or equals $lrmc(q)$. Also, the total net benefits for output q_e will be positive; this follows since the total net benefits at output q_d clearly are positive—to the extent of the consumers' surpluses, since $ar(q_d)$ is equal to $lratc(q_d)$—and since $mb(q) \geq lrmc(q)$ for $q = q_d$ up to $q = q_e$.

However, the higher-demand case would present difficult problems for private firms which were faced with competition. In such a case competition would "push" the price below long-run average total cost or to a price $p(q_e) = ar(q_e) = lrmc(q_e) = srmc_2(q_e)$, therefore producing long-run defi-

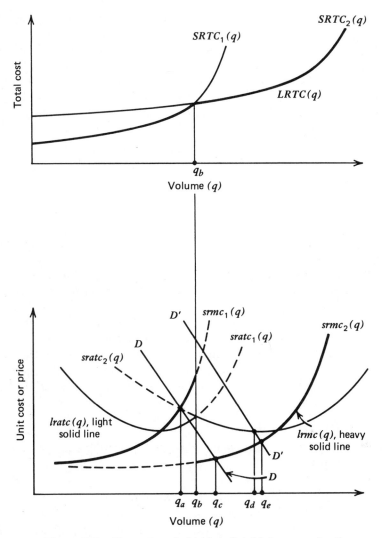

Figure 7-2. Illustration of a highly indivisible long-run situation.

cits and indicating that firms would not attempt such an expansion. On the other hand, with no competition and for the illustration as scaled, firms would find the situation profitable but at a lower level of output, one at which the marginal revenue equals the long-run marginal cost. It is also worth noting that for the diagram as drawn and scaled it appears that a profit-maximizing firm without competition would not expand beyond facility 1. As noted above, however, this would not be *socially* desirable.

The lower-demand case (with curve DD) is less straightforward and obvious than the first. In this situation it is clear that expansion *at least* up to an output of q_a is desirable (economically), since the marginal benefit is at least as large as the long-run marginal cost from $q = 1$ to $q = q_a$ and since the total net benefits are positive. The next question, however, is not so easy to answer: Should we expand from facility 1 to facility 2 and expand output from q_a to q_c? The answer is affirmative if and only if the incremental benefits are at least as large as the incremental long-run costs. Thus, to justify expansion to q_c, we must satisfy ourselves that the following inequality holds:

$$\sum_{q=q_a}^{q_c} mb(q) \geq \sum_{q=q_a}^{q_c} lrmc(q) \tag{7-9}$$

In this instance the exact shapes of the demand and cost functions will be required in order to determine the answer.

Finally, it should be noted that similar kinds of situations can arise with respect to the determination of the financial prospects for facility expansion. In noncompetitive situations, if the marginal revenue function were to intersect the "sawtoothed" long-run marginal cost function in much the same fashion as did the *DD* demand function, then it would be necessary to examine both the marginal and incremental revenues and costs. In such situations the use of benefit–cost analysis and (perhaps) multiobjective decision making should be used as described in the following chapters. That is, we would compare the time stream of benefits and costs for both the larger and smaller facilities and then select the alternative with greater net social benefits.

7-5 ECONOMIC PLANNING FOR NONCONSTANT OR FLUCTUATING DEMAND CASES

Thus far the discussion has dealt solely with long-run economic planning for cases in which demand curves are constant, both from hour to hour and year to year. Needless to say, this is a gross oversimplification and to some extent weakens our ability to apply the straightforward deterministic approach which was outlined in the previous sections of this chapter. The principles with respect to the justification of extra capacity and output—and their costs—remain unchanged, however. The difficulties and complexities arising from considering the highly dynamic nature of investment planning and fluctuating demand make it necessary to place the investment planning problem within the more usual type of benefit–cost analysis framework in which particular facility designs, staging plans, and pricing policies are analyzed and evaluated with respect to their year-by-year costs and benefits (or revenues, where necessary). The benefit–cost analysis and evaluation procedure which will be followed throughout the remainder of this text employs the net present value (or net present worth) method. We shall use the terms *net present value, net present worth*, and *total discounted net benefit* interchangeably. While less common than the benefit–cost ratio, internal rate-of-return, or equivalent annual cost methods within the engineering and planning community, this procedure avoids a number of practical and technical difficulties and inconsistencies which often arise with use of the last three methods (as discussed in Chapter 8).

In the remainder of this section benefit–cost analysis procedures will be applied to design situations involving three different types of demand fluctuations: first, with respect to intertemporal (or year-to-year) demand changes, while assuming there are no intratemporal (or hour-to-hour) demand fluctuations; second, with respect to intratemporal demand fluctuations, while assuming there are no intertemporal changes; and third, with respect to both (that is, joint) intratemporal and intertemporal changes.

7-5-1   INTERTEMPORAL DEMAND CHANGES AND LONG-RUN PLANNING

The essential questions of planning are: how much and what type of investment to undertake *now* in light of the available technology and our expectations about present and future costs, demands, and benefits. To begin to answer this question, we must first determine a time or planning horizon in which costs and benefits will be considered. In addition, we must consider alternative staging strategies within this planning horizon. For example, we should explicitly consider the possibility of delaying facility construction. To conduct the analysis, we require knowledge of year-to-year demand expectations, year-to-year cost functions for each staging plan and alternative investment, and year-to-year discount rates, all properly accounting for the uncertainties of man and nature and for divergences between market and opportunity values. Further, there are problems involving the extra delays, interruptions, and other such costs occurring during construction and maintenance periods, and there are the practical considerations of workable pricing mechanisms, and of steady versus fluctuating prices and so forth.

Our general procedure for considering these problems will be to sum the (discounted) annual consequences of each specific investment and staging plan (that is, each alternative) over the entire planning horizon. The analysis will be identical to that in the previous section except that we must consider each year of the planning horizon separately, and we must explicitly consider different implementation schedules over time. As a result, the calculations are more numerous, but the essential principles and approach remain unchanged.

While it is necessary to anticipate and account for the entire stream of expected future costs and benefits in the process of making decisions about today's commitments, once a decision is made about present actions, there is clearly no firm commitment being made with respect to future ones. One commitment does not *require* the other, after the fact; on the other hand, the earlier action can and probably will affect later actions, even in the face of changes in expected benefits or costs, if for no other reason than because of the fact that earlier commitments (usually) can be regarded as sunk or irrevocable.

Another important aspect based upon the analyses and conclusions earlier in this chapter is that is not necessary to place fixed and variable costs on commensurate scales with respect to *specific* time intervals and their output levels. That is, while resources committed for fixed factors of production during (say) year t can be placed on a commensurate time value of money scale with commitments made during other earlier or later years, such fixed costs are nonseparable with respect to the output level during year t or succeeding years. Thus, they need *not* be "spread" or averaged over the volume occurring during year t and the remaining years during the planning horizon. It will be necessary to deal with fixed or nonseparable costs in terms of their relationship to facility size and output capacity and the time period in which they are committed.

The long-run economic objective (while assuming no intratemporal demand fluctuations and thus that flow throughout the tth time period or year is constant) is to determine the investment plan which will maximize the (expected) total discounted net benefits resulting over an n-year analysis period (or n-year planning horizon),[2] subject, of course, to the restriction that the total discounted net benefits are positive. In short, the null alternative (which will produce total discounted net benefits equal to zero) is always preferable to a plan which will result in negative total discounted net benefits, aside from social or other external considerations. Also, as detailed throughout the preceding sections, the best pricing policy (from the standpoint of economic efficiency and maximizing total net benefits) will be to adopt marginal cost pricing. Again, for this initial discussion, the implementation of one or another pricing policy is regarded as "costless" (at least on a relative basis). Satisfying this longer-term problem, given (just) intertemporal demand fluctuations, can no longer be regarded as a straightforward or deterministic problem. Rather, it must be characterized as a compound decision problem based on expectations of future costs and benefits for each alternative. Thus, the decision problem may be formalized as a decision tree or dynamic programming problem. Also, it must be recognized that the costs and benefits during any future year t will be dependent or conditional upon the prior staging plan or actions which were taken during years 1 to $t - 1$.

---

[2]Throughout, it is assumed that expected costs and benefits will be used; other strategies (such as MINIMAX and MAXIMAX) will not be considered.

The problem can be formulated as follows:
Let

$NSC(x_t|x_1,\ldots,x_{t-1})$ = nonseparable or fixed costs incurred at start of year t for plan x_t *given* that plans $x_1,\ldots,$ x_{t-1} were adopted in previous years (written $x_t|x_1,\ldots,x_{t-1}$)

$SRVC(q_t, x_t|x_1,\ldots,x_{t-1})$ = total variable costs incurred for output q_t during year t for plan $x_t|x_1,\ldots,x_{t-1}$

$srmc(q_t, x_t|x_1,\ldots,x_{t-1})$ = short-run marginal cost at output q_t during year t for plan $x_t|x_1,\ldots,x_{t-1}$

$mb_t(q_t)$ = marginal benefit during year t at output q_t

Then, for efficient utilization and maximum total net benefits during year t for plan x_t, given the adoption of plans $x_1,\ldots,x_{t-1}$ during prior years,

$$\text{Equilibrium price} = p_t(x_t|x_1,\ldots,x_{t-1}) \tag{7-10}$$

$$= srmc(Q_t, x_t|x_1,\ldots,x_{t-1}) \tag{7-11}$$

$$= mb_t(Q_t) \tag{7-12}$$

where

Q_t = equilibrium flow or output during year t for plan $x_t|x_1,\ldots,x_{t-1}$

These equilibrium flows and prices for this simple intertemporal demand case (while ignoring intratemporal fluctuations) could be determined analytically by setting the appropriate marginal benefit and short-run marginal cost expressions equal to each other and solving for the equilibrium flow (and then back-substituting to find the price as in Chapter 3). For example, using Equations (4-18) and (5-3) for plan $x_t|x_1,\ldots,x_{t-1}$ during year t, we get[3]

$$\frac{\alpha_t}{\beta_t} - \frac{Q_t}{\beta_t} = \tau_x + \frac{\nu}{(V_{\max} - \delta_x Q_t)} + \frac{\nu\delta_x Q_t}{(V_{\max} - \delta_x Q_t)^2} \tag{7-13}$$

This expression can be solved for the equilibrium flow Q_t. Then, if Q_t is back-substituted into either Equation (4-18) or (5-3), the equilibrium price can be determined.

---

[3]Each of the parameters for the marginal cost function should be subscripted both with respect to year t and facility plan $x_t|x_1,\ldots,x_{t-1}$, but for simplicity, only part of these subscripts were used. Also, Equation (4-18) was modified by substituting Equation (4-15) for $sravc_x(q)$ and collecting terms.

Also,

$$SRVC(Q_t, x_t | x_1, \ldots, x_{t-1}) = k_t \sum_{q_t=1}^{Q_t} srmc(q_t, x_t | x_1, \ldots, x_{t-1}) \qquad (7\text{-}14)$$

and

$$TB(Q_t, x_t | x_1, \ldots, x_{t-1}) = k_t \sum_{q_t=1}^{Q_t} mb_t(q_t) \qquad (7\text{-}15)$$

$$TR(Q_t, x_t | x_1, \ldots, x_{t-1}) = k_t Q_t p_t(x_t | x_1, \ldots, x_{t-1}) \qquad (7\text{-}16)$$

in which $SRVC$, TB, and TR are the total variable costs, total benefits, and total revenues, respectively, during the tth year for the equilibrium flow and staging plan indicated in the argument; also, in these equations k_t is the number of time intervals during year t having equilibrium flow Q_t and assumes that the flow throughout the year is constant. Consequently, if the output or flow units are trips *per hour* in year t, then the time interval would be an hour and k_t would be equal to 8760.

Also, it will be assumed (simply for computational convenience) that the variable costs, benefits, and revenues occur at the *end* of the year during which they are incurred or accrued (i.e., at the end of the tth year); this is in contrast to the nonseparable (or "fixed") costs which are assumed to be incurred at the *start* of year t.

Once the costs, marginal benefits, and revenues have been enumerated—for all years during the n-year planning horizon and for all plans or combinations of facility size and staging sequences—it will then be possible to reduce the costs and benefits to a comparable time base (in order to account for the time value of money) and to compare alternative facility plans and staging sequences. For this purpose the year-by-year cost and benefit totals in Equations (7-14) to (7-16) together with the nonseparable costs will be discounted, totalled, and compared in two ways. First, *increments* of expenditure and benefit will be compared *working backward from year n* to insure the economic feasibility of increments. Two, those plans for which all increments of expenditure during the n years are economically justifiable will then be compared in terms of their accumulated n-year total net benefits (discounted to the present). This procedure is outlined as a two-step procedure for computational reasons. That is, if the analysis is made incrementally—as will be detailed—the computations can be foreshortened relative to a procedure whereby *every* plan is discounted to the present.

To illustrate the above points, consider the simple example shown in Figure 7-3 in which four different facility sizes or expansion plans are analyzed for the planning horizon of 2 years (i.e., *through* year 2). The first step of the analysis would be to examine the incremental costs and

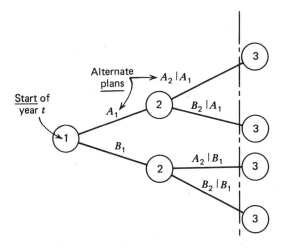

Figure 7-3.   Illustration of alternative facility and staging plans.

benefits from the *start* of year 2 to its end. Thus, for each of the four plans, the year 2 variable costs and benefits will be discounted to the start of year 2, netted, and compared with any nonseparable (or fixed) costs incurred at the start of year 2. All plans for which the incremental (or second year) benefits do not exceed the incremental costs will be rejected; recall in this regard that at the end of each year throughout the planning horizon the facility can be abandoned, thus reducing from that year forward the total net benefits to zero (which clearly is preferable to negative total net benefits). In turn, each of the plans which was not rejected upon examination of the last increments will be analyzed in terms of the incremental costs and benefits during the nth and $n - 1$th years combined. The total net benefits computed before (i.e., the total net benefits discounted to the *start* of the nth year, or second year in this case) will be added to the benefits accruing during the $n - 1$th year; the $n - 1$th-year variable costs will be subtracted from these total 2-year benefits and the net will then be discounted to the start of the $n - 1$th year and then compared with the nonseparable costs (if any) which were made at the start of the $n - 1$th year. Again, all plans for which the net of these benefits and costs (or total discounted net benefits for the last 2 years) are not positive will be rejected. Finally, all plans having positive total discounted net benefits can be compared to determine which is the most preferable (i.e., which plan accrues the largest total discounted net benefits).

If overall *financial* feasibility for the total n-year period is also a requirement for alternative plans and projects, as might be recommended for increasing returns cases, the year-by-year revenues and costs *for the best plan* (i.e., for the plan having the highest total discounted net benefit) can then be discounted and totalled; if the total discounted net revenues for the best plan are positive, then both economic and financial feasibility requirements will be satisfied.

The year-to-year discounting (working backwards from year n) required for the incremental benefit and cost analysis can be accomplished by successively applying a 1-year discount factor as follows:

$$DF_1 = 1\text{-year discount factor} = \frac{1}{1+i} \qquad (7\text{-}17)$$

where i is the interest rate expressed in decimal form. For example, if the benefit and cost increments for the last or nth year of the planning horizon are to be placed on a comparable time-value basis (which we will assume to be the *start* of the nth year), the total net benefits discounted to the start of year n would be as follows:

$$
\begin{aligned}
TDNB_n(x_1,\ldots,x_n) = \ & DF_1[TB(Q_n, x_n|x_1,\ldots,x_{n-1}) \\
& - SRVC(Q_n, x_n|x_1,\ldots,x_{n-1})] \\
& - NSC(x_n|x_1,\ldots,x_{n-1})
\end{aligned}
\qquad (7\text{-}18)
$$

where $TDNB_n(x_1,\ldots,x_n)$ is the total net benefits discounted to the start of year n for the staging and facility plan shown in the argument of the expression.

More generally, for carrying out the incremental analysis the total net benefits for years t through n when discounted to the start of year t would be as follows:

$$
\begin{aligned}
TDNB_t(x_1,\ldots,x_n) = \ & DF_1[TDNB_{t+1}(x_1,\ldots,x_n) \\
& - SRVC(Q_t, x_t|x_1,\ldots,x_{t-1}) \\
& + TB(Q_t, x_t|x_1,\ldots,x_{t-1})] \\
& - NSC(x_t|x_1,\ldots,x_{t-1})
\end{aligned}
\qquad (7\text{-}19)
$$

For those cases in which financial feasibility is also required, the factor for discounting revenues or costs accrued or incurred at the end of the tth year to their present value would be

$$DF_t = \frac{1}{(1+i)^t} \qquad (7\text{-}20)$$

Applying this factor, the total net revenues for the n-year planning horizon, all discounted to the start of year 1, would be as follows (for staging plan $x_1,\ldots,x_n$):

$$TDNR(x_1,\ldots,x_n) = \sum_{t=1}^{n} DF_t[TR(Q_t, x_t|x_1,\ldots,x_{t-1})$$

$$- SRVC(Q_t, x_t|x_1,\ldots,x_{t-1})$$

$$- NSC(x_t|x_1,\ldots,x_{t-1})(1+i)] \qquad (7\text{-}21)$$

However, when t is equal to 1 in the summation [Eq. (7-21)], the argument $(x_t|x_1,\ldots,x_{t-1})$ simply becomes x_1, and when t is equal to 2 in the summation, the argument becomes $x_2|x_1$.

The benefit–cost (or, more specifically, net present value) procedure outlined above will permit the analyst to examine the economic and financial feasibility of investments and increments of investment. Furthermore, this procedure will permit the analyst to take into account the alternatives of doing nothing now (or later), of abandoning existing facilities at any time during the planning horizon, and of withholding expansion or investment until a later year. (Specifically, requiring increments of investment as well as the overall investment to have total discounted net benefits equal to or greater than zero implicitly accounts for these alternatives.) However, the extent to which the procedure will lead to the "optimum" investment and staging program depends on the ingenuity of engineers, planners, and designers and their ability to create "useful and worthwhile" designs, to estimate the best expansion plans and the best technology for providing services, and to determine the plan for which extra benefits just equal the extra costs for the last increment of expenditure.

Finally, it should be noted that this procedure *with* the accompanying pricing policy requires the use of prices which can (and probably will) vary from year to year; the degree to which they would vary depends on the lumpiness or divisibility of the technology, on demand shifts from year to year, on the staging plan, and on the nature of the returns to scale (i.e., are they constant, increasing, or decreasing?).

7-5-2 INTRATEMPORAL DEMAND FLUCTUATIONS AND LONG-RUN EFFICIENCY

The problems of peak loads or intratemporal demand fluctuations complicate investment, pricing, and efficiency planning enormously but are of great importance. In this section both simple and complex peak-load situations will be treated, though in all cases it will be assumed that intratemporal demand functions change only from hour to hour and remain constant from day to day and from year to year; also, intratemporal demand *cross*-relations generally will be ignored.

The first case to be discussed will be that in which the demand fluctuations during the day can be characterized by two demand functions, one for the demand during n_p peak-load hours and a second for the demand during n_o off-peak-load hours; the demand during each hour of the peak period will be identical, and that during each off-peak period hour will be identical. This does not imply that the peak period must consist of n_p consecutive hours, however; for example, if n_p were 5 hours, the morning peak load could be 2 hours long and the afternoon peak load could be 3 hours long, with each peak-load hour having the same demand and equilibrium flow. As noted above, the hour-to-hour demand *cross*-relations are ignored. That is, it is assumed that travelers, when deciding whether to travel and which hour to select if one does travel, will consider only the price of travel during the hour in question. For instance, when deciding whether to make a trip during the peak period, the traveler will consider only the peak period price rather than consider the off-peak period price as well. In essence, this is to assume that the peak and off-peak periods are not competing choices for potential travelers. While this assumption is clearly unrealistic, its use does permit us to depict the situation graphically and with less complexity than would otherwise be necessary. Chapter 5 provides an explanation of the appropriate treatment for competing choice situations.

Let us assume that we are confronted with the long-run cost functions and peak and off-peak period demand functions shown in Figure 7-4. Note that the long-run marginal cost is assumed to be constant, thus indicating that (for the total cost functions as shown) the long-run average total cost is continually declining. Two possibilities for the *lratc* function are indicated on the diagram. Using the long-run economic efficiency principles outlined earlier, we can see that the "best" facility would be that for which total cost was lowest when the output was q_o *if* the demand were constantly at D_o but that the "best" would correspond to output q_p *if* the demand were constantly at D_p. Moreover, it can be shown that in either of the two cases the total net benefits would be positive when the *lratc(q)* function applied; however, total net benefits may or may not be positive when the *lratc'(q)* function was appropriate.

With fluctuating demand, determination of the best facility size cannot be made by simply examining the long-run marginal cost curve. We might attempt to choose the best facility for one particular period (such as the peak travel period), but this policy may result in *much* lower net benefits than might be obtained from intermediate facility sizes. The relevant principle is to determine the net benefits during each period for the various facility sizes and then to choose the facility which maximizes the total nonnegative net benefit, which is the sum of all individual periods' net benefits.

In general, for any facility x the daily total net benefits can be computed as follows when there are r different demand periods:

$$TNB_x = \sum_{h=1}^{r} k_h \sum_{q=1}^{q_{h,x}} [mb_h(q) - srmc_x(q)] - 24F_x \qquad (7\text{-}22)$$

where F_x is the hourly fixed cost for facility x, $mb_h(q)$ is the hourly marginal benefit during the hth demand period for a flow of q, and $q_{h,x}$ is the hourly equilibrium flow for the hth demand period with facility x. In this equation the hth demand period includes k_h hours of flow. This formulation of total net benefit applies regardless of whether there are constant, increasing, or decreasing returns to scale. The planning problem is to identify the facility size, x, which maximizes the total nonnegative net benefits.

For situations in which facility sizes are discrete, a planner need only calculate the total net benefits for each possible facility size and then choose the facility with the largest nonnegative net benefits. In situations of perfect divisibility the same principle exists, although the method of identifying the best facility is more difficult due to the large number of

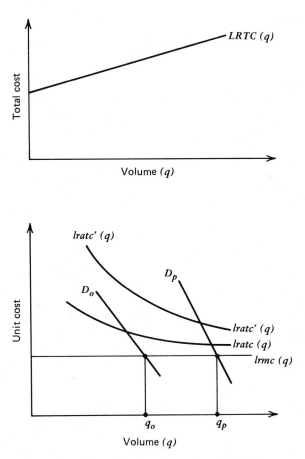

Figure 7-4. Illustrative long-run cost and demand curves.

alternatives. Under certain circumstances a planner may simply follow the procedure of continuously expanding the facility size until the long-run incremental total net benefit due to expansion is zero; the incremental benefits may be calculated from Equation (7-22) for each change in facility size, such as from facility x to facility y:

$$\Delta TNB_{xy} = TNB_y - TNB_x$$

$$= \sum_{h=1}^{r} k_h \sum_{q=q_{h,x}}^{q_{h,y}} mb_h(q) - 24(F_y - F_x)$$

$$- \sum_{h=1}^{r} k_h [SRVC_y(q_{h,y}) - SRVC_x(q_{h,x})] \quad (7\text{-}23)$$

The conditions under which this guideline may be employed require that only *one* optimum facility size exists. As long as a single optimum short-run price exists and equilibrium volumes increase with increased facility size, this condition will occur. With the possibility of more than one facility size for which the total incremental net benefits are zero, it is necessary to identify each of these facilities and then directly compare their total net benefits to determine the best facility.

While the approach described above insures that the best facility size will be chosen, it does not insure that the best facility will be either economically desirable or financially feasible. To be economically feasible, the facility must have total benefits larger than total costs; that is,

$$\sum_{h=1}^{r} k_h \sum_{q=1}^{q_{h,x}} [mb_h(q) - srmc_x(q)] \geq 24F_x \quad (7\text{-}24)$$

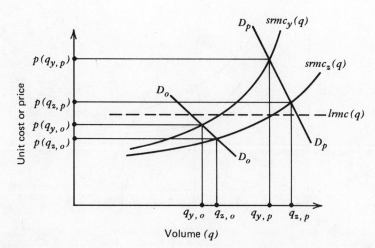

Figure 7-5. Cost and demand relations for two-period intratemporal demand case and for two facility sizes.

In some cases a financial constraint may be imposed so that total payments might be required to exceed costs:

$$\sum_{h=1}^{r} k_h[q_{h,x}p(q_{h,x}) - SRVC_x(q_{h,x})] \ge 24F_x \qquad (7\text{-}25\text{a})$$

or

$$\sum_{h=1}^{r} k_h q_{h,x}[p(q_{h,x}) - sravc_x(q_{h,x})] \ge 24F_x \qquad (7\text{-}25\text{b})$$

In addition, financial requirements for operators might be imposed; this possibility is discussed further below.

One interesting condition concerning the optimal facility size was derived by M. Boiteux.[4] According to Boiteux, the facility of optimum scale or capacity for situations with periodic loads or, say, with peak and off-peak demand functions as shown in Figure 7-5 will be that facility for which the total costs for the equilibrium peak and off-peak flows will be minimized (under short-run marginal cost pricing and while clearing the market).[5] From this, Boiteux concluded that for the "optimum" facility (say x) and for short-run marginal cost pricing, the following condition holds[6]:

$$\sum_{h=1}^{r} k_h srmc_x(q_{h,x}) = lrmc \sum_{h=1}^{r} k_h \qquad (7\text{-}26)$$

However, Boiteux noted that this condition applies only "...*when the development [or long-run marginal] cost is constant and the expenditure [or total cost] curves for plants of various capacities are congruent and differ only in position*. If the outputs [or equilibrium flows] are not very different or if the [$LRTC_x(q)$] curves do not alter shape greatly when the capacity

---

[4]M. Boiteux, "Peak-Load Pricing," *Journal of Business* **33**(2), 157–179 (1960); this work is also included in J. R. Nelson (ed.), *Marginal Cost Pricing in Practice*, Prentice-Hall, Englewood Cliffs, NJ, 1964. Also, it should be noted that some of of his mathematical results may appear different from those formulated here since the output time interval used by Boiteux was 12 hours; further, it may be helpful to note that Boiteux uses the term *development cost* in place of long-run marginal cost and *differential cost* in place of short-run marginal cost. Finally, he applied the term *plant of flexible capacity* to facilities having characteristics of the sort discussed here.

[5]Ibid., pp. 169, 177, 178.

[6]Ibid., pp. 169; notation and time-scale has been changed to conform to that used here. The Boiteux solution can also be applied to situations wih more than two different (intratemporal) demand functions.

of the plant is changed, the formula holds as a first approximation."[7] [Emphasis added.]

For the Boiteux solution, the tolls for the optimum facility x would be equal to the difference of short-run marginal costs and the short-run average variable costs (assuming, again, that short-run average variable costs are equivalent to the perceived travel payments); thus, during the hth demand period, the toll for facility x would be

$$T_{h,x} = srmc_x(q_{h,x}) - sravc_x(q_{h,x}) \qquad (7\text{-}27)$$

While this particular solution ensures that the total payment by trip-makers (tolls plus average variable or perceived travel costs) would more than cover the total *variable* costs for the "optimum" facility, it does not insure that the total net benefits are positive, that the total net revenues are positive, or that the total toll revenues at least equal the fixed facility costs. Thus, while total net benefits are maximized (by virtue of short-run marginal cost pricing), neither economic nor financial feasibility is assured, *a priori*.

7-5-3 JOINT CONSIDERATION OF INTERTEMPORAL AND INTRATEMPORAL DEMAND FLUCTUATIONS

In most instances the analyst should take account of both intertemporal and intratemporal demand fluctuations in his search for the "best" investment and staging plan. To undertake such an assignment, a benefit–cost analysis and decision-tree approach comparable to that outlined for the intertemporal situation in Section 7-5-1 or Chapter 8 would be suitable.

First, let us define

$NSC(x_t|x_1,\ldots,x_{t-1})$ = nonseparable (fixed) costs incurred at start of year t for plan x_t given that plans $x_1,\ldots,$ x_{t-1} were adopted in previous years

$SRVC(q_{h,t}, x_t|x_1,\ldots,x_{t-1})$ = total variable costs for flow $q_{h,t}$ during the hth demand period of year t for plan $x_t|x_1,\ldots,x_{t-1}$

$srmc(q_{h,t}, x_t|x_1,\ldots,x_{t-1})$ = short-run marginal cost for output $q_{h,t}$ during the hth demand period of year t for plan $x_t|x_1,\ldots,x_{t-1}$

$mb_{h,t}(q_{h,t})$ = marginal benefit for output $q_{h,t}$ for plan $x_t|x_1,\ldots,x_{t-1}$

---

[7]Ibid., pp. 169, 170, reprinted by permission of the University of Chicago Press. Also, Boiteux's reference to congruency simply means that the short-run marginal cost functions for different capacity levels differ from one another only by a horizontal translation.

For most efficient utilization and maximum net benefits during the hth demand period of year t for plan x_t given the adoption of plans $x_1,\ldots,x_{t-1}$ during previous years, the following conditions must hold:

$$\text{Equilibrium price} = p_{h,t}(x_t|x_1,\ldots,x_{t-1}) \tag{7-28}$$

$$= srmc\,(Q_{h,t},\,x_t|x_1,\ldots,x_{t-1}) \tag{7-29}$$

$$= mb_{h,t}(Q_{h,t}) \tag{7-30}$$

where $Q_{h,t}$ = equilibrium flow during hth demand period of year t for plan $(x_t|x_1,\ldots,x_{t-1})$

As before, the equilibrium flow and price can be determined analytically (while ignoring cross-elasticities) by setting the marginal benefit and short-run marginal cost expressions equal to each other. Also,

$$SRVC\,(Q_t,x_t|x_1,\ldots,x_{t-1}) = m_t \sum_{h=1}^{r} k_h \sum_{q_{h,t}=1}^{Q_{h,t}} srmc\,(q_{h,t},\,x_t|x_1,\ldots,x_{t-1}) \tag{7-31}$$

and

$$TB\,(Q_t,x_t|x_1,\ldots,x_{t-1}) = m_t \sum_{h=1}^{r} k_h \sum_{q_{h,t}=1}^{Q_{h,t}} mb_{h,t}(q_{h,t}) \tag{7-32}$$

$$TR\,(Q_t,x_t|x_1,\ldots,x_{t-1}) = m_t \sum_{h=1}^{r} k_h\, Q_{h,t}p_{h,t}(x_t|x_1,\ldots,x_{t-1}) \tag{7-33}$$

in which $SRVC$, TB, and TR are the total variable costs, total benefits, and total revenues during all demand periods of year t for the staging plan indicated in the argument; Q_t is intended to merely represent the combined equilibrium flows during the year t. Also, k_h is the number of time intervals in the hth demand period, with each interval having flow $Q_{h,t}$, and m_t is the number of identical demand periods occurring during the year t. Consequently, if the output units are trips per hour, then k_h would be the number of hours (during a day) having a flow $Q_{h,t}$ and the sum of k_h over all h (i.e., $h=1,\ldots,r$) would be 24; if all days during the year t had an identical set of demand functions, m_t would be equal to 365.

From here on, the analysis of the total net benefits (or total net revenues) and treatment of year-by-year discounting and incremental effects would be identical to that outlined in Section 7-5-1. The formulas, shown earlier in Equations (7-17) to (7-21), are entirely applicable when using the joint intratemporal functions for $SRVC$, TB, and TR which were developed in Equations (7-31) to (7-33), together with the definition for NSC which was given at the outset of this section.

7-6   DECISION ANALYSIS WITH UNCERTAINTY

There is an additional and very important consideration which should be included in the analysis of investment and staging plans which was outlined in the previous section. As we noted in Chapter 3, estimates of system or service usage which will occur in the future have a great deal of uncertainty associated with them. Moreover, estimates of the costs of construction and operation in future years are also uncertain. This uncertainty complicates the analysis, but a reasonable and prudent planner can and should consider its implications in making investment decisions.

It should be apparent that different alternatives will be more or less desirable as the expected volume or associated costs change. For example, smaller facilities would likely be more desirable than larger ones when the underlying demand for a service is lower than originally expected. In addition, more flexible services and systems are likely to be more beneficial when a great deal of uncertainty accompanies estimates of volume levels and costs. With a more flexible system, it is possible to make decisions to change the scale of service at a later date in light of the actual changes in volumes or costs.

One tedious but straightforward manner in which to consider such uncertainties is to estimate the *expected* net benefits of an investment and staging alternative. This procedure requires identification of the various possibilities or conditions which are likely to occur and determination of a probability or chance that each of these conditions might occur. These different conditions might correspond to different growth rates in population or economic activity. The total net benefits resulting from each investment and staging alternative under each condition or possibility is then calculated using the method described in Section 7-5. Subsequently, the expected net benefits are calculated by summing the net benefits under each condition multiplied by the probability that the condition occurs:

$$E[TDNB] = \sum_{z=1}^{m} \Pr\{z\} TDNB_n(x_1,\ldots,x_n|z) \qquad (7\text{-}34)$$

where z is a particular condition, m is the number of possible conditions, $\Pr\{z\}$ is the probability that z will occur, and total discounted net benefit $TDNB(\cdot)$ is as defined in Section 7-5. Note that the sum of the probabilities associated with all the possible conditions must equal 1.

An illustration of this procedure appears in Figure 7-6 for the case in which two different conditions might occur in year 2. These two conditions might occur if a major industrial plant had some chance of locating within the study area, so the analysis is conducted under the assumption that the plant will not be present ($z = 1$) and that the plant will be ($z = 2$).

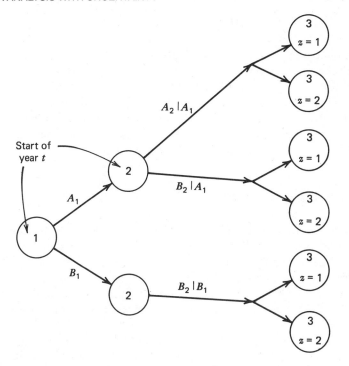

Figure 7-6. Alternative facility and staging plans for a two-year horizon with two possible exogenous events.

In this analysis, the decision is whether to implement alternative A or B in year 1 and, in year 2, whether to switch to alternative B from alternative A (if it was chosen in year 1). Another example in which two alternatives might be considered is the case in which an economic recession may or may not occur. The net benefits resulting from each of the future conditions are estimated, along with the probabilities for all z, and then the expected net benefits are calculated using Equation (7-34).

Uncertain events which may occur during the planning horizon may make subsequent changes in the investment and staging plans desirable. For example, future planned expansions might be cancelled if the growth in system usage was much lower than expected. The analysis should be conducted based upon the assumption that such cancellations might occur given the outcome of events up until that point in time. Such changes are simply a realization that decisions deferred to a later date may take advantage of knowledge developed in previous periods. Selling unneeded vehicles is a practical example of a rational response of this type. Thus, the costs associated with low-volume situations would likely be lower for investment alternatives which carry with them the possibility of flexible operations and cost reductions.

In many cases it may be adequate to consider the result of a few extreme cases of cost and demand function shifts, and then interpolate to find intermediate values. Even in planning situations in which a full-scale analysis of the type illustrated in Figure 7-6 would be too costly to be practical, planners should realize that investment plans which incorporate a certain amount of flexibility in operation under different conditions are likely to be more effective than rigid alternatives.

7-7 CONCLUDING REMARKS

The earlier sections of this chapter outlined the interactions among cost, demand, and pricing under very idealized circumstances, but nonetheless provided a general framework to guide the designer and planner in his search for better designs and technologies. Furthermore, in these introductory remarks the conflict between economic efficiency and financial feasibility which can exist was noted, along with some of the reasons for permitting one aspect or another to override.

However, once it becomes necessary to account for the demand fluctuations that invariably exist, either intertemporally (year to year) or intratemporally (hour to hour or season to season), or both, the last of which is usually the case, the idealized and deterministic structure for decision making on questions of the best investment and output level does not appear suitable. Rather, in its stead, it becomes necessary to detail particular plans and to analyze their particular consequences on the more usual benefit–cost basis. The details of this type of analysis were introduced to permit full accounting of the time-value aspects as well as intratemporal and intertemporal demand fluctuations (while ignoring crosselasticities, however). Finally, it should be noted that feasibility analysis was mainly considered in this chapter for marginal cost pricing, though some of the ramifications stemming from other policies were noted. Further, no note was made of the practical difficulties or costs of implementing such a pricing policy or of the distributional aspects involved. These issues will be considered in Chapter 13.

CHAPTER 8

BENEFIT–COST ANALYSIS FOR MUTUALLY EXCLUSIVE ALTERNATIVES—PRINCIPLES AND METHODS

The subject of benefit–cost analysis—whether termed that or an engineering economy study or an alternatives analysis or a feasibility analysis—is not a new one. While the "names" have changed, the substance and the content have remained unchanged for many years. Nor have the principles changed. Rather, it is the planner's understanding of the subject (or lack thereof) and use (or abuse) which seem to have undergone a change, though one which hardly appears to have improved upon the process. Thus, it is important to carefully review the principles underlying benefit–cost analysis and the methods to be employed for analyzing mutually exclusive alternatives.

At the outset it is important to emphasize that in most senses benefit–cost analysis is little different from long-run economic planning as discussed in previous chapters. The principles to be used are virtually identical, the major difference being that in benefit–cost analysis only a subset of specific alternatives is analyzed. That is, benefit–cost analysis is directed solely at the analysis of a specific set of technological or policy alternatives while long-run economic planning as discussed earlier is directed at identification of the best alternative among a much wider range of technological possibilities. Further, benefit–cost analyses will tend to be much more detailed than the more general long-run economic planning and to take account of other important aspects—such as variation in demand, either from hour to hour (or intratemporally) or from year to year (or intertemporally).

8-1   PROPER SPECIFICATION OF MUTUALLY EXCLUSIVE ALTERNATIVES

The essential questions for benefit–cost analysis are directed at analyzing the *economic* desirability of mutually exclusive alternatives. The term *mutually exclusive* implies that one and only one of the alternatives can be undertaken. Importantly, when a list of mutually exclusive alternatives has been specified for analysis, the *null or "do-nothing" alternative* should always be part of the process. The null alternative is simply that of doing nothing. More precisely, it is providing no transport service and thus incurring no costs and accruing no benefits. When an entirely new facility is being proposed, there seems to be no misunderstanding about the existence and treatment of the null alternative. But when an agency is considering the improvement of services on an *existing* transit line or highway, the analyst *often and incorrectly specifies* the null alternative as the "status quo" or existing alternative. Sometimes this is done implicitly by virtue of simply analyzing the incremental benefits and costs between the existing facility or system and its improvement. This is tantamount to assuming that the existing service will be continued or improved, regardless of its economic merits.

There is one exception to our definition of the null alternative which occurs occasionally in the case of disinvestment in existing facilities. In such a case abandonment may involve shut-down or demolition costs and, thus, the null alternative as defined above is not available. This case is relatively rare, however, since most facilities will have some salvage or residual land value to offset some or all of the demolition costs.

Also, the usual practice is to overlook consideration of the null (or do-nothing) alternative, as previously defined. That is, most analysts treat the existing (or status quo) alternative as the null alternative. In this instance the analyst has *implicitly* concluded that the benefits associated with the use of the existing system *do* outweigh the costs of operating and maintaining it (to include the foregone opportunity value associated with its fixed way and facilities). In practice, this is equivalent to saying "No facility or system, once built and in operation, can be abandoned—*regardless*." In a rapidly changing society and economy constantly bombarded with new technology and developments, it would be hard to justify such a position. While we seldom question the wisdom of abandoning obsolete plants and facilities *if privately owned*, we nonetheless see no contradiction when we take an opposite view with respect to abandoning obsolescent *publicly owned* systems or facilities. The difference in viewpoint is neither defensible nor understandable.

The proper specification of mutually exclusive alternatives can also be explained by example. Suppose, for instance, you had attempted to carry out a benefit–cost analysis for BART (the San Francisco Bay Area Rapid Transit System) prior to its construction. Most analysts would simply analyze the extra costs incurred to build and operate BART as compared to the extra benefits stemming from its operation. Other planners would argue that by virtue of building BART certain additional highways would not have to be built, and thus that an additional benefit item for BART would be the avoided costs of additional highway construction. In either case the full set of mutually exclusive alternatives has been mis-specified. For the first the existing highway and transit facilities (prior to BART) are implicitly assumed to be the null alternative and thus their benefits and costs are ignored. In the second case two mutually exclusive alternatives are improperly intermeshed. In contrast, the proper list of mutually exclusive alternatives (involving the existing highway and transit system, BART, and new highways) might be as follows:

Null Alternative: abandonment of existing transit and highway system, as well as no BART and no new highways.

Existing (or Status Quo) Alternative: existing transit and highway system *without* either BART or new highways.

New Alternative 1: existing transit and highway system *plus* BART but *no* new highways.

New Alternative 2: existing transit and highway system *plus* BART *and* some new highways.

New Alternative 3: Improved operating and pricing strategies for the existing transit and highway system.

In turn, the benefits and costs for each of these mutually exclusive alternatives (other than the null, which has zero benefits and costs) should be evaluated.

The acceptance or rejection of one alternative is not dependent upon another. That is, if one does not build one alternative, such as "New Alternative 1" above, then one does not have to build highways or some other transit system instead. Nor does the construction of BART mean that some new highways are necessarily avoided or "saved."

A story involving former Secretary Robert McNamara highlights this principle. As the story goes, one day McNamara's son informed his father (a champion of benefit–cost analysis) that he had saved a quarter by walking home from school rather than taking the bus, whereupon his father asked why he hadn't decided *not* to take a taxi home and thus to save $2.50 instead.

8-2   BASIC PRINCIPLES UNDERLYING BENEFIT–COST ANALYSIS

The benefit–cost analysis principles are designed to determine whether *any* of a set of mutually exclusive alternatives is economically worthwhile and, if so, which of the alternatives is the most desirable in an economic sense. Benefit–cost analysis methods are used to insure that (1) no project will be considered economically acceptable unless its total net benefits are positive and (2) the project having the highest nonnegative total net benefits is selected as the best.

The analysis methods are designed to take account of the time period in which cost commitments are made or benefits accrued, and to insure that costs incurred or benefits accrued during different time periods are placed on a commensurate value scale. In essence, this is simply to recognize the "time value of resources" and the fact that resources committed in the present or near future are more costly than those committed farther in the future.

8-2-1   DEFINING THE PLANNING HORIZON OR ANALYSIS PERIOD

All alternative projects *must* be analyzed for the *same* analysis period or planning horizon if we are to properly account for reinvestment of any earnings or benefits accrued prior to the end of the analysis or planning period, especially when one project may have a shorter terminal date than another (whether replaced or not).[1] Briefly, the analyst is concerned with (1) examining the benefit and cost conditions which are expected to occur over the same analysis period or planning horizon for all alternatives, regardless of when or whether certain capital items are to be replaced or terminated early, and (2) determining whether any initial capital outlays should be made at the present and, if so, which level of outlay is best based on expected future benefits and costs. For the first, if one project among the set of alternatives is terminated early, the analyst must concern himself with the other opportunities that are available for using the capital funds (which would have been used for replacement) and what returns (i.e., benefits or revenues) can be accrued from them. Similarly, when benefits or revenues are accrued in early years, either prior to the end of the analysis period or prior to the end of any project's terminal date, the analyst cannot ignore the problem of properly accounting for the reinvestment (or use) of the early-year benefits or revenues for the remainder of the analysis period. Some of these matters will be clarified in later examples (Sections II-3 and II-4).

There are many ways of designating the analysis period and insuring that alternative projects are properly compared with respect to the costs and benefits. For one, we can simply adopt an arbitrary length of time over which the cost and benefit circumstances are to be analyzed. This period might be chosen to seem suitable in terms of the service or physical

---

[1]See E. Solomon, "The Arithmetic of Capital-Budgeting Decisions," in E. Solomon (ed.), *The Management of Corporate Capital*, The Free Press of Glencoe, London, 1959, pp. 74 ff.

lives of the facilities involved or in terms of other appropriate aspects. For another, we may—again, arbitrarily—set the analysis period or planning horizon to be equal to what we believe to be "the foreseeable future," or the period of time over which we can comfortably or fairly reliably predict benefits and costs. A third (and common but undesirable choice) is to set the analysis period equal to the least common multiple of the physical or service lives of the alternatives being compared. (For instance, if alternative 1 will be replaced at the end of 5 years, alternative 2 at the end of 15 years, and alternative 3 at the end of 25 years, the least common multiple will be 75 years.) The problem with the third approach is not so much with the length of time established but with the analysis method *usually* (though admittedly not necessarily) utilized in combination with the "least common multiple" approach. Specifically, it usually is employed when the costs are to be expressed in terms of equivalent annual costs computed by multiplying the initial capital outlay (for each alternative) times the capital recovery factor for its service or physical life. Accordingly, use of this approach results in the implicit assumptions that (1) capital items will always be replaced at the end of their initially designated service life (for however many times as are necessary over the "least common multiple" life) and (2) the replacement costs of the capital items in future years will be exactly the same as they were when the project was initiated. Inasmuch as these two assumptions appear to be at odds with real-world considerations (such as changes in the future with respect to the service lives, factor prices, and appropriate technology), a different and simpler analysis method seems more appropriate. Briefly, it appears more straightforward to arbitrarily designate the analysis period (according to our expectations about the "foreseeable future"), and then to estimate the year-by-year cost outlays, whether for initial purchase or replacement and whether service lives change or not, as they are expected to occur over the planning horizon. By so doing, future cost outlays can easily reflect changes due to variations in factor prices or in the technology employed.

8-2-2 ESTIMATING BENEFITS AND COSTS

Once the alternatives have been specified, estimates must be made of the year-by-year volume they will experience and, in turn, the year-by-year costs and benefits associated with that pattern of usage. Importantly, the values for these items should be measured *in constant dollars* and thus not reflect inflation or deflation. It is possible to conduct an analysis in inflated or nominal dollar amounts. However, use of such nominal dollar amounts typically requires applying an inflation factor during the forecasting phase and then removing the inflation during the evaluation phase. It is analytically simpler and conceptually clearer to simply restrict the analysis to costs and benefits as measured in constant dollars.

The yearly costs and benefits calculated for a project should represent the actual benefits and costs resulting from the project with respect to the viewpoint adopted for analysis. As an example, suppose that the federal government is considering an investment, and so a national viewpoint is adopted. In this case dollar amounts which do not represent a commitment of goods or services may be excluded from the benefit and cost totals since they represent a transfer payment. No tax payments should be included within the totals in this case *unless* such taxes represent the payments for services associated with the construction, maintenance, operation, or usage of the alternative being analyzed. If for example extra police were hired by the local government to provide control or security for the alternative, and the costs thereof were to be borne by the local government and paid out of city taxes, then any city tax payments to that extent should be included as a cost item. By contrast, any local property taxes levied against motor vehicles probably should be excluded. Chapters 4 and 5 discussed the definition and measurement of such benefit and cost items.

The costs and revenues associated with *borrowed* money deserve particular attention in specifying and determining the time stream of costs and benefits. Borrowed money has an economic opportunity cost since these funds cannot thereby be used for alternative investments. Some projects require borrowed money during the construction phase or later when replacing equipment and repairing facilities, such funds then being repaid from later project revenues or from other internal earnings (such as tax revenues) available to the firm or agency sponsoring the project. As an

TABLE 8-1. Example of an Alternative's Benefit and Cost Stream with and without External Borrowing Costs

Year	Internal Cash Flow without Borrowing Considerations		Borrowing Costs and Revenues		Cash Flow with Borrowing Costs and Revenues Added	
	Benefit	Cost	Revenue	Cost	Benefit	Cost
0	0	600	600	0	600	600
1	512	100	0	412	512	512
2	512	150	0	237	512	387
3	400	250	0	0	400	250
4	560	800	0	0	560	800
5	800	500	0	0	800	500

Note: Dollar amounts are in thousands of constant dollars. A 6% borrowing rate is assumed for financing.

example, suppose a 5-year project has an internal cash flow stream without considering financing as shown in the first few columns in Table 8-1 and assume the initial outlays are to be financed by borrowing \$600K in year 0, an amount which is paid back in the next 2 years from project net revenues including a 6% interest charge on unpaid balances. The combined cash flow for the project, including external financing revenues and payments, is shown in the final two columns of Table 8-1. While an additional capital infusion of \$240K is required in year 4, in this example it is assumed that the added capital is obtained from internal sources or retained earnings rather than from external borrowing. Obviously, though, other financing schemes could be considered, thereby leading to different combined cash flow streams; more attention will be devoted to this prospect in Section 9-4 of Chapter 9.

Importantly, to determine the economic acceptability of a project and the best among a set of mutually exclusive projects, the benefit–cost analysis must consider the total cash flow stream of benefits and costs, to include any borrowing costs and revenues. *Accordingly, for the discussions and analysis methods described in subsequent sections of this chapter, it will be assumed that all cash flow streams one way or another do account for any borrowing considerations.*[2]

With the estimation of the time stream or benefits and costs for each alternative, we can define

$C_{x,t}$ = expected costs or outlays (whether capital or operating) for
           alternative x during year t

and

$B_{x,t}$ = expected benefits from alternative x during year t.

The stream of costs and benefits over n years might be as shown in Table 8-2. In turn, two other items of information must be specified: (1) the planning horizon or analysis period (n in Table 8-2) and (2) the minimum attractive rate of return (or, say, "cutoff rate") or, equivalently, the opportunity cost of capital (or MARR).

---

[2]However, to the extent that any year by year cash flow imbalances are financed *either* from internal equity sources or retained earnings available to an agency or firm *or* from external borrowing at an interest rate which is *equal* to the MARR (i.e., the discount rate used for benefit–cost analysis, as described in the next section), then the cash stream need not explicitly include financing considerations but can be accomplished by a straightforward analysis of the internal cash flow stream. Specifically, in both of these cases any financing of year to year cash flow imbalances is assumed to be charged at an interest rate equal to MARR, a cost which—when discounted—nets out to zero.

TABLE 8-2.   Year-by-Year Costs and Benefits for
Alternative x Over n Years

Year t	Costs During Year t^a	Benefits During Year t^a
0	$C_{x,0}$	$B_{x,0}$
1	$C_{x,1}$	$B_{x,1}$
$\vdots$	$\vdots$	$\vdots$
t	$C_{x,t}$	$B_{x,t}$
$\vdots$	$\vdots$	$\vdots$
n	$C_{x,n}$	$B_{x,n}$

[a]It is assumed that costs or benefits are incurred or accrued in *lump-sum* at the *end* of year t. The costs or benefits during any year t can be zero. The variable n is the analysis period or planning horizon. Also, if project x has some "salvage value" at the end of n years, that value should be included within $B_{x,n}$, the benefits for year n.

8-2-3   SETTING THE OPPORTUNITY COST OF CAPITAL OR MINIMUM ATTRACTIVE RATE OF RETURN

For *all* benefit–cost analysis methods it will be necessary to specify an interest rate (or discount rate), *directly or indirectly*. Often, and especially when using the internal rate-of-return method, the interest rate to be specified is referred to as the "minimum attractive rate of return" (MARR), a rate which reflects the interest which can be earned from other alternative opportunities which are foregone. This term is equivalent to that used by economists, that is, the opportunity cost of capital or an interest rate with reflects the earnings which will be foregone from other investment opportunities if the capital is to be committed to a project in question. To a large extent the specification of an "appropriate" interest rate, MARR or opportunity cost of capital is arbitrary and thus open to question. As a consequence, it may be desirable to carry out the analysis for a range of interest rates (which may reflect private market rates, on one extreme, and judgments about the social rate of discount, on the other); this range may vary widely, perhaps as much as from 4 to 20%. Given this wide range of possibilities, and the different judgments with respect to private versus social rates of discount, it seems appropriate to discuss the basis of these possibilities and differences.

To begin, resources can be consumed (or enjoyed) now by the current generation or conserved for future use by either the current or future generations; put another way, programs can be undertaken principally for the benefit of the current generation or they can be conducted mainly in the interest of future generations. On the one hand the discount rate reflects the strengths of peoples' individual preferences with respect to foregoing today's enjoyment until next year, with a higher rate expressing a higher preference for consumption and enjoyment *now* relative to that at a later date. Suppose, for instance, your personal rate of time preference was 10%. Such a rate of time preference implies that a dollar of enjoyment or consumption 1 year from now is worth 10% less than a dollar of enjoyment now; or stated somewhat differently, you will be willing to forego a dollar's worth of enjoyment today *only* if you can receive *at least* $1.10 worth of enjoyment 1 year hence. On the other hand the discount rate also reflects the productivity of alternative investments. That is, if you forego consumption and enjoyment today, the resources which you otherwise would have consumed could be invested in alternative opportunities and thus earn more resources for more consumption and enjoyment in later years. If, for instance, the rate of productivity for some investment is 15%, then each dollar invested now rather than consumed will result in $1.15 worth of resources being available for consumption or reinvestment 1 year hence. In turn, the market discount or interest rate (in a perfectly competitive economy) would be determined by a balance between individual's time preferences with regard to substituting future consumption for present-day consumption and the productivity of alternative investments. Individually, and thus collectively, people would continue to invest (and thus forego consumption until a later date) so long as the rate of productivity for increments of investment was larger than their rate of time preference for increments of present versus future consumption. The market discount rate would be determined by that rate which just balances these two rates—that is, when the marginal rate of productivity (or rate of productivity from the last dollar of investment) is equal to the marginal rate of time preference (or rate of time preference for the last dollar of foregone consumption).

Aside from the difficulties of measuring this (ideal) market rate or discount rate (at which the marginal rate of time preference is equal to the marginal rate of return on investments), and aside from the distortions of governmental action and of less than a perfectly competitive economy, some economists argue that the rate of time preference and the feelings of individuals with respect to the welfare of future versus current generations is affected by the opportunities for collective action. Marglin argues this position as follows:[3]

> *The objection to the market solution is that individuals may have preferences that, although an integral part of their attitudes toward consumption now versus consumption later, are inexpressible in the market place. In particular,*

[3]S. Marglin in A. Maass, M. M. Hufschmidt, R. Dorfman, H. A. Thomas, Jr., S. A. Marglin, and G. M. Fair, *Design of Water Resource Systems*, Harvard University Press, Cambridge, MA, 1962, pp. 194 ff. See also remarks on pp. 47 ff.

none of us is able to put into effect in the market place his preferences with regard to other people's consumption. I may well place less of a premium on my own consumption now as opposed to the consumption of an unknown member of a future generation at some specified date in the cooperative context of public investment, in which I know a sacrifice on my own part will be matched by sacrifices by all other members of the community, than in an individualistic market arrangement in which I have no such assurance.

An often used example to illustrate certain aspects of such collective action and social considerations would be the California redwood trees. On the one hand purely economic considerations (in all likelihood) would indicate the wisdom of chopping down the commercially important sequoias and using the wood for homes and furniture, in addition to lumber by-products. To do so, however, would mean that many future generations as well as some members of the current generation would completely forego the opportunity of enjoying the beauty, majesty, and grandeur of these giants for perhaps four to five centuries. As a consequence, some argue that it is socially desirable to forego some of our economic gains merely to preserve this option for those yet unborn and unable to express their preferences in the marketplace.

However, a discount rate to reflect the time preferences under such conditions, or a *social* rate of time preference (sometimes called the social rate of discount), would be virtually impossible of measurement or explicit determination and if used in the justification of *public* investments would appear to have two unattractive features.[4] First, the use of different discount rates for the public and private sectors of the economy will not lead to the most efficient investment planning (from the standpoint of the economy and *aside* from matters of income distribution, both intratemporally and intertemporally). Margolis (in reviewing the Eckstein and McKean books) summarizes other views as well as the important issues as follows:[5]

Essentially Eckstein proposes as a discount rate, the rate at which the taxpayers privately value the funds which they provide, through taxation, to finance the project. He calls this rate the social cost of federal capital and he estimates it at 5 to 6%.[6] He defends this use of a private rate by urging that the

---

[4]An excellent discussion of these aspects may be found in M. Hufschmidt, J. Krutilla, and J. Margolis, "Standards and Criteria for Formulating and Evaluating Federal Water Resources Developments," Report to Bureau of the Budget, Washington, D.C., June 1962, pp. 11ff.

[5]J. Margolis, "The Economic Evaluation of Federal Water Resource Developments," *The American Economic Review*, March 1959, pp. 102-103.

[6]This rate was established prior to 1958. The rate recommended in 1983 for federal projects was 10%. For Eckstein's discussion on interest rate selection, see O. Eckstein, *Water Resource Development*, Harvard University Press, Cambridge, MA, 1958, Chapter IV, Section 3.

*agencies should accept the ethical judgment that consumers' sovereignty with
regard to intertemporal choice should dominate. Therefore, a private rate of
interest should be used in determining the choice of projects and the size of
public investments.*

*Eckstein and Krutilla-Eckstein both recognize that in the political process the
future is not valued solely in terms of the preferences of the current population; the beneficiaries should be future generations as well as the current one.
But they use the time preferences of the current generation of taxpayers as the
basis for the choice of a discount rate.* Actually there is no basis other than an
arbitrary one upon which to select the particular generation or generations
whose preferences should be regarded. *If, for example, we should select a later
generation their preferences might be to keep the current generation at a
minimum consumption level.*

*Though the economist cannot decide which generation's welfare should be
maximized and therefore cannot "scientifically" choose a discount rate, he can
be helpful in the selection of an appropriate social rate of time preference. . . . In
the specific area of water resources the economist can carry through the
analysis at several rates, one of which would be Eckstein's social cost of federal
capital and he can then inform the Congress of the time implications of the
different rates. [Emphasis added.]*

A second and related problem is that the benefits of public investments
may accrue to individuals or groups who have different time preferences.
In line with their individual preferences, should the different benefits be
discounted at different rates?[7] If so, we should consider the incidence of
benefits and the subsequent reinvestment of such benefits. The result
would be a composite or average discount rate.

Another approach to estimation of the rate of social time preference
was outlined in the 1961 report of Hufschmidt et al. to the Bureau of the
Budget; this method calls for determining its value by "discovering the
marginal rate implicit in the Administration's goal of a certain rate of
economic growth. This value judgment with respect to growth rate contains an implicit balancing at the margin of the Administration's time
discount rate and social productivity of investment."[8] Importantly,
though, the panel of consultants added the following qualification:[9]

*One cannot really expect the Administration to hit upon a rate of growth
regarded as optimal without much more knowledge of the economy's investment opportunities than we possess today. Thus the broad-brush targets of*

---

[7]For a thorough discussion of this point along with aspects of reinvestment of benefits by the
beneficiaries, see R. Lind, (ed.), *Discounting for Time and Risk in Energy Policy*, Resources for
the Future, Washington, D.C., 1982.

[8]Hufschmidt et al., op. cit., p. 15.

[9]Ibid.

growth and investment rates which determine the marginal rate of time discount should themselves be revised in light of the marginal rate of discount implicit in them. In short, optimal rates of investment, growth, and marginal rate of discount are properly determined iteratively.

Another matter to be considered in the selection of the "proper" interest rate is that of risk, and a third is that of taxation.

Two aspects of risk (and uncertainty) might be accounted for:[10] (1) the uncertainties of estimating accurately the future costs and benefits of a project and (2) aversion to assuming risk on the part of individuals or organizations. While the uncertainties of cost and benefit prediction are often implicitly accounted for by increasing the discount rate over what it would be with no risk or uncertainty, a more appropriate way of handling the problem would be to incorporate the uncertainties into the computation of the year-to-year estimates of cost and benefit and to use the expected values. With uncertainties varying from year to year and generally increasing over time, these adjustments should clearly be made year by year rather than on some arbitrary, constant, and overall interest rate increase basis. Furthermore, this type of treatment will permit differentiation between uncertainties (or risks) and the time value of money, rather than combine the two aspects on some implicit and unidentifiable basis.

In addition to accounting for inaccuracies in estimating costs or benefits because of risk or uncertainty, it may also be necessary to make adjustments for "risk aversion"—either in calculating the true market value aside from "risk aversion" or in specifying a proper discount rate where "risk aversion" is preferable. Risk aversion applies to the preferences of individuals (or firms) with respect to undertaking investments with differing degrees of risk; some people, for example, are "risk averters" and are unwilling to invest in situations unless there is minimal or no risk, regardless of how high the *expected* return might be, while others or "risk takers" would hesitate to invest in situations unless there is at least some chance of a very large return (relative to the expected return).[11]

More specifically, risk averters generally would be unwilling to undertake investments unless the quoted return is higher than the expected

---

[10]This subject will only be treated in brief terms; also, little distinction will be made between "risk" and "uncertainty." For a thorough and straightforward treatment of investment planning under uncertainty, see H. Bierman and S. Smidt, *The Capital Budgeting Decision*, 3rd ed., Macmillan, New York, 1971, Part III. For a brief discussion of the relationship between risk and the discount rate, see Hirshleifer et al., op. cit., pp. 139 ff.

[11]There is considerable commonality between these risk aversion extremes and those implicit in situations which utilize MINIMAX and MAXIMAX objective functions for probabilistic decision making. For a simple reference and introduction to this subject, see M. Wohl and B. V. Martin, *Traffic System Analysis*, McGraw-Hill Book Co., New York, 1967, Section 8.3. For a more complete discussion, see D. Luce and H. Raiffa, *Games and Decisions*, Wiley, New York, 1957.

return (or so-called risk aversion premium), while risk takers might be willing to invest in situations having quoted returns less than the expected rate if high returns were a reasonable possibility. A simple example of the latter would be gamblers who are willing to place bets in a house crap game (e.g., on each roll of the dice, those betting on "boxcars" or 12 receive a payoff of 30 to 1; however, they can expect a payoff only once every 36 rolls, thus producing a negative expected value).

The existence of these positive and negative "risk aversion" or "risk-taking" premiums for individuals and firms within the private sector of the economy is emphasized mainly to indicate that investment analysts may find it necessary to make certain adjustments when viewing data obtained from the private sector. This is not to say, though, that the rate of discount used for evaluating public investments should reflect either an attitude of conservatism (or "risk aversion") or the reverse; in fact, it probably is more reasonable to take the position that public investment should be based simply on expected values and reflect neither risk aversion nor risk taking.[12]

Two other aspects are of importance to a determination of an appropriate discount rate; they involve the dollar value of resources (or matters of depreciation or appreciation) and taxation.

In situations of inflation or deflation Hirshleifer et al. recommend that all present and future costs and benefits be measured in constant dollars (that is, assuming that the dollar value is stable) and that "the discount rate should be adjusted to correspond to what would be the ruling rate if in fact people were confident that dollars would have constant purchasing power."[13] As a practical rule for adjusting the discount rate under current inflationary trends, it would be appropriate to reduce the market discount rate since it probably reflects a built-in allowance for continuing inflation expectations. (That is, when inflationary trends are expected to continue, the market discount rate is probably adjusted upwards to account for this. Thus, if market rates are used for application to analyses involving constant dollar values, they should be adjusted downwards by the inflation trend adjustment factor.)

Federal, state, and local taxation directly affects the net or after-tax yield of private firms and thus is of importance in determining the true productivity of incremental investment.[14] Foremost, it should be recognized that the private sector of the economy will tend to balance or

---

[12]For coverage of other aspects of this subject, see the previous references and Hufschmidt et al, op. cit., pp. 34 ff.

[13]Hirshleifer et al., op. cit., p. 143.

[14]In addition to the remarks and references to follow, see the treatment of this subject by McKean, op. cit., pp. 163 ff.

equilibrate the marginal rate of time preference and the marginal rate of *after-tax* productivity (or marginal rate of *after-tax* return on investment) rather than the true or overall productivity; this result stems from federal, state, and local tax payments and deduction allowances, but requires an assumption that taxes do *not* represent a proxy for costs of certain public services which were provided for them by government agencies. If one accepts the assumption that taxes do not represent a *cost* associated with the investments, then the yield or return of concern here is the before-tax return or overall productivity; also, it would seem that the market solution caused by taxation policy (i.e., balance at the marginal rate of after-tax productivity) is probably not the best solution from a standpoint of economic efficiency and will not directly permit determination of the marginal rate of before-tax productivity. Even so, Hirshleifer et al. attempted to estimate the marginal rate of productivity (and in so doing to reflect the equity and debt relationships) and suggested (in 1960) that an appropriate figure was in the range of 9 to 10% for private utility investments,[15] after correction for taxation and inflation. However, if one regards corporation income taxes as costs associated with the production of goods or services, the appropriate discount rate would be around 5% according to the same authors.[16] As a concluding comment on (their 1960) recommendations for the "proper" discount rate for public investments, Hirshleifer et al. say:[17]

Even for utility investments in the private sphere, we have seen that the capital market will supply funds only for projects promising (with the average degree of riskiness experienced in that sector) to yield about 9% or 10%. Unfortunately, public investment decision processes have on the whole a far worse record of over optimism, so that the lowest discount rate for public projects we would recommend in practice, unless and until their record improves, is around 10%.

This view contrasts with that taken by the panel of consultants to the Bureau of the Budget (in 1962):[18]

As a temporary expedient, in place of a social rate of time discount plus cutoff benefit-cost ratio, the Panel recommends that a rate synthesizing social time discount and opportunity cost be used. Pending a full-scale investigation by the Council of Economic Advisors of the value of the social rate of discount and the magnitude of opportunity costs, an interim rate of 4 to 5% would appear to be appropriate.

[15]Hirshleifer et al., op. cit., p. 146. See also their additional comments on pages 144–148.

[16]Ibid., p. 147.

[17]Ibid., p. 161.

[18]Hufschmidt et al., op. cit., p. 67.

In practice, an analyst may have little choice in the discount rate used for analysis: the applicable rate is often prescribed by a decision maker or a higher level of government. In the absence of such restrictions, analysts would be well advised to conduct their analyses at different discount rates to determine the *sensitivity* of investment choices to the discount rate. Sensitivity analysis of this type is described in Chapter 10.

8-3 BENEFIT–COST ANALYSIS METHODS

Among the many available benefit–cost analysis methods, the following will be discussed: (1) net present value (or net present worth) method; (2) benefit–cost ratio method; and (3) internal rate-of-return method. For these methods *discounted* benefits and costs will be used; however, since some analysts use *equivalent annual* costs and benefits instead, the distinction between the two measures will be discussed below. Also, a later section (14-1) will touch upon another type of analysis procedure, the cost-effectiveness method.

Economists almost universally find the net present value method superior to all others, both because it is simple and because it is unambiguous in indicating which alternative has the highest economic potential. None of the others is so straightforward and some, unfortunately, may provide ambiguous or incorrect economic indicators as commonly applied. As a consequence, the widespread use of the internal rate-of-return method by engineering economists, as well as the appeal of the benefit–cost ratio and annual cost methods to other groups, warrants a thorough discussion.

Throughout, the following terms and definitions will be used:

i = interest or discount rate (i.e., the minimum attractive rate of return or opportunity cost of capital), expressed in decimal form

n = length of analysis period or planning horizon, in years

$C_{x,t}$ = expected costs (capital or operating) to be incurred for project x during year t

$B_{x,t}$ = expected benefits (or revenues) to be accrued from project x during year t

For convenience it will be assumed that the benefits or costs, $B_{x,t}$ or $C_{x,t}$, occurring during year t will be accrued or committed *in lump sum at the end of year t*. Typically, for other than the "do-nothing" or abandonment alternative (i.e., the alternative for which $C_{x,t} = B_{x,t} = 0$ for all t), there will be some initial cost outlays at the *beginning* of the first year (i.e., when $t = 0$), although the benefits or revenues will not usually (but not necessarily) begin to accrue until at least a year later (i.e., when $t \geq 1$). In any case, though, the formulation is perfectly general and will apply to all situations. The cost and benefit streams during the n-year planning horizon for any project x will look as shown in Table 8-2.

A year-by-year cash flow tabulation of the benefits and costs for all alternatives (where, say, there are m alternatives and thus x varies from $x = 1, 2,\ldots, m$) could be displayed in much the same manner as that indicated for project x in Table 8-2, and then ordered for analysis. *Commonly*, the m alternatives are ordered in ascending order such that the alternative having the lowest initial cost in year $t = 0$ is the first or alternative 1 (i.e., $x = 1$ corresponds to the lowest initial cost alternative), the alternative having next lowest initial cost in year $t = 0$ is that for which $x = 2$, and so forth, until the alternative having highest initial cost in year $t = 0$ is alternative m (i.e., $x = m$ for it). *While such an ordering procedure will be suitable for the net present value and benefit–cost ratio methods, this ordering procedure would not be appropriate for the internal rate-of-return method*. In the latter case a different procedure *should* be used, one which will be explained in Section 8-4-2.

8-3-1 DISCOUNTED VERSUS EQUIVALENT ANNUAL COSTS OR BENEFITS

Calculations for all benefit–cost analysis methods can be carried out while using either discounted or equivalent annual costs or benefits. While the final decisions—as to which alternatives are worthwhile and which is the most economical—will not differ for the two measures of costs and benefits, numerical results will not be the same. However, since some analysts and textbooks stress the use of one method, and others emphasize the second, it seems useful to review the two techniques. At the outset, though, we should note that for most benefit–cost analysis the use of discounted benefits and costs will be simpler and require fewer calculations; accordingly, for all discussions other than that in this section, discounted values will be used exclusively.

With either discounted or equivalent annual costs and benefits, the objective is simply to account for the time value of money. That is, the objective is to account for the fact that a dollar of resources expended today is more costly than one expended in later years. Similarly, a dollar of benefit accrued today is more valuable than one to be accrued in some future year.

The *first* and simplest way to account for the time value of money and to place all present and future costs or benefits on a commensurate value scale is to discount them to their present value or present worth (i.e., their value *today* or at year t-0). Thus, the discounted value of the costs or benefits occurring in some year t for alternative x would be as follows:

$$[PVC_{x,t}]_i = (P|F, i, t)C_{x,t} = (pwf'_{i,t})C_{x,t} \tag{8-1}$$

and

$$[PVB_{x,t}]_i = (P|F, i, t)B_{x,t} = (pwf'_{i,t})B_{x,t} \tag{8-2}$$

where $[PVC_{x,t}]_i$ is the discounted present value of the costs during year t, $[PVB_{x,t}]_i$ is the discounted present value of the benefits during year t, and $pwf'_{i,t}$ or $(P|F, i, t)$ is the (single payment) present value factor for a cost or benefit occurring during year t when the interest rate (or opportunity cost of capital) is i. The present value factor is:[19]

$$(P|F, i, t) = pwf'_{i,t} = \frac{1}{(1 + i)^t} \qquad (8\text{-}3)$$

This formulation assumes *annual* compounding of interest at a per annum rate of i (though i is expressed in the formula as a decimal fraction).[20] In turn, for project x the discounted values for a stream of costs and benefits occurring over n years such as those shown in Table 8-1 would be

$$[TPVC_{x,n}]_i = \sum_{t=0}^{n} (P|F, i, t) C_{x,t} = \sum_{t=0}^{n} \frac{C_{x,t}}{(1 + i)^t} = \sum_{t=0}^{n} [PVC_{x,t}]_i \qquad (8\text{-}4)$$

and

$$[TPVB_{x,n}]_i = \sum_{t=0}^{n} (P|F, i, t) B_{x,t} = \sum_{t=0}^{n} \frac{B_{x,t}}{(1 + i)^t} = \sum_{t=0}^{n} [PVB_{x,t}]_i \qquad (8\text{-}5)$$

where $[TPVC_{x,n}]_i$ and $[TPVB_{x,n}]_i$ are the total discounted costs and benefits, respectively, for an n-year period and interest rate i.

The *second* way to account for the time value of money and to place all present and future costs or benefits on a commensurate value scale is to convert the stream of costs and benefits to an equivalent annual cost or benefit figure. Essentially, the problem is to determine an equal annual amount which is exactly equivalent to either the year-by-year cash flow stream or the discounted value as computed by Equation (8-1), (8-2), (8-4), or (8-5). This is entirely analogous to the procedures used to determine the equal payments which are charged by banks or credit firms for mortgages or installment loans, though usually the creditor will make monthly rather than annual payments—the latter being the case here.

The most straightforward technique for determining the equivalent annual cost or benefit for a stream of benefits and costs would be to

---

[19]The notation $(pwf'_{i,t})$ has been widely used in the engineering economy literature until the past 5 to 10 years, but is rapidly being replaced by the notation $(P|F, i, t)$. Either may be read as the factor for computing P (the present value) given F (the future value), i (the interest rate), and t (the number of years in the future).

[20]In those cases when interest is compounded quarterly, monthly, or daily, and so forth, a slightly different formulation would be required. For simple references, see Bierman and Smidt, op. cit., pp. 55 ff., or Au and Au., op. cit., pp. 56 ff.

multiply the total discounted costs or benefits, as computed with Equation (8-4) or (8-5), times the capital recovery factor. Thus,

$$[EAC_{x,n}]_i = (A|P, i, n)[TPVC_{x,n}]_i = (crf_{i,n})[TPVC_{x,n}]_i \qquad (8\text{-}6)$$

and

$$[EAB_{x,n}]_i = (A|P, i, n)[TPVB_{x,n}]_i = (crf_{i,n})[TPVB_{x,n}]_i \qquad (8\text{-}7)$$

where $crf_{i,n}$ or $(A|P, i, n)$ is the capital recovery factor for an interest rate i and an n-year analysis period, and $[EAC_{x,n}]_i$ and $[EAB_{x,n}]_i$, respectively, are the equivalent annual cost and equivalent annual benefit for n and i.

The capital recovery factor used in Equations (8-6) and (8-7) can be computed as follows:

$$(A|P, i, n) = crf_{i,n} = \frac{i(1 + i)^n}{(1 + i)^n - 1} \qquad (8\text{-}8)$$

However, the capital recovery factor shown in Equation (8-8), as well as its use in (8-6) and (8-7), applies only to equivalent *annual* payments and to *annual* compounding of interest.

An example using both the discounted and equivalent annual payment methods of representing a 5-year cash flow stream for an interest rate of 5% is shown in Table 8-3. Essentially, we can represent the 5-year cash flow stream of costs shown in column 2 *either* by the total discounted cost

TABLE 8-3.   Discounted and Equivalent Annual Costs for a 5-Year Cash Flow Stream and an Interest Rate of 5%

Year t	$C_{x,t}$ Costs Incurred at End of Year t for Alternative x	$[PVC_{x,t}]_{5\%}$ Discounted or Present Value of $C_{x,t}$	$[EAC_{x,5}]_{5\%}$ Equivalent Annual Cost for the 5-Year Stream	Present Value of Equivalent Annual Cost in Year t
0	$200K	$200K	0	0
1	60K	57.14K	$125.22K	$119.26K
2	70K	63.49K	125.22K	113.58K
3	80K	69.11K	125.22K	108.17K
4	90K	74.04K	125.22K	103.02K
5	100K	78.35K	125.22K	98.11K
Total		$542.13K		$542.14K

$$[TPVC_{x,5}]_{5\%} = \sum_{t=0}^{5}[PVC_{x,t}]_{5\%} = \$542.13K$$

$$[EAC_{x,5}]_{5\%} = (A|P, 5\%, 5)[TPVC_{x,5}]_{5\%} = \$125.22K$$

of \$542.13K in a lump sum *now* or by an equal amount of \$125.22K in 5 successive years beginning 1 year from now. That is, if we determine the present value of the five equal annual payments, as shown in column 5, the total discounted value is \$542.14K, the small \$0.01K difference being due to rounding.

The two methods for placing present and future costs or benefits on a commensurate value scale, as described above, are entirely general and will apply to any stream of costs or benefits. It will apply whether or not there are any costs or benefits occurring in year 0 or now, as well as in situations when the year-to-year costs or benefits vary, as they did in Table 8-3. However, most descriptions of these methods are applied to a less general case and can be misleading. Thus, it will be helpful to take such a case and point to the difficulties which can arise.

Suppose, for example, we anticipate an initial and immediate capital outlay of \$200K, to be followed by annual operating costs of \$80K a year starting 1 year from now. Moreover, let us assume that at the end of the fifth year the facility must be replaced at a cost of \$200K in addition to the annual operating cost, and that there will be no salvage value at the end of a 10-year period. The 10-year stream of capital and operating costs would then be as shown in Table 8-4.

For this special case in which the annual operating costs are the same from year to year and in which the capital replacement costs are identical to the initial capital costs, it can be shown that the equivalent annual costs can be computed simply by adding the annual operating costs to the product of the initial capital costs and the capital recovery factor for its replacement life. That is,

$$[EAC_{x,n}]_i = \text{annual operating cost} + (A|P, i, n_c)(C_{x,0}) \qquad (8\text{-}9)$$

where $(A|P, i, n_c)$ is the capital recovery factor for an initial capital replacement life of n_c years. The equivalence between Equation (8-9) and the formulation given in Equations (8-4) and (8-6) is indicated in Table 8-4. Importantly, this method of placing the capital costs on an equivalent annual basis will be correct *only* if the future replacement costs are identical with the initial year outlays *and if* they occur exactly at n_c-year intervals. Should either of these conditions be violated, then the simplified formulation in Equation (8-9) will not apply. Thus, since one would rarely encounter such "neat and tidy" conditions, it is recommended that analysts use the more general formulation described previously.

8-3-2   NET PRESENT VALUE METHOD

With the net present value method the stream of benefits and costs are discounted to their present value or present worth (that is, to their value *now*) and then netted to determine the resultant *net* present value. Thus, for any alternative x the net present value for the n-year analysis period when the interest rate is i or $[NPV_{x,n}]_i$ would be

$$[NPV_{x,n}]_i = [TPVB_{x,n}]_i - [TPVC_{x,n}]_i \qquad (8\text{-}10)$$

$$= \sum_{t=0}^{n} \frac{B_{x,t}}{(1+i)^t} - \sum_{t=0}^{n} \frac{C_{x,t}}{(1+i)^t} = \sum_{t=0}^{n} \frac{B_{x,t} - C_{x,t}}{(1+i)^t} \qquad (8\text{-}11)$$

TABLE 8-4. Equivalent Annual Costs for a 10-Year Cash Flow Stream and a 5% Interest Rate

Year t	Costs Incurred at End of Year t	
	Capital	Operating
0	$200K	0
1	0	$80K
2	0	$80K
3	0	$80K
4	0	$80K
5	$200K	$80K
6	0	$80K
7	0	$80K
8	0	$80K
9	0	$80K
10	0	$80K

Using Equation (8-9)

$$[EAC_{x,10}]_{5\%} = \$80K + \$200K(A|P, 5\%, 5) = \$80K + \$200K(0.23097) = \$126.19$$

Using Equations (8-4) and (8-6)

$$[EAC_{x,10}]_{5\%} = \left[\sum_{t=1}^{10} \frac{\$80K}{(1+0.05)^t} + \$200K + \frac{\$200K}{(1+0.05)^5} \right](A|P, 5\%, 10)$$

$$= \$80K(P|A, 5\%, 10)(A|P, 5\%, 10) + \$200K(A|P, 5\%, 10)$$

$$+ \$200K(P|F, 5\%, 5)(A|P, 5\%, 10)$$

$$= \$80K + \$200K(0.12950) + \$200K(0.7835)(0.12950)$$

$$= \$126.19$$

Note: $(P|A, 5\%, 10) =$ uniform series present value factor $= 1/(A|P, 5\%, 10)$. Also, it can be shown that $(A|P, 5\%, 10) + (P|F, 5\%, 5)(A|P, 5\%, 10) = (A|P, 5\%, 5)$. To show this, substitute for the capital recovery factors using the formula given in Equation (8-8). Hint: $(1+i)^{10} - 1 = [(1+i)^5 + 1][(1+i)^5 - 1]$.

The net present value must be determined for each alternative from $x = 1, 2, \ldots, m$. All alternatives which have a nonnegative net present value can be regarded as economically feasible while the best alternative will be that having the highest nonnegative net present value.

The method is straightforward and will guarantee that public or private agencies maximize net social benefits, however these are measured and for whatever planning horizon or interest rate is chosen. Where the opportunity cost of capital (i.e., the interest rate for other foregone investments) is unknown or subject to question, the calculations can be repeated for different rates and the final results compared for similarities or differences in ranking or acceptability. Also, if the net present value increases when moving from a lower initial (or total) cost alternative to a higher initial (or total) cost one, then one may be certain that the discounted incremental or extra benefits outweigh the discounted extra costs; otherwise the net present value would not have increased.

In sum, there is no more easily applied, unambiguous, complete, and less tedious benefit–cost analysis method than this one. Moreover, the method is equally applicable to situations in which there is a budget constraint and the problem is to select the most worthwhile *set* of projects among a larger group of alternatives. In such a case one simply combines those projects whose total initial costs are less than or equal to the budget constraint but whose combined total net present value is largest.

8-3-3 BENEFIT–COST RATIO METHOD

In some sense the benefit–cost ratio method—*when properly applied*—is little different than the net present value method. The identical benefit and cost measures are used to compute the benefit–cost ratios and proper interpretation will invariably lead to the same decisions about which alternatives are economically feasible and about which one is the best, economically speaking. The only differences are that extra computations are required for the benefit–cost ratio method and that proper interpretation of the ratios is confusing in some cases.

To begin, one may order alternatives for analysis in a number of different ways, though we will assume that alternatives are placed in ascending order with respect to the initial-year cost or $C_{x,0}$ for $x = 1, 2, \ldots, m$.[21] After the alternatives are ordered, there are two steps in applying the benefit–cost ratio method, though it is extremely important to note that often the first of these two steps is improperly ignored.

---

[21]This is the usual ordering method, though fewer problems can result if the alternatives are placed in ascending order with respect to the total discounted value of the costs or $[TPVC_{x,n}]_i$ for $x = 1, \ldots, m$.

The *first* step is undertaken in order to determine whether any alternative is economically worthwhile. Simply, we determine the benefit–cost ratio for the lowest-ordered alternative as follows:

$$[BCR_{1,n}]_i = \frac{[TPVB_{1,n}]_i}{[TPVC_{1,n}]_i} \geqslant 1.0 \qquad (8\text{-}12)$$

$[BCR_{1,n}]_i$ is the benefit–cost ratio for alternative 1 over an n-year analysis period for an interest rate i. If the ratio is equal to or larger than 1, then alternative 1 can be regarded as acceptable. That is, if the ratio is at least as large as 1.0, then we know that the total discounted benefits are at least as large as the total discounted costs and that the net present value is nonnegative. If, however, the ratio for the lowest cost alternative is less than 1.0, then it will be rejected and the ratio will be computed for the next higher initial cost alternative. This process is repeated until we identify the lowest ordered alternative having a benefit–cost ratio equal to or greater than 1.0. If all alternatives have ratios less than 1.0, then all should be rejected, economically speaking. Let us assume, however, that alternative x is the lowest-ordered alternative having an acceptable benefit–cost ratio; thus,

$$[BCR_{x,n}]_i = \frac{[TPVB_{x,n}]_i}{[TPVC_{x,n}]_i} \geqslant 1.0 \qquad (8\text{-}13)$$

Put differently, we know that it is better to undertake alternative x than any of the lower-ordered alternatives.

The *second* step is to determine whether or not it is worthwhile to undertake an even higher-ordered alternative. That is, we must justify any additional increments of cost. For this purpose we compute the incremental benefit–cost ratio for the additional expenditures. Pairwise comparisons are made between successively higher-ordered alternatives, starting with the lowest-ordered alternative which is acceptable, as indicated by Equation (8-13). Specifically, for an n-year analysis period and an interest rate of i, the incremental benefit–cost ratio for the increments in benefit and cost between the lowest-ordered acceptable alternative x and the next higher-ordered one will be $[IBCR_{x/x+1,n}]_i$, where $x/x+1$ simply means alternative $x + 1$ as compared to alternative x, as follows:

$$[IBCR_{x/x+1,n}]_i = \frac{[TPVB_{x+1,n}]_i - [TPVB_{x,n}]_i}{[TPVC_{x+1,n}]_i - [TPVC_{x,n}]_i} \geqslant 1.0 \qquad (8\text{-}14)$$

If the incremental ratio is equal to or larger than 1.0, then alternative $x + 1$ will be more desirable than alternative x and, in turn, the incremental ratio will be computed for alternative $x + 2$ as compared to $x + 1$. On the other hand, if the incremental ratio for alternatives x and $x + 1$ is less

TABLE 8-5. Example for the Benefit–Cost Ratio Analysis Method Benefits and Costs of Alternatives (in $1000s)

	Alternatives			
	1	2	3	4
$C_{x,0}$	50	55	60	65
$[TPVB_{x,n}]_i{}^a$	175	258	360	320
$[TPVC_{x,n}]_i{}^b$	180	200	300	250
$[BCR_{x,n}]_i{}^c$	0.97	1.29	1.20	1.28
$[NPV_{x,n}]_i{}^d$	−5	58	60	70

[a] Present value of benefits.
[b] Present value of costs.
[c] Benefit cost ratio = $[TPVB_{x,n}]_i/[TPVC_{x,n}]_i$.
[d] Net present value = $[TPVB_{x,n}]_i − [TPVC_{x,n}]_i$.

than 1.0, then alternative $x + 1$ will be rejected and the incremental ratio for alternative $x + 2$ as compared to alternative x will be computed. As we shall later see, however, the above rules strictly apply *only* when both the numerator and denominator are positive.

Pairwise comparisons are continued until we identify the highest-ordered alternative which satisfies both of the criteria set forth by Equations (8-13) and (8-14). Importantly, do *not* use the highest benefit–cost ratio—as computed by Equation (8-13)—as the criterion for choosing the best alternative. Choosing the alternative with the largest ratio results in maximizing the return per dollar of cost, but this is not the same as maximizing the net present value or benefits less costs.

For incremental ratios one should not be confused by the fact that the numerator *and/or* denominator of the incremental benefit–cost ratio will sometimes be negative but should recognize that in such cases the criterion (of being at least as large as 1.0) can change. Specifically, when *both* the numerator and the denominator are negative, the next higher-ordered alternative is preferable to the lower-ordered one whenever the incremental benefit–cost ratio is equal to or *less* than 1.0, but when just the denominator is negative, the higher-ordered alternative is always preferable; when just the numerator is negative, the lower-ordered alternative is always preferable. The example shown in Table 8-5 will highlight these principles.

Four alternatives have been analyzed and have initial-year costs, as well as total discounted costs and benefits, all as shown in Table 8-5. The analysis should proceed as follows:

1. The benefit–cost ratio for the lowest-ordered alternative ($x = 1$) is 0.97 or less than 1.0 and, therefore, it is rejected, according to the criterion in equation (8-12);

2. The benefit–cost ratio for alternative 2 is 1.29, thereby indicating that alternative 2 is the lowest-ordered acceptable alternative;

3. The incremental benefit–cost ratio for alternative 3 as compared to alternative 2 is equal to ($360 – $258) divided by ($300 – $200) or 1.02; thus, alternative 3 is more desirable than alternative 2, using the criterion shown in equation (8-14);

4. The incremental benefit–cost ratio for alternative 4 as compared to alternative 3 is equal to ($320 – $360) divided by ($250 – $300), or –$40/–$50, which is equal to 0.8; however, since both the numerator and denominator are negative and since the incremental ratio is less than 1.0, alternative 4 is preferable to alternative 3. (More simply, in this case the benefits were reduced when we moved from alternative 3 to alternative 4, but the costs were reduced even more, thus resulting in overall economies and a gain in net benefits.)

Overall, alternative 4 is the highest-ordered alternative for which both sets of ratios satisfied the criteria and therefore is the best or most economically acceptable alternative. Moreover, we should note that the alternative with the highest benefit–cost ratio (alternative 2 with a ratio of 1.29) is clearly not the best alternative. In fact, to have used the highest benefit–cost ratio as the choice criterion would have resulted in foregoing two alternatives which would have brought about higher total net benefits. Note, further, that both the net present value and benefit–cost ratio analysis methods would have resulted in the choice of alternative 4 as the best alternative, the difference between the methods being simply that the latter requires more computation and is less straightforward in application. Properly and fully applied, though, the benefit–cost ratio method will always identify the most economical alternative.

8-3-4 INTERNAL RATE-OF-RETURN METHOD *AS USUALLY DEFINED*

The internal rate of return method, *as defined in this section*, has been popularized by engineering economists, though it often has been *improperly* understood, explained, or used. Most importantly, this method *can and sometimes will* result in *incorrect* economic choices being made, despite the frequent assertion that all benefit–cost analysis methods will—if properly used—lead to correct economic decisions. (However, some supplemental rules and calculations can insure that this method—when properly defined—will result in correct decisions. These rules will be covered in Section 8-4.)

Accordingly, this method will be presented in some detail, will be applied to a series of simple and more general cases, and then will be compared to and contrasted with the results obtained from the net present method, both here and in Appendix II. Hopefully, these examples and the accompanying discussion can clarify the matter and thus permit analysts to discard those methods which either can or will give incorrect or ambiguous answers when evaluating mutually exclusive projects.

The discounted internal rate-of-return method as usually defined has two essential steps,[22] following the ordering of mutually exclusive alternatives. Again, the rule to be followed in this section will be the usual one, to order alternatives in ascending order with respect to their initial-year costs. Then, the *first* step will be to determine the internal rate of return for the lowest initial-year cost alternative (i.e., determine the rate of return for alternative $x = 1$). By definition, the internal rate of return is the interest rate or discount rate for which the discounted benefits over n years are just equal to the discounted costs. Identical results will be forthcoming if equivalent annual benefits and costs are used instead of discounted benefits and costs, though more calculations will be required for the former. Thus, for any alternative x, the internal rate of return or r_x is that interest rate which satisfies the following condition:

$$[TPVB_{x,n}]_{r_x} = [TPVC_{x,n}]_{r_x} \qquad (8\text{-}15)$$

or

$$\sum_{t=0}^{n} \frac{B_{x,t}}{(1 + r_x)^t} = \sum_{t=0}^{n} \frac{C_{x,t}}{(1 + r_x)^t} \qquad (8\text{-}16)$$

where

$$\frac{1}{(1 + r_x)^t} = \text{discount factor for internal rate-of-return method} \qquad (8\text{-}17)$$

Alternatively, the internal rate of return can be defined as the discount rate (or rates) at which the net present value of the alternative is zero. That is, Equation (8-15) can be rewritten as follows:

$$[NPV_{x,n}]_{r_x} = [TPVB_{x,n}]_{r_x} - [TPVC_{x,n}]_{r_x} = 0$$

or

$$[NPV_{x,n}]_{r_x} = \sum_{t=0}^{n} \frac{B_{x,t}}{(1 + r_x)^t} - \sum_{t=0}^{n} \frac{C_{x,t}}{(1 + r_x)^t} = 0 \qquad (8\text{-}18)$$

Once the internal rate of return for the lowest-cost alternative is determined, we must ask whether this alternative is acceptable or not. For this

[22]J. H. Lorie and L. J. Savage, "Three Problems in Rationing Capital," in E. Solomon (ed.), *The Management of Corporate Capital*, The Free Press of Glencoe, London, 1959.

purpose, a minimum attractive rate of return (MARR) which reflects the earning possibilities for foregone alternatives (or opportunity cost of capital) must be stated. This interest rate serves as a "yardstick" or "cutoff" rate for accepting or rejecting projects; that is, projects which do not earn that much will be rejected. Thus, if r_x is at least as large as the MARR or opportunity cost of capital, then alternative x is judged to be economically acceptable *by this method*. (Some later examples will show that this is not necessarily a correct criterion.)

While some analysts claim that a desirable feature of the rate of return method is that the interest rate is determined rather than specified, it is obvious that such a view is misleading. While the unknown interest is determined, some "cutoff" rate or MARR *must also* be specified in order to judge the acceptability of any given project. Importantly, this cutoff rate or MARR is *the* interest rate which is used in the net present value and benefit–cost ratio methods. Thus, the three methods are identical in terms of the information and data required to carry them out.

The internal rate of return, r_x, for individual projects, starting with the lowest initial cost alternative (i.e., starting with $x = 1$), is determined until the lowest initial cost project having an acceptable internal rate of return (i.e., r_x greater than MARR) is ascertained. This alternative, say alternative x, then becomes the lowest-cost acceptable alternative.

To determine the internal rate of return for projects having a short planning horizon or analysis period (say 2 or 3 years) is a simple matter requiring little more than rudimentary algebra. But in more usual planning situations, when we are faced with a 20- to 30-year planning horizon and with benefits and costs which vary from year to year, the task of determining the rate of return will be quite arduous, requiring lengthy trial-and-error calculations. This factor should not be passed off as trivial.

However, to demonstrate the mechanics of the internal rate-of-return method, let us determine the rate of return for the simple 2-year example

TABLE 8-6. Benefits and Costs for Alternative x Over a 2-Year Period

Year t	$B_{x,t}{}^a$	$C_{x,t}{}^b$
0	0	100
1	60	0
2	72	0

[a]Benefits net of operating costs during year t (in $1000s).
[b]Capital outlays during year t (in $1000's).

shown in Table 8-6. Given these benefit and cost data, we must find r_x such that the following identity is satisfied:

$$\frac{100}{(1 + r_x)^0} = \frac{0}{(1 + r_x)^0} + \frac{60}{(1 + r_x)^1} + \frac{72}{(1 + r_x)^2} \tag{8-19}$$

Then

$$100 = \frac{60}{(1 + r_x)^1} + \frac{72}{(1 + r_x)^2} \tag{8-20}$$

or

$$100(1 + r_x)^2 - 60(1 + r_x) - 72 = 0 \tag{8-21}$$

Solving Equation (8-21) algebraically yields

$$r_x = 0.20 \text{ or } 20\%$$

From Descartes' Rule of Signs, the number of *positive or zero* real roots for Equation (8-21) cannot *exceed* the number of changes in sign for the equation, which in this case is one. Negative roots are of no interest for our purposes.

Of considerable importance, this first step in applying the internal rate-of-return method is aimed at determining whether any alternative is worthwhile undertaking, economically speaking. That is, it provides an answer to the question: Is anything worth doing? If this first step is overlooked or ignored, as is often the case for benefit–cost analysis of public transport projects, then the method will only identify the best of the mutually exclusive alternatives being analyzed and provide no information about the acceptability of any of the alternatives.

The *second* step in the internal rate-of-return method is to determine the incremental internal rate of return for projects having an initial cost higher than the lowest initial cost alternative which is acceptable. Again, if alternative x is the lowest initial cost alternative which is acceptable, then the incremental internal rate of return for the extra benefits and costs between x and the next higher initial cost alternative, or $x + 1$, must be determined. By definition, the incremental internal rate of return, or $r_{x/x+1}$, is the interest rate or discount rate for which the extra discounted benefits (of $x + 1$ over x) are just equal to the extra discounted costs (of $x + 1$ over x). Thus, for alternative $x + 1$ compared to alternative x, the incremental internal rate of return is that interest rate which satisfies the following identity:

$$[TPVB_{x+1,n}]_{r_{x/x+1}} - [TPVB_{x,n}]_{r_{x/x+1}} = [TPVC_{x+1,n}]_{r_{x/x+1}} - [TPVC_{x,n}]_{r_{x/x+1}} \tag{8-22}$$

or

$$\sum_{t=0}^{n} \frac{B_{x+1,t} - B_{x,t}}{(1 + r_{x/x+1})^t} = \sum_{t=0}^{n} \frac{C_{x+1,t} - C_{x,t}}{(1 + r_{x/x+1})^t} \qquad (8\text{-}23)$$

where

$$\frac{1}{(1 + r_{x/x+1})^t} = \text{discount factor for increment between } x \text{ and } x + 1 \qquad (8\text{-}24)$$

Once the lowest initial cost alternative (say x) having an acceptable rate of return (i.e., $r_x \geq$ MARR) is determined, then pairwise calculations for increasingly higher initial cost alternatives are made using Equation (8-22) or (8-23). If $r_{x/x+1}$, the internal rate of return on the increment, is at least as large as the MARR, then alternative $x + 1$ is accepted as better than x. If not, then alternative $x + 1$ is rejected, and a pairwise comparison is made between x and $x + 2$, and so forth for successively higher-cost alternatives, until the highest initial cost alternative having satisfied both sets of rate-of-return calculations is determined. Under the internal rate-of-return method the highest initial cost alternative satisfying these conditions will be selected as the best, economically speaking.

Also, if we rearrange the terms of Equation (8-23), we obtain

$$\sum_{t=0}^{n} \frac{B_{x+1,t} - C_{x+1,t}}{(1 + r_{x/x+1})^t} = \sum_{t=0}^{n} \frac{B_{x,t} - C_{x,t}}{(1 + r_{x/x+1})^t} \qquad (8\text{-}25)$$

in which the left-hand side is the net present value of alternative $x + 1$ for a discount rate of $r_{x/x+1}$ and the right-hand side is the net present value of alternative x for a discount rate of $r_{x/x+1}$. *In other words, the incremental rate of return for the increment between two alternatives is simply the discount rate at which the net present value of the two alternatives is equal.*

To illustrate the mechanics of the internal rate-of-return method, consider its application to the four alternatives shown in part (a) of Table 8-7. For our purposes, let us assume that the MARR is 10%. The analysis and interpretation would proceed as follows:

1. The rate of return for the lowest-cost alternative ($x = 1$) is 7.8%, or lower than the MARR of 10%; thus, alternative 1 would be rejected;

2. The rate of return for the next higher initial-year cost alternative ($x = 2$) is 12.9% and therefore is higher than the MARR of 10%; thus, alternative 2 is the lowest-cost acceptable alternative;

3. The next step is to determine whether any higher-cost alternative has an incremental rate of return which is as large as the MARR; the incremental rate of return of alternative 3 as compared to alternative 2, or $r_{2/3}$, is 8.7%, or below the MARR of 10%; thus, alternative 3 must be rejected;

TABLE 8-7. First Example for the Internal Rate-of-Return Method for a MARR of 10%

Year	Alt. 1		Alt. 2		Alt. 3		Alt. 4	
t	$B_{1,t}$	$C_{1,t}$	$B_{2,t}$	$C_{2,t}$	$B_{3,t}$	$C_{3,t}$	$B_{4,t}$	$C_{4,t}$
(a)								
0	0	$100K	0	$105K	0	$111K	0	$115K
1	$54K	0	$61K	0	$62K	0	$63K	0
2	$58K	0	$65K	0	$71K	0	$75K	0
r_x	7.8%		12.9%		12.6%		12.7%	

$$r_{2/3} = 8.7\%$$
$$r_{2/4} = 10.5\%$$

	Alt. 1	Alt. 2	Alt. 3	Alt. 4
(b) $[NPV_{x,2}]_{10\%}$	−$2.98K	+$4.17K	+$4.04K	+$4.26K
(c) $[BCR_{x,2}]_{10\%}$	0.970	1.040	1.036	1.037

$$[IBCR_{2/3,2}]_{10\%} = 0.978$$
$$[IBCR_{2/4,2}]_{10\%} = 1.008$$

181

4. Finally, the incremental rate of return for alternative 4 as compared to alternative 2, or $r_{2/4}$, is 10.5% or slightly higher than the MARR of 10%; therefore, alternative 4 is preferable to alternative 2. Thus, alternative 4 is found to be acceptable and the most profitable among the four choices shown in Table 8-7(a).

Importantly, one should *not* simply compute the internal rate of return (or r_x) for each of the alternatives and then regard the alternative having the highest rate of return as the best one. That is, a lower rate of return does not by itself indicate that the overall profitability is lower. Referring again to Table 8-7(a), it can be seen that use of the highest rate-of-return rule would have resulted in the incorrect choice of alternative 2 rather than alternative 4. Further, for the data in Table 8-7(a) and a MARR of 10%, net present value and benefit–cost ratio calculations have been made, as shown in Table 8-7(b) and (c). Both sets of data show that alternative 4 is acceptable and the best among the four alternatives.

8-3-5 INCONSISTENCIES OF THE THREE METHODS

One point deserves emphasis: all of the three benefit–cost analysis methods provided consistent and identical results and rankings for the particular example in Table 8-7. Unfortunately, though, other situations can and do arise when neither consistent nor identical results will be obtained. Consider, for instance, the example shown in Table 8-8. Using the net present value and benefit–cost methods and the results shown in Table 8-8(b) and (c), alternative 1 is acceptable and best. To the contrary,

TABLE 8-8. Second Example for the Internal Rate-of-Return Method for a MARR of 10%

	Year t	Alternative 1		Alternative 2	
		$B_{1,t}$	$C_{1,t}$	$B_{2,t}$	$C_{2,t}$
(a)	1	0	$10,000	0	$11,000
	1	$2,000	0	$5,304	0
	2	2,000	0	5,304	0
	3	12,000	0	5,304	0
	r_x	20%		21%	
		$r_{1/2} = 15.7\%$ *and* 271%			
(b)	$[NPV_{x,3}]_{10\%}$	$2,486.85		$2,190.26	
(c)	$[BCR_{x,3}]_{10\%}$	1.25		1.20	
		$[IBCR_{1/2,3}]_{10\%} = 0.70$			

however, use of the internal rate-of-return method as described in Section 8-3-4 would result in choosing alternative 2 as the most acceptable or would lead to an ambiguous answer. *But neither alternative 2 nor an ambiguous answer is correct*. Rather, alternative 1 is clearly acceptable and the best for a MARR of 10%. Succinctly, the problem rests with the internal rate-of-return method as usually defined. Accordingly, analysts are strongly advised to avoid use of the internal rate-of-return method *as usually defined* for project selection or, instead, to adopt the revised procedure outlined in the following section. A full discussion of the pitfalls for this method is provided in Appendix II.

8-4   REVISED RULES FOR THE INTERNAL RATE-OF-RETURN METHOD

It is shown in Appendix II that the internal rate-of-return method *as usually defined* can lead to ambiguous or incorrect decisions about a project's acceptability or about which project among a set of mutually exclusive alternatives is best. Moreover, use of the internal rate-of-return method—however defined—will invariably require more lengthy and arduous calculations than would use of either the net present value or benefit-cost ratio methods. For these reasons other methods should generally be used to pick the best acceptable alternative. Once the best alternative is selected, the internal rate of return(s) for that alternative could be calculated. If desired, however, the internal rate-of-return method can be revised so as to provide correct and consistent economic decisions. Here, we will outline a new ordering procedure and a new set of decisions rules for the method so that the decisions resulting from its use will be correct and unambiguous. Accordingly, any analyst who insists on employing the internal rate-of-return method should use these revised rules rather than the more usual ones described earlier in Section 8-3-4.

8-4-1   REVISED IRR DECISION RULES FOR DETERMINING PROJECT ACCEPTABILITY

An appropriate and consistent set of decision rules is outlined below for determining project acceptability when using the internal rate-of-return method. The rules widely apply for both single and multiple rates of return, for borrowing or investment situations, and for pure or mixed projects. They are as follows:

1. Determine the sum of the undiscounted (net) annual cash flows of the project over the n-year analysis period, that is,

$$S = \sum_{t=0}^{n} [B_{x,t} - C_{x,t}] = [NPV_{x,n}]_{0\%} \qquad (8\text{-}26)$$

where S is the sum of (net) annual cash flows; $B_{x,t}$ and $C_{x,t}$ are the benefits and costs, respectively, for project x during year t of the n-year analysis period.

2. Determine r_x, the internal rate of return for project x (i.e., determine the non-negative discount rate or rates at which the discounted benefits just equal the discounted costs over the n-year analysis period). If there are multiple rates of return, list them in ascending order, as follows: $r_x', r_x'', r_x''', r_x'''', \ldots$; *however, exclude all nonpositive rates from this list; also, list each positive repeating rate separately.*

3. When there is a *single* internal rate of return (r_x) *or* no positive rate of return *and* the sum of the annual cash flows is not equal to zero, accept or reject project x according to the following rules:

Condition	Sum of Annual Cash Flows is Positive	Sum of Annual Cash Flows is Negative
MARR $< r_x$	Accept project	Reject project
MARR $> r_x$	Reject project	Accept project
No positive r_x	Accept project	Reject project

When MARR and the internal rate of return are equal, one would be indifferent between acceptance and rejection.

Applying these rules to the example in Table 8-9, we would reject the project if the MARR was below 20%, accept it if the MARR was above 20%, and be indifferent between acceptance and rejection if MARR was just equal to 20%.

4. When there are *multiple* rates of return *and* the sum of the annual cash flows is not equal to zero, accept or reject project x according to the following rules, where r_x' is the first positive IRR, r_x'' is the second positive IRR, and so on:

Condition	Sum of Annual Cash Flows is Positive	Sum of Annual Cash Flows is Negative
MARR $< r_x'$	Accept	Reject
$r_x' <$ MARR $< r_x''$	Reject	Accept
$r_x'' <$ MARR $< r_x'''$	Accept	Reject
$r_x''' <$ MARR $< r_x''''$	Reject	Accept

Note: Reversal pattern continues for additional rates of return.

TABLE 8-9. Third Example of the Internal Rate-of-Return Method

Year	Cash Flow
0	+220
1	−144
2	−144
Sum of annual cash flows	−68
Internal rate of return	20%

Also, when MARR and an internal rate of return are equal, one would be indifferent between acceptance and rejection.

For the example in Table 8-10, whose annual cash flow sum is positive, the project would be accepted for a MARR below 8.52%, rejected for a MARR between 8.52 and 18.66%, accepted for a MARR between 18.66 and 73.57%, and rejected for a MARR above 73.57%. By contrast, for the example in Table 8-11, whose annual cash flow sum is negative, the project would be rejected for a MARR below 3.85%, accepted for a MARR between 3.85 and 4.99%, and rejected for a MARR above 4.99%.

TABLE 8-10. Annual Cash Flows (in $10,000's) for a Bridge Improvement

End of Year t	Benefits B_t	Costs C_t	Benefits Less Costs $B_t - C_t$
0	—	50	−50
1	61	55	+6
2	63	0	+63
⋮	⋮	⋮	⋮
9	77	0	+77
10	79	705	−626
11	81	610	−529
12	83	495	−412
13	85	0	+85
⋮	⋮	⋮	⋮
29	117	0	+117
30	119	0	+119

Rates of return: $r'_x = 8.52\%$, $r''_x = 18.66\%$, $r'''_x = 73.5\%$
Sum of net annual cash flows = +785

TABLE 8-11.   Annual Cash Flows (in \$10,000's) for a Local Streetcar
Extension Example

End of Year t	Benefits B_t	Costs C_t	Benefits Less Costs $B_t - C_t$
0	0	175	−175
1	0	1265	−1265
2	250	0	+250
3	240	0	+240
4	230	0	+230
5	220	0	+220
⋮	⋮	⋮	⋮
19	80	0	+80
20	70	0	+70
21	60	0	+60
22	0	1900	−1900

$$r'_x = 3.85\%, \ r''_x = 4.99\%$$

Sum of net annual cash flows = −240

5. When the sum of the undiscounted (net) annual cash flows, or S, is
    zero, a more complex procedure must be adopted. Stated succinctly, we
    need to know the slope of the discounted cash flow function, evalu-
    ated for an interest rate of zero. To this end, recall that the discounted
    value of the project's cash flow steam, for an interest rate i, is

$$f(i) = \sum_{t=0}^{n} \frac{B_{x,t} - C_{x,t}}{(1+i)^t} \tag{8-27}$$

where $f(i)$ is the discounted value of the cash flow stream, expressed
as a function of the interest rate i. In turn, the slope of the above
discounted cash flow function is simply equal to the derivative of the
function with respect to i, or

$$f'(i) = -\sum_{t=1}^{n} \frac{t[B_{x,t} - C_{x,t}]}{(1+i)^{t+1}} \tag{8-28}$$

where $f'(i)$ is the slope of the discounted cash flow function for a
project, expressed as a function of the interest rate i. When the slope
of the function is evaluated at i equal to zero, the slope will be as
follows:

$$f'(0) = -\sum_{t=1}^{n} t[B_{x,t} - C_{x,t}] \tag{8-29}$$

an expression which can easily be evaluated. Do not overlook the negative sign for the slope in Equation (8-29).

When there is a *single* internal rate of return and thus r_x is equal to 0%, accept the project when the slope, as computed by Equation (8-29), is positive and reject it when the slope is negative.

When there are *multiple* rates of return, the acceptance or rejection decision rules for a project having an undiscounted cash flow stream equal to zero *and* a slope as computed with Equation (8-29) will be as follows:

Condition	Slope of Discounted Cash Flow Function at $i = 0\%$	
	Positive	Negative
$\text{MARR} < r_x'$	Accept	Reject
$r_x' < \text{MARR} < r_x''$	Reject	Accept
$r_x'' < \text{MARR} < r_x'''$	Accept	Reject
$r_x''' < \text{MARR} < r_x''''$	Reject	Accept

Note: Reversal pattern continues for additional rates of return.

Also, when the MARR and an internal rate of return are equal, one will be indifferent between acceptance and rejection.

For both projects in Table 8-12 the sum of the undiscounted cash flows are zero and thus the above decision rules apply. Accordingly, and using Equation (8-29), the slope of the discounted cash flow function (at i equal to 0) is −200 for alternative 1 and +200 for alternative 2. Thus, alternative

TABLE 8-12.   Fourth Example of Cash Flows and the Internal Rate-of-Return Method

Year	Alternative 1	Alternative 2
0	−100	−300
1	+600	+900
2	−1100	−700
3	+600	+100
Sum of annual cash flows	0	0
Rate of return r_x	$r_1' = 100\%$ $r_1'' = 200\%$	$r_2' = 81.6\%$
	$r_{1/2}' = 85.1\%$	

Note: Zero rates of return have been excluded for r_1, r_2, and $r_{1/2}$

1 is acceptable when MARR is between 100 and 200% and unacceptable when MARR is below 100 or above 200%. Alternative 2 is acceptable when MARR is between 0 and 81.6% and unacceptable when MARR is above 81.6%. (Recall, however, that when listing and labeling the internal rates of return any nonpositive (i.e., ≤ 0) rates must be excluded.)

8-4-2   REVISED PROCEDURE FOR ORDERING MUTUALLY EXCLUSIVE ALTERNATIVES

An appropriate procedure for ordering mutually exclusive alternatives is crucial to a proper analysis and determination of the best project. The pitfalls of ordering on the basis of increasing initial costs are all too evident for examples similar to Tables 8-13 and 8-14. To avoid these and other problems, a revised ordering procedure has been developed, as follows:

1. Determine the sum of the undiscounted (net) annual cash flows for all alternatives, as defined in Equation (8-26).

2. List all alternatives in ascending order with respect to their annual cash flow sums (as computed above). However, if the annual cash flow sums for two or more alternatives are equal, determine the slope of each of their discounted cash flow functions evaluated at i equal to zero, as defined in Equation (8-29), and then list these alternatives in ascending order with respect to the algebraic value of the slopes. (Thus, the alternative which has the most positive or least negative slope will be the highest-ordered alternative. Also, it is possible though highly unlikely that two or more alternatives would have equal cash flow sums *and* equal slopes for their discounted cash flow

TABLE 8-13.   Cash Flows and Internal Rates of Return for an Example

Year	Alternative 1	Alternative 2
0	−100	−100
1	0	+20
2	+144	+120
Sum of annual cash flows	+44	+40
Rate of return	$r_1 = 20\%$	$r_2 = 20\%$
	$r_{1/2} = 20\%$	

Note: r_x is the internal rate of return for alternative x. $r_{1/2}$ is the internal rate of return for the increment in benefits and costs between alternatives 1 and 2.

TABLE 8-14.   Annual Cash Flows (in $10,000's) for Oil Pump Alternatives

Year	Alternative 1		Alternative 2		Difference
t	$B_{1,t}$	$C_{1,t}$	$B_{2,t}$	$C_{2,t}$	$\Delta B_1 - \Delta C_t$
0	0	100	0	110	−10
1	70	0	115	0	+45
2	70	0	30	0	−40
Sum of net annual flows					
	+40		+35		−5
Rate of return					
	$r_1 = 25.69\%$		$r_2 = 26.16\%$		$r'_{1/2} = 21.92\%$
					$r''_{1/2} = 228.08\%$

Note: $\Delta B_t = B_{2,t} - B_{1,t}$ and $\Delta C_t = C_{2,t} - C_{1,t}$. r_x is the internal rate of return for alternative x. $r'_{1/2}$ and $r''_{1/2}$ are the internal rates of return for the increment in benefits and costs between alternatives 1 and 2.

functions; in such a case it would be necessary to use the second or perhaps third derivative of those functions to determine the appropriate ordering.)

Using the above rules, the appropriate ordering can differ markedly from the usual ordering rule which calls for ordering alternatives according to the initial-year costs or outlays. For instance, the above rules would reverse the ordering of the alternatives as they are shown in Tables 8-13 and 8-14.

8-4-3   REVISED DECISION RULES FOR DETERMINING THE BEST ALTERNATIVE

The decision rules for using the internal rate-of-return method to properly and consistently determine the best among a set of mutually exclusive alternatives are described below. Of equal importance, though, is the necessity for a proper ordering of the alternatives for subsequent analysis; thus, it is mandatory that the ordering procedure described in Section 8-4-2 (or some variation thereon) be adopted as part of the project selection process. The overall set of rules are as follows:

1.   List all mutually exclusive alternatives in ascending order according to the procedure described in Section 8-4-2.
2.   Beginning with the two lowest-ordered alternatives, determine $r_{1/2}$, the internal rate of return for the increments in benefits and costs between the two alternatives; if there are multiple rates of return, list them in ascending order as follows: $r'_{1/2}$, $r''_{1/2}$, $r'''_{1/2}, \ldots$; *however,*

exclude all nonpositive rates from this listing and list each positive repeating rate separately.

3. When there is a *single* positive rate of return, the higher-ordered alternative of the two being compared will be preferable when MARR is less than $r_{1/2}$; when MARR exceeds $r_{1/2}$, the lower-ordered alternative will be better. Neither alternative is better when MARR just equals $r_{1/2}$. However, when there is a single rate of return which is equal to zero, the higher-ordered alternative will be preferable for any MARR value.

4. When there are *multiple* rates of return, the better of the two alternatives being compared can be determined from the following rules:

Condition	Preference Rule for the Better of Two Alternatives
MARR $< r'_{1/2}$	Higher-Ordered Alternative
$r'_{1/2} <$ MARR $< r''_{1/2}$	Lower-Ordered Alternative
$r''_{1/2} <$ MARR $< r'''_{1/2}$	Higher-Ordered Alternative
$r'''_{1/2} <$ MARR $< r''''_{1/2}$	Lower-Ordered Alternative

Note: Reversal pattern continues for additional rates of return.

Also, when MARR is equal to one of the rates of return, neither alternative is preferable.

5. Apply the above preferability test (i.e, in rule 4 shown above) to successively higher-ordered alternatives until the highest-ordered alternative is found that is preferable to lower-ordered ones. That is, if alternative 2 is preferable to alternative 1, then apply the test to alternative 3 as compared to alternative 2, and so forth. But if alternative 1 is preferable to alternative 2, then apply the test to alternative 3 as compared to alternative 1, and so forth.

6. Whenever all internal rates of return are nonpositive or indeterminate, the higher-ordered alternative will be preferable.

Let us apply these rules to the examples in Table 8-13, 8-14, and 8-12.

For the Table 8-13 example we first note that the two projects should be reordered with alternative 1 being the higher-ordered one. Accordingly, we conclude that alternative 1 is preferable if MARR is less than 20% and that alternative 2 is preferable if MARR is greater than 20%.

For the Table 8-14 example we again see that the two alternatives should be reordered with alternative 1 being the higher-ordered one. In turn, we conclude that alternative 1 is preferable if MARR is less than 21.92% or if MARR exceeds 228.08%; alternative 2 is preferable if MARR is between 21.92 and 228.08%.

For the Table 8-12 example it is first necessary to determine the slope of the discounted cash flow function (evaluated at i equal to zero) to properly order the alternatives. In this case the slope for alternative 1, as determined by Equation (8-29), was −200 and that for alternative 2 was +200. Therefore, using the ordering rules in Section 8-4-2, alternative 2 is the higher-ordered alternative among the two and thus the ordering shown in Table 8-12 is correct. Accordingly, if MARR is less than 85.1%, alternative 2 is preferable, and if MARR is above 85.1%, alternative 1 is preferable.

8-4-4   DETERMINING THE BEST ACCEPTABLE ALTERNATIVE

In the interest of brevity, no comprehensive treatment of this obviously important aspect of economic analysis is included here. Suffice it to say, however, that to jointly consider the aspects of acceptability and preference one simply follows the following procedure: (1) Order all mutually exclusive alternatives, using the procedure described in Section 8-4-2; (2) determine the lowest-ordered *acceptable* alternative, using the rules described in Section 8-4-1; and (3) determine the highest-ordered alternative, using the rules described in Section 8-4-3, which is found to be preferable to all lower-ordered *acceptable* alternatives.

8-4-5   SUMMARY OF REVISED IRR METHOD

The internal rate-of-return method has long been widely used to determine the acceptability of projects, as well as the best among mutually exclusive ones. Even so, conflicts, ambiguities, and inconsistencies can result from the method *as usually applied*. These problems began receiving intensive attention about 30 years ago.[23] More recently, sophisticated but complex procedures have been introduced to obviate the problems by introducing external investment or borrowing rates, by computing the adjusted or reinvestment corrected rate of return, or by adopting other computational methods to incorporate similar matters.[24] Fuller treatment of these matters appears in Appendix II.

---

[23]J. Lorie and L. J. Savage, "Three Problems in Capital Rationing," *Journal of Business*, October 1955; E. Solomon, "The Arithmetic of Capital Budgeting Decisions," *Journal of Business*, April 1956.

[24]See, among others, the following references: T. Au and T. P. Au, *Engineering Economics for Capital Investment Analysis*, Allyn and Bacon, Boston, 1983, Section 9.8; L. E. Bussey, *The Economic Analysis of Industrial Projects*, Prentice-Hall, Englewood Cliffs, NJ, 1978, Sections 7.10 and 7.11; E. J. Mishan, *Cost-Benefit Analysis*, Praeger Publishers, New York, 1976, p. 228; D. Teichroew et al., "An Analysis of Criteria for Investment and Financing Decisions Under Certainty," *Management Science* **12**(3), 151–179 (1965); M. Wohl, "Common Misunderstandings about the Internal-Rate-of-Return and Net Present Value Economic Analysis Methods," *Transportation Research Record* **731**, 1–19 (1979).

However, the question still remains: Can internal rate(s) of return be used to consistently and unambiguously determine project acceptability and the best project among mutually exclusive ones? The answer is affirmative *if* one modifies the ordering procedure and decision rules as described here. Also, the decisions which result will be identical to those stemming from the use of the net present value or benefit–cost ratio methods. Given the complexity of the internal rate-of-return method's rules, it is generally preferable to apply these latter methods. Once the most desirable alternative is selected, the internal rates(s) of return and other figures of merit (such as the effective rate of return described in Appendix II) can be computed as supplemental indicators.

CHAPTER 9

THE FINANCIAL IMPLICATIONS OF PRICING AND INVESTMENT DECISIONS

The financial implications of pricing and investment decisions are another widely discussed aspect of planning for transportation. Consideration of economic efficiency—which has been discussed in the previous three chapters—may result in policies which imply either financial deficits or profits to service providers and transport agencies. Even if the net social benefits of an investment are positive, there is no guarantee that service providers will experience a financial profit. The existence of financial deficits is of great interest to decision makers and the public, so it is worthwhile to consider both the financial implications of different policies and the impact of decisions which are intended to maximize the financial profits to a firm or agency.

From a social perspective the question of financial deficits or profits to specific organizational entities is secondary to the broader question of whether or not any particular facility or activity has social benefits in excess of social costs, that is, positive net social benefits. If this is the case, it may be possible in some cases to cover the deficit of the service providers by taxing the beneficiaries. Assessing the extent of benefits to individuals and collecting a tax may be exceedingly difficult and very expensive, however. There are not only practical but theoretical difficulties in assessing taxes in direct proportion to benefits. In particular, such charges must be assessed so that individuals do not perceive a connection between the tax and their benefits or usage of a facility, else the tax will change the level of demand.

Concern for the deficit operations of public transportation arises first from the desire to restrict the amount of subsidy which is derived from general tax revenues. Of course, any form of taxation is politically undesirable and costly in the sense of both financial and economic losses to the economy as a whole. Moreover, with a restriction on the total level of public spending (as often occurs at the local level of government), funds spent on public transportation cannot be spent on other socially desirable projects. The most common result of this concern with financial deficits is the imposition of a budget target on public transportation providers. For example, in making investment decisions and programming for a budget, public transportation agencies might be prohibited from incurring a deficit which is larger than some set amount of public funds.

A second reason for a concern with the financial implications of different policies arises from arguments of equity. Many accept the fairness principle that the actual beneficiaries of a service should pay the costs of the service, rather than the public as a whole. This principle has been embodied in such financial devices as the federal highway trust fund, which disburses funds for roadway construction and improvement which are derived entirely from roadway users' taxes. Since the users of a transportation facility incur costs in addition to tolls, fare, and taxes, it seems reasonable to include these payments in the analysis of such overall equity and to consider whether total user payments exceed total social costs of providing a particular service or facility.

We shall distinguish two separate areas for the analysis of the financial implications of pricing and investment decisions. The first is concerned with the relationship between total user payments for service and overall social costs. While this concern is not directly related to the financial situation of providers such as transit operators, it is quite relevant to the principle or belief that beneficiaries of services should pay the total cost of providing service. The most important question in this regard is whether or not the total user costs or payments (which are equal to the price of travel multiplied by volume) exceed the total social costs of a service. Since the social benefits of a service include both the total user payments and the value of consumers' surpluses, it should be apparent that social benefits would exceed social costs if user payments exceed social costs.

The second level of analysis with respect to financial implications concerns the financial profit or loss of particular service providers. One might ask, for example, if the revenues derived from tolls or fares (equal to the volume multiplied by the fare) exceed the costs incurred by the service provider. The level of such revenues and private costs may comprise only a small portion of the total social costs and benefits of a service, but the financial deficits of service providers must be covered from general tax revenues or other sources. A second question in this analysis concerns the possible profits which might be earned from pricing and investment decisions which are intended to maximize financial profits.

The plan of this chapter is as follows. First, we shall discuss the relationship between user payments and social costs, including the case in which decisions are intended to maximize the level of net user payments. Following this, we shall consider the implications of pricing and investment policies which are intended to maximize the financial profits of service providers. Maximization of net user payments, financial profits, or net social benefits *alone* represents *single*-objective planning and decision making. An alternative approach is to consider more than one objective in making decisions. One technique for such consideration is to set a target for one objective—such as the budget target mentioned above—and then make pricing and investment decisions so as to maximize net social benefits while insuring that the target is met. For example, planners might wish to maximize net social benefits while requiring service providers to break even financially (i.e., have revenue equal to their own costs). Pricing and investment planning with this type of strategy is discussed in Section 9-3. General techniques for considering more than one objective directly will be considered in Chapter 10. Before taking up that subject, however, this chapter closes with a discussion of the problem of financial objectives and the analysis of risky investments. This final section is intended to provide some perspective concerning financial analysis and concerns when the result of undertaking particular investments is uncertain.

9-1 USER PAYMENTS AND COSTS

Before discussing financial analysis for service providers, it is useful to consider the relationship between the total user payments and the costs incurred in providing a facility or service. Recall that different pricing policies and price levels affect total net benefits to the extent that the quantity demanded and thus output, costs, and benefits are affected. Total net benefit will be maximized at an output level equal to q_A in Figure 9-1, where the marginal benefit is equal to the short-run marginal cost, or $mb(q_A) = srmc_x(q_A)$.

The total user payments (equal to the total amount of user cost incurred in travel) are similarly related to the output level, but bear a different relationship to pricing policy and are maximized under different output and pricing conditions. To illustrate this relationship, a marginal payment curve is shown in Figure 9-1. The marginal payment curve indicates the increase in total payments which results from increasing output level by one unit. In calculating changes in the total payments for a given service, it must be kept in mind that tripmaking can be increased only by reducing price, and, therefore, that the extra payment by an additional tripmaker must be balanced against the reduction in unit price for each of the previous tripmakers. To calculate total payments, and in turn marginal payments, the demand curve DD may be regarded as an average payment curve; that is, the demand curve expresses the average payment (i.e., price) per traveler or $ap(q)$ to be obtained from q travelers. Thus,

$$TUP(q) = q \cdot ap(q) \qquad (9\text{-}1)$$

where $TUP(q)$ is the total payment from q travelers including all components of the price (money, travel time, effort) valued by the travelers. For a linear demand function in which

$$ap(q) = \frac{\alpha}{\beta} - \frac{q}{\beta} \qquad (9\text{-}2)$$

the total payment function is

$$TUP(q) = \frac{q\alpha}{\beta} - \frac{q^2}{\beta} \qquad (9\text{-}3)$$

In turn, the marginal payment at output q, or $mp(q)$, is defined as follows:

$$mp(q) = \frac{\partial TUP(q)}{\partial q} = \frac{\Delta TUP(q)}{\Delta q} \qquad (9\text{-}4)$$

$$= TUP(q) - TUP(q-1) \qquad (9\text{-}5)$$

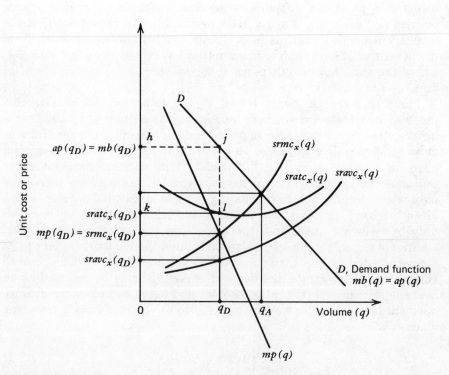

Figure 9-1. Short-run cost and demand relations for a fixed facility and high-demand under noncompetitive conditions.

Taking the derivative of $TUP(q)$ as expressed in Equation (9-3), the marginal payment curve is

$$mp(q) = \frac{\alpha}{\beta} - \frac{2q}{\beta} \qquad (9\text{-}6)$$

for a linear demand curve. This marginal payment function is plotted in Figure 9-1.

Several things are worth noting about the marginal payment function. First, the marginal payment can take on both positive and negative values; the former indicates that output increases—which can occur only if the price is reduced for a given service and demand curve—will lead to total payment (or user cost) increases so long as $mp(q)$ is positive. Negative values of $mp(q)$ indicate that total payments will be decreased if price is reduced and thus output is increased; accordingly, when $mp(q)$ is negative, total payments can be increased only by increasing the price and reducing output. *Also, it can be seen that the positive and negative mp(q) values will correspond, respectively, with the elastic and inelastic regions of the demand function.* Lastly, the marginal payment will be zero (meaning of course that a small price change will not affect the total user payments) whenever the demand is unit elastic with respect to price (i.e., when $\epsilon_p = -1$).

From arguments similar to those for maximizing net benefits, total net payments (equal to the difference between total payments and total social costs) are maximized by restricting flow to the point at which the short-run marginal cost equals the marginal payment or $srmc_x(q) = mp(q)$. In Figure 9-1 maximum net payments are equal to the area of the rectangle $hjlk$, or

$$[mb(q_D) - sratc_x(q_D)]q_D \qquad (9\text{-}7)$$

To achieve an equilibrium flow rate of q_D, a toll equal to $mb(q_D)$ minus $sravc_x(q_D)$ would be required, assuming that without a toll individuals each have user payments equal to the short-run average variable cost or $sravc_x(q_D)$. However, it should also be clear from the discussion within Chapter 6 that it would *not* be possible to restrict output to q_D and to maximize total user payments with a price of $ap(q_D)$ unless there was no competition.

Why should a planner be interested in changes in total payments? While the marginal payments curve does not have the normative or theoretical significance that the marginal benefit function has (which was discussed above), or the practical financial significance of the marginal revenue function (which is discussed below), there are a few circumstances in which changes in total payments may be of interest. The first is the case in which consumer surplus is excluded from consideration, that is, the benefit is assumed to be equal to the user cost incurred in travel. This approach is occasionally advocated by highway engineers or may be appropriate if the consumer surplus is negligible (i.e., with a perfectly elastic or a horizontal demand function) or unmeasurable. Excluding the consumer surplus, the most advantageous flow level is that which maximizes total net payments. A second circumstance in which total payments may be of interest is in the analysis of the incidence of costs and the degree of subsidy provided to various groups.

In some cases total payments may be less than the total social costs of providing a particular service. This certainly would be true for the *very low demand* case shown earlier in Figure 6-6. Under certain conditions this will also hold true for the *low-demand case* described in Chapter 6 and deserves further attention since it may be common for many public transport facilities. For low-demand cases the demand function will intersect the short-run average total cost function to the left of its minimum average total cost-point. It is difficult, of course, to say with any preciseness how typical this case really is. It would be our guess that commuter railroads, rail transit systems, and some toll roads may find this representation appropriate. Clearly, if total payments are less than total costs, the facilities will not be financially feasible in the sense that toll or fare revenues cannot cover operating and fixed costs. However, these facilities may still be economically justifiable since total benefits may still exceed total costs.

The discussion above pertains to maximizing net user payments given a particular facility or service and in the absence of competition. The relationship of user payments to costs over the long run in which facility size can be altered can also be of interest. In particular, we can consider cases of increasing or decreasing long run returns to scale.

Figure 9-2 shows the *low-demand* case in which increasing returns to scale exist (i.e., a falling average cost curve). In this instance the marginal payment function $mp(q)$, which represents the increase in total user payments which accompany a unit change in volume, would be as shown in the figure. Each unit of increase in capacity and volume up to q_F will result in extra total payments in excess of the long-run marginal costs because in the range of volume from 0 to q_F the marginal payment $[mp(q)]$ is equal to or greater than the long-run marginal cost $[lrmc(q)]$. A price set equal to the average payment at q_F so that $p(q_F) = ap(q_F) = mb(q_F)$ would result in total payments which are larger than long-run total costs. At a different price and volume, however, it is possible to have situations in which payments would not exceed costs. In particular, maximum net social benefits occur with an equilibrium price of $p(q_A)$ and volume q_A. Thus, the preferable facility size would be that which has the least total costs for an output level of q_A, and, in this situation, total payments would be less than total costs. However, we should also point out that the former result [with an output of q_F and a price of $p(q_F)$] could only occur in the absence of competition and that the latter result [with an output of q_A and a price of $p(q_A)$] would be an unlikely outcome unless subsidies were provided.

Next, we examine the results for *high-demand* cases having decreasing returns to scale (or rising long-run average total costs), as shown in Figure 9-3 for the $D'D'$ demand case. Under these circumstances, *and in the absence of competition*, capacity and output could be expanded up to level q_G, at which point the marginal payment and long-run marginal cost would be equal or $mp(q_G) = lrmc(q_G)$. The market clearing price for these

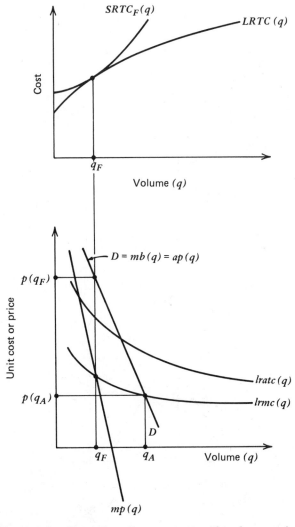

Figure 9-2. Illustration of long-run costs with scale economies.

conditions would be $p(q_G) = ap(q_G)$, an average payment which is above the short- and long-run average total cost. The facility of lowest long-run total cost for an output of q_G would be built and operated at that level. Again, though, less than the best facility and output level—from the standpoint of maximum long-run total net social benefits—would result; that is, a facility of capacity and output equal to q_C would be more desirable economically with a price $p(q_C) = ap(q_C) = lrmc(q_C) = srmc(q_C)$.

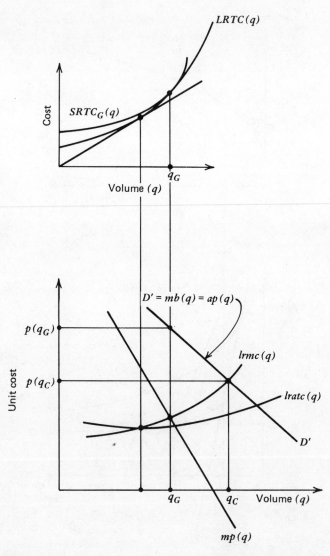

Figure 9-3. Illustration of long-run costs with scale diseconomies.

With the possibility of competition, the excess returns obtained in Figure 9-3 at a volume of q_G would offer a (perhaps irresistible) temptation to competitors. At volume q_G average payments $p(q_G)$ are substantially greater than average and marginal costs. Competitors could introduce lower prices and thereby attract some trips, profitably at that.

As a final note, all the preceding discussion can be applied to strictly financial analysis with a suitable substitution or redefinition of the demand and cost functions. Financial analysis in this sense is concerned with the money revenues and the private costs incurred by the provider. In essence, demand functions estimated with respect to monetary charges can be substituted for those estimated with respect to total user cost or price, as illustrated in Figures 9-1 to 9-3. Chapter 3 described the use and analytical difficulties of such specialized functions. Similarly, and as discussed below, cost functions can be defined with respect to costs incurred by providers rather than total costs to users or society. With these provisions and changes, financial analysis to maximize money profits can be conducted as described in the next section.

9-2   PROFIT MAXIMIZATION AND FINANCIAL IMPLICATIONS FOR SERVICE PROVIDERS

Analysis of financial implications to service providers is similar to the analysis of net user payments presented in the previous section. However, the analysis must be undertaken for a different set of demand and cost curves, namely, the demand function with respect to fares or tolls, $D(f)$, and the costs which are incurred by the service provider alone. Complications also arise in the analysis with respect to competing providers and investment planning.

Development of demand curves as a function of fares or tolls was discussed in Chapter 3. By considering the volume which will result at different fare levels, it is possible to construct a demand function which indicates the equilibrium volume at each fare or toll level. In developing this curve, however, it is important to consider equilibrium changes in volume since, as the fare changes, the volume using a service changes and other components of user cost (such as travel time) can and often will change and, in turn, affect the demand and equilibrium volume level. Thus, the variation in other components of user cost must be considered in the prediction of actual volume changes due to fare changes.

Cost functions for service providers may be developed in a manner similar to the development of *social* cost functions in Chapter 5. Included in such functions are the components of total costs which are incurred directly by the service provider, such as wages or maintenance expenses. In addition, transfer payments from the service provider should also be included as a cost item since these payments do represent a financial expense even though they are not a social cost. Examples of such transfer payments include bond payments and taxes. We shall call the total costs incurred by a service provider a *private* cost function, from which we can calculate marginal and average private costs at any volume level in the same way that marginal and average social costs were calculated from the social cost function.

Demand functions with respect to money price or fare and private cost functions for one facility size are shown in Figure 9-4. The curves are all short-run functions since a change in the facility size would alter other

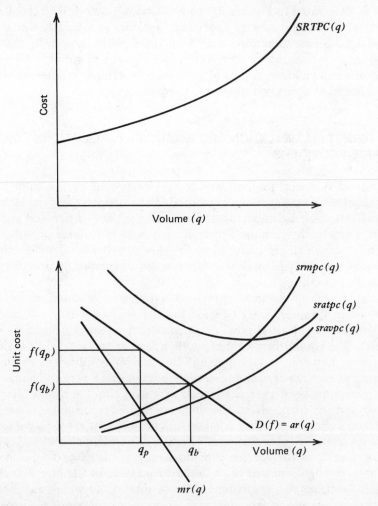

Figure 9-4. Private costs and equilibrium demand with respect to fares for an unprofitable service. The addition of p to the notation for the cost functions [e.g., $srmpc(q)$ rather than $srmc(q)$] denotes a private rather than social cost function.

components of user cost and shift the expected volume at any fare level. Thus, while the demand function with respect to user price is stable for a specific facility type and size, the demand functions defined with respect to fare would shift as the facility size or service is altered. Moreover, and as discussed in Chapter 3, the effects of changes in usage and thus in travel time and crowding for the situation depicted in Figure 9-4 can be incorporated in the demand function $D(f)$ for the facility shown in Figure 9-4.

The private financial effect of any pricing and investment decisions may be calculated after private costs have been estimated. Total revenue is simply the product of the equilibrium volume and the fare or toll charged for service. Private costs are indicated by the private total cost curve at any particular volume level for whatever facility size or activity level is chosen.

In a manner analogous to the identification of prices which maximize total net payments or total net benefits, it is also possible to identify the fare level which will maximize financial profits to the service provider. *In the absence of competition* the fare level should be set such that resulting volume has the marginal private cost equal to the marginal revenue. In Figure 9-4 fare should be set at $f(q_p)$ while volume is q_p. Volume increases above q_p would result in marginal and incremental costs larger than the incremental contribution to revenue. A volume level below q_p would result in the provider receiving less total net revenues. With a volume of q_p we have the profit maximizing volume for a *monopoly* supplier, that is, a supplier without competition. (Figure 9-4 depicts the *very-low-demand* case.)

Figure 9-4 illustrates a case in which revenues cannot cover the total costs of operation since the fare $[f(q_p)]$ which results in the maximum profits is less than the average total private cost at volume q_p. Over the long run a private operator would not attempt to operate service under these conditions without receiving some form of subsidy or attempting some sort of value of service pricing. In the short run, however, the operator would find the operation profitable since the fares would more than cover the short-run total variable costs and thus contribute something to overhead. The long run is, of course, a different matter, during which the operator must abandon the service, obtain a subsidy, or change his pricing policy. *With competition*, the operator—in the short run— would have little choice but to set his price at $f(q_b) = srmpc(q_b)$ until such time as he could abandon the service or obtain a subsidy. In this case the provider would have total revenue in excess of his total short-run variable costs, but the excess would contribute far less to covering overhead than would the former noncompetitive pricing case.

One possibility for a pricing change is to charge differential fares so that travelers who value a trip highly would be required to pay more, while others would pay less. A pertinent example would be higher fares for long trips (e.g., zone fares). In this way some of the consumers' surpluses may be extracted by the operator. With sufficient differentiation the average fare *may* be high enough to cover costs. Unfortunately, this type of differential pricing is often impossible or impractical (as discussed in Chapter 13). Moreover, we should not overlook the fact that an operator would not be able to extract either a maximum profit fare of $f(q_p)$ or a higher differential fare unless he found himself in an uncompetitive (or monopoly) situation and was able to take advantage of it. As in the case in which net user payments were maximized, it should be clear that operations to maximize profit generally do not result in the maximization of net social benefit.

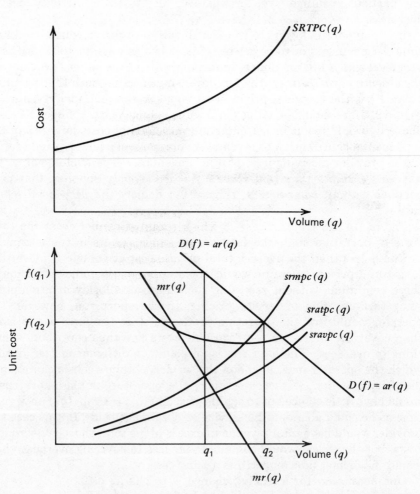

Figure 9-5. Private costs and equilibrium demand with respect to fares for a profitable service.

In contrast to Figure 9-4, demand cases in which profits could be obtained are not uncommon in public transportation, especially facilities in high demand such as urban turnpikes, bridges, or tunnels. An example is illustrated in Figure 9-5. *In the absence of competition* and in pursuit of maximum profits, a private operator could set the fare level at $f(q_1)$ and accumulate a profit of the fare minus his average costs, or $f(q_1)$ minus $sratpc(q_1)$, from each traveler. Price regulations have often been advocated in such cases to reduce the amount of such profits and increase net social benefits by restricting the fare charged for service. Alternatively, with the possibility of new service operators, competition would also serve to reduce the fare level and drive the fare to $f(q_2)$, a situation which would still be profitable for the operator.

Figure 9-6 illustrates the situation with the same demand curve as before, but with the existence of two operators offering identical service (and the same service as was offered originally) and having marginal cost functions as shown. In the absence of collusion between the operators, each one would be willing to offer a lower fare to attract new travelers, but only so long as the fare charged exceeded their marginal private costs.

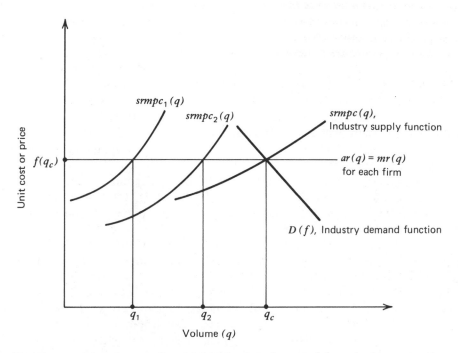

Figure 9-6. Private costs and equilibrium for the industry and for each of two competing service providers.

This conclusion stems from the fact both firms must charge the same price, or $f(q_c)$, and therefore each firm faces a horizontal and constant marginal revenue function [i.e., $ar(q) = mr(q) = f(q)$ is constant and the same for each firm]. In the figure the competition for travelers would result in a fare level of $f(q_c)$, with one provider serving a volume of q_1 and a second provider serving a volume of q_2 for a total volume of $q_1 + q_2 = q_c$. Also, in this case both firms would have total revenues exceeding their total variable costs. The excess for provider 1 would be equal to $q_1 \cdot f_c$ minus the sum of its short-run marginal private costs from $q = 1$ to q_1.

Investment decisions which are intended to maximize the profitability of a transportation operator must also consider the shifts in demand due to variations in components of user cost other than fare changes. For example, expansion of a service or facility will generally result in a higher quality service to users, and the expected volume at any fare level would increase. The profit-maximizing investor must consider the trade-off between extra costs incurred in expansion and the additional volume, and hence revenue, derived from service improvement. Necessary conditions for the most profitable investment decisions in the case of a highly flexible facility or service options are dependent upon the interrelationships among the demand, marginal revenue, and marginal cost functions and upon the pricing policy and degree of competition. First, let us assume that the operator faces long-run scale economies as depicted in Figure 9-2 and that for this discussion the cost functions shown are private ones. Accordingly, in the absence of competition, the operator would expand capacity and output so long as the marginal payment (or revenue) was at least as large as the long-run marginal cost. With demand constant at DD, the short- and long-run marginal cost would be equal (for an output of q_F and for the facility of lowest total cost at output q_F), and it would be necessary to charge a fare equal to $p(q_F)$ in order to clear the market. However, if there was perfect competition among the firms (who potentially could be providing the services), then no profit-maximizing firm might enter the market [since competition would drive the fare level to $p(q_A)$, a level far below the average total cost]. Second, if the operator faced long-run diseconomies as depicted in Figure 9-3 (and again if we we assume that the cost functions are private ones), service would be provided whether or not there was competition. In the absence of competition the operator would expand capacity and output so long as the marginal payment (or revenue) was at least as large as the long-run marginal cost. Thus, the lowest total cost facility for an output of q_G would be built and a fare of $p(q_G)$ would be charged. However, with perfect competition, and with equal services provided by all operators, all operators would be forced into charging the same price which, in this case, would be $p(q_C)$. That is, operators would expand beyond q_G since the fare to clear the market would always be higher than the long-run marginal cost. In effect, then, competition would cause each operator to have a constant marginal revenue equal to $p(q_C)$ and $lrmc(q_C)$. With constant demand the short- and long-run marginal cost would be equal. However, a complete representation of this decision process and problem in a two- or three-dimensional figure is difficult since a different demand curve must be indicated for each different output level. Consequently, analysis might proceed for comparison of discrete alternatives (as in Chapter 7 but with private cost functions) or be multidimensional (similar to the analysis of equilibrium in Chapter 3).

As a simplified example, suppose that a single service provider (with no competition) estimated that demand functions during two equal periods of the year were $q_1 = 700 - 250f_1$ and $q_2 = 900 - 210f_2$ where q_1 and q_2 are the volumes per hour in periods 1 and 2, respectively, and f_1 and f_2 are the corresponding monetary charges. Further, suppose that the variable private cost in each period is $1.80 per trip and annual fixed costs are $180 per hour. To maximize profit in each period, we wish to find the volume at which (short-run) marginal private cost equals marginal revenue. Using Equation (9-6) with $mr(q)$ substituted for $mp(q)$, the two marginal revenue functions are

$$mr(q_1) = \frac{\alpha}{\beta} - \frac{2q_1}{\beta}$$

$$= \frac{700}{250} - \frac{2q_1}{250}$$

$$= 2.80 - 0.008q_1 \qquad (9\text{-}8)$$

and

$$mr(q_2) = \frac{900}{210} - \frac{2q_2}{210} = 4.29 - 0.010q_2$$

In each case short-run marginal private cost, $srmpc(q)$, is $1.80 [since $srmpc(q) = sravpc(q)$ when the latter is constant], so the profit maximizing volume in period 1 is found by setting $srmpc(q_1)$ equal to $mr(q_1)$; thus

$$1.8 = 2.80 - 0.008q_1 \qquad (9\text{-}9)$$

which yields a profit maximizing volume of

$$q_1^* = \frac{2.80 - 1.80}{0.008} = 125 \qquad (9\text{-}10)$$

which occurs at a monetary charge of $f_1^* = $2.30 per trip. Similarly, the profit-maximizing volume in period 2 is $q_2^* = 270$ with a charge of $f_2^* = $3.00 per trip. Average revenues per hour are [($2.30)(125) +

($3.00)(270)]/2 = \$548.75, which exceed costs [of \$180 + \$1.80(125 + 270)/2 = \$535.50] by \$13.25 per hour. This excess represents a profit for the service.

As a side note, suppose that the service provider is prohibited from charging different tolls in the two periods. In this case we can construct an average demand function of $q = (700 + 900)/2 - [(250 + 210)/2]f = 800 - 230f$ for an average hour during the year. With this demand function an analysis similar to that above reveals a profit-maximizing charge of \$2.60, with average volume of 200 and period volumes of $q_1 = 50$ and $q_2 = 350$. Average revenue per hour is then \$520, which is less than average cost per hour (180 + 360 = \$540) by \$20 per hour. Consequently, the restriction to a uniform charge implies that the service will operate at a loss.

9-3 ECONOMIC EFFICIENCY WITH A BUDGET TARGET

Whenever financial deficits to service operators are a concern, decisions concerning pricing and investment policies for public transportation are generally undertaken with a budget target or constraint. In these cases a maximum allowable deficit is agreed upon prior to investment and pricing decisions, although the budget might be subsequently altered and the analysis conducted again if the original target was too constricting or additional funds were obtained. In this case transportation services should be operated so as to maximize net social benefits while staying within the financial target. Mathematically, the public service provider should attempt to choose fares and activity levels so as to maximize total net benefits:

$$TNB = \sum_{i=1}^{q} mb(i) - \sum_{i=1}^{q} srmc(i) - F \qquad (9\text{-}11)$$

subject to the budget target (stated as a negative deficit)

$$f \cdot q - SRTPC(q) \geq B \qquad (9\text{-}12)$$

where $f \cdot q$ is the total private revenue and $SRTPC(q)$ is the total private cost. The value B represents the allowable budget deficit. If $B = 0$, then the provider must at least break even with fare revenue.

A number of economists have considered the problem of pricing rules for public enterprises with such budget targets. With different services, fluctuating demand, or the ability to differentiate among users, the pricing rule to maximize net social benefits while attaining a budget target may be simply summarized: charge in proportion to what the traffic will bear.

This rule is often called the "Ramsey rule" of pricing.[1] In brief, providers should recoup more costs in markets which are more *insensitive* to price changes.

Recall that the price which maximizes net social benefits is that which equals short-run marginal costs. If the revenue resulting from such prices exceeds the deficit target plus the private costs of service, then additional charges are not required. In many cases, however, additional and higher fares would have to be imposed in order to meet the budget target. These additional charges should be concentrated in markets which have numerically lower (that is, less negative) price elasticities.

Mathematically, the rule for setting additional charges as a proportion of price is that the additional charges should be inversely proportional to the elasticity of demand with respect to price for each service or in each period:[2]

$$\frac{m_1}{p_1}\epsilon_1 = \frac{m_2}{p_2}\epsilon_2 = \cdots \frac{m_i}{p_i}\epsilon_i = \cdots \frac{m_n}{p_n}\epsilon_n \qquad (9\text{-}13)$$

where m_i is the additional fare (above p_i) imposed in period i, p_i is the original price in period i [equal to $srmc(q_i)$], and ϵ_i is the elasticity of demand in period i. The same rule would be applied among n different traveler groups, services, or locales.

In practice, this rule implies that periods (or markets) which are more sensitive to price changes should be charged less. Periods with equal demand elasticities should have equal proportional increases in the price level, implying that the *absolute* amount of excess or additional charges will be higher in periods which already have high prices. In the context of transportation, peak travel periods typically have little sensitivity to price changes (i.e., an elasticity near zero) and relatively high prices. Thus, excess fares imposed to meet a budget target should probably be concentrated during peak travel periods.

Investment decision making should also consider the impact on budget targets and the additional or excess fares which must be charged in order to meet such budget targets. While more computations are required, it is possible to calculate the required prices for all alternatives [which would be $m_i + srmc(q_i)$ for all i in each case] and then proceed with the same analysis as that in Chapter 7.

As a numerical illustration, consider the two-period service described in the last section. For simplicity, suppose that no user costs exist other than

[1]For a fuller yet straightforward mathematical development, see A. A. Walters, *The Economics of Road User Charges*, Johns Hopkins Press, Baltimore, 1970, pp. 115–117.

[2]F. P. Ramsey, "A Contribution to the Theory of Taxation," *Economic Journal* **37**, 47–61, (1927).

the monetary charge for service. In this special case short-run marginal *private* costs equal short-run marginal costs to society. The charges which maximize net social benefit are found by identifying the intersection of the short-run marginal cost and marginal benefit (i.e., the inverse demand) functions. For period 1 in the previous example this is

$$srmc(q_1) = mb(q_1)$$

$$1.80 = \frac{700}{250} - \frac{q_1}{250} \tag{9-14}$$

implying that the most desirable volume is $q_1 = (2.80 - 1.80)\ 250 = 250$ trips per hour, which occurs with a charge of \$1.80 per trip. Similarly, the economically efficient volume in period 2 is 522 trips per hour. Unfortunately, the service would operate at an average loss of \$180 per hour at these volumes and their corresponding charges. To indicate which period should receive a greater increase in charge, note that the equilibrium toll elasticity in period 1 is $\epsilon_1 = -\beta(p/q) = (-250)(1.8/250) = -1.80$, while the elasticity in period 2 is $\epsilon_2 = -0.72$. Using the inverse elasticity rule [Eq. (9-13)], we expect that a greater increase should occur in period 2. Indeed, by trial and error or by analytical solution,[3] the charges which maximize net social benefit subject to the restriction that the providers break even are \$2.20 for f_1 and \$2.70 for f_2 (to the nearest tenth of a dollar), so that the increase in the period 2 charge is about twice that for period 1.

9-4 FINANCING CAPITAL COSTS

The preceding discussion concerned the relationship between revenues and costs for a facility or service once built and in operation. We should also deal with the financial problem created by capital costs or temporary deficits. A common example is that of new capital investments which have large construction or purchase costs in the initial years and have benefits and revenues which only begin accruing after completion of the project's construction. With such an unbalanced cash flow stream the problem of financing the initial costs arises. An example appears in Table 9-1 in which the private expenses exceed the revenues in the early years of the project. This problem of financing capital outlays or temporary deficits is in addition to the problem addressed above, that is, to insure that reve-

---

[3]An analytical solution is found by maximizing net social benefits subject to the restriction that revenues equal costs. Mathematically, that is, max $TNB_1 + TNB_2$ subject to $(TR_1 + TR_2)/2 = F + (SRVC_1 + SRVC_2)/2$. In terms of q_1 and q_2, this is: Maximize $[q_1 700/250 - (q_1^2 + q_1)/2(250) - 1.8q_1 + q_2 900/210 - (q_2^2 + q_2)/2(210) - 1.8q_2]$ subject to $[(q_1 700/250 - q_1^2/250) + (q_2 900/210 - q_2^2/210)] = 1.8(q_1 + q_2)/2 + 180$. This problem can be solved with the use of the technique of Lagrange multipliers.

nues from user fees or other sources are sufficiently high to cover the private costs in the long run.

There are many financial mechanisms available for handling cash flow imbalances. They include financing from current revenues (from other projects or general taxes), using working capital, issuing stock, initiating joint ventures with private firms, issuing revenue bonds, borrowing short term funds, receiving subsidies from other levels of governments (which simply shifts the financing problem to the other level of government), and so forth. Generally, the financing problem is one of insuring that adequate funds are made available at the lowest possible cost.

As a general note, the cost of borrowing to finance a project depends upon the relative levels of the minimum attractive rate of return (MARR) and the borrowing interest rate. If the borrowing interest rate exceeds MARR, then it is preferable to borrow as little as possible since the interest rate paid for borrowed funds exceeds the return from alternative investments. In contrast, when MARR exceeds the borrowing rate, the net return from a project increases as the proportion of borrowed funds increases. This latter situation provides an incentive for "leveraging," in which a small amount of equity capital and a large proportion of borrowed money are used for projects. In the former case (when MARR is less than the borrowing rate), initial capital or other expenses covered by borrowed funds are generally repaid as quickly as possible and following that, "sinking funds" of accumulated or retained earnings may be established to cover any future periodic or rehabilitation expenses.

An important initial consideration in planning a financial mechanism is to decide whether or not the alternative selected for implementation is to be financed as a separate entity or as part of an ongoing program of capital investment. For example, federal grants for some roadway projects are part of an ongoing program funded from the Highway Trust fund. Revenues derived from gasoline and other excise taxes are used to cover new grants each year on a pay-as-you-go basis without borrowing. Pay-as-you-go financing simply means that the year by year revenues (such as gasoline and excise tax receipts) must cover any additional year by year capital expenditures. At the other extreme revenue bonds may be issued which are pledged to be repaid solely from the revenue received by a new facility or service.

For planning the financing of a particular project in isolation, its benefits and costs can be considered simultaneously with alternative financing schemes. Thus, a time stream of benefits and costs can be combined with the time stream of financing revenues and expenses; an example appeared in the two right-hand columns of Table 8-1. Otherwise, the alternative financing schemes can be evaluated separately in terms of their net present values. The alternative financing plan with the largest net present value can then be chosen. The net economic feasibility of the project— from the private or local viewpoint—can then be calculated as the sum of the net present value of the project itself plus the net present value of the financing scheme.[4] However, if alternative investment plans are considered solely in terms of their *internal* benefits and costs, the implicit assumption is made that financing is accomplished without new borrowing or with borrowing at a rate equivalent to the MARR. Choice among financial schemes and project alternatives can then be made on the basis of maximizing net present value.

As an example, suppose that we wish to consider financing the first two years' costs for a project with the cash flow stream shown in Table 9-1. To emphasize that our analysis is financial in nature and restricted to private costs and benefits, we label the cash stream as "revenues" and "expenses" in Table 9-1. With a MARR of 18% the basic project aside from financing has a net present value of $152K. For simplicity in this problem, the cash streams in Table 9-1 are presumed to be in after-tax, constant dollar amounts.

One possible alternative is to finance the project entirely from internal equity funds. With a MARR of 18% the use of internal equity funds implies that capital will be diverted from other projects which could earn a positive return at an 18% discount rate. With such internal financing the project's net present value is $152K, which is calculated with a MARR of 18% from the project's cash flow stream in Table 9-1.

TABLE 9-1.   An illustration of Two Project Financing Alternatives

	Project Cash Flow		Overdraft Financing		Bond Financing	
Year	Revenues	Expenses	Loan Revenues	Repayment Expenses	Bond Revenues	Repayment Expenses
0	0	700	700	0	800	100
1	0	900	900	0	1000	100
2	600	100	0	500	0	420
3	600	100	0	500	0	420
4	600	100	0	500	0	420
5	600	100	0	500	0	420
6	600	100	0	500	0	420
7	600	100	0	67	0	420
8	600	100	0	0	0	420
Net Present Value at i = 18%						
	152.34		116.61		106.07	

Note: Dollar amounts in thousands. Overdraft financing charge is 15% per year. Bond financing is at 12.3% plus expenses of issuing bonds, the latter of which are spread equally over years 0 and 1.

[4]For a more extensive discussion, see R. Brealey and S. Myers, *Principles of Corporate Finance*, McGraw-Hill, New York, 1981, Chapter 19.

An alternative financing scheme is to arrange a short-term loan or overdraft arrangement with a bank. As shown in the cash flow stream for the overdraft alternative in Table 9-1, this plan involves overdrafts until year 8. Interest charges on overdrafts are assumed to be at an interest rate of 15%. Note that all excess revenues in years 2 to 6, plus part of the year 7 revenues, are applied to repay this overdraft. The net present value of the overdraft is $117K evaluated at the MARR, so the combined net present value of the project together with overdraft financing is $152K + $117K = $269K. This alternative is preferable to equity financing since the firm is borrowing money at a 15% rate rather than diverting funds from other investment opportunities, which have a rate of return of 18% or more.

Table 9-1 also shows a possible financing scheme with revenue bond financing. In this example bonds in the amount of $800K at the present and $1000K at the end of year 1 are issued at a rate of 12.3% and repaid in years 2 to 8. However, there are expenses associated with preparing and issuing the bonds in this example. These expenses amount to $100K for years 0 and 1. With these issuing costs the combined net present value of the project together with revenue bond financing is $152K + $106K = $258K. Thus, overdraft financing (with a combined net present value of $269K) is the most desirable alternative financing plan in this example. In practice, a variety of other financing plans could also be examined.

Note that the same results would be obtained if the project cash flow and the financial plan cash flows were combined and the joint or combined cash flow evaluated. For example, the sum of project and overdraft cash flows consists of net revenues of $433K in year 7 and $500K in year 8. This combined cash flow has a net present value of

$$NPV = \$433K(P|F, 18\%, 7) + \$500K(P|F, 18\%, 8)$$

$$= \$433K(0.3139) + \$500K(0.2660) = \$269K$$

which is identical to the combined net present value of the two cash streams evaluated separately.

Obviously, financing options can affect the choice of mutually exclusive alternatives, as well as their acceptability. As an example, consider the two two-year alternatives shown in Table 9-2. For a MARR of 10%, and ignoring financing, alternative II would be superior to alternative I; this same result would be obtained for any MARR $\leq 10.62\%$. However, suppose that available cash is limited to $500 and that the remainder of each alternative's initial investment would be financed by borrowing money at an interest rate of 15%. In this case, both alternatives would require borrowed funds, though only one year would be required for their repayment for alternative I. With this 15% financing and ignoring any uncer-

TABLE 9-2. An Example of Financial Effects on Project Selection[a]

| | Alternative I | | | Alternative II | | |
Year	Internal Cash Stream[b]	Financing Cash Stream	Combined Cash Stream	Internal Cash Stream[b]	Financing Cash Stream	Combined Cash Stream
0	−1000	+500	−500	−2000	+1500	−500
1	+600	−575	+25	+1200	−1200	0
2	+600	0	+600	+1160	−604	+556
$[NPV_{x,2}]_{10\%}$	+41	−23	+19	+50	−90	−40

[a] Amounts are rounded to closest integer.
[b] Cash stream without considering financing.

tainty in cash flows, alternative I is more desirable than alternative II for any positive MARR. This result arises from the financial "cost" of borrowing money; that is, for a MARR of 10%, the net present value of each alternative declined since the borrowing rate exceeded the MARR.

Finally, we should note the effects of tax deductions and the like on financial analysis. For public agencies this is not necessarily relevant, but private firms can often realize tax benefits from capital investments in the form of depreciation allowances and investment credits which reduce income tax liabilities. This difference between public and private providers is the primary motivation for financial schemes such as private ownership of equipment with public agency leasing and operation. The private "owners" can take advantage of depreciation and other allowances and pass on some portion of these savings to the public agency operator in the form of lower leasing charges. In any event, financing alternatives should be evaluated after tax payments or savings are removed from the revenue or expense side of the cash flow profile.

In contrast to the individual project finance discussed above, transportation investments are commonly treated as parts of ongoing programs of investments. The advantages of treating projects in this fashion stem from the pooling of risks and revenues which can occur. New projects can often be funded from current revenue rather than borrowing. Risks of failure can be spread among numerous projects, which also reduces the costs of any required borrowing. A disadvantage of such pooling is that new projects may not be sufficiently well scrutinized to insure that they are economically desirable on their own.

With consideration of multiple independent projects, the problem of capital rationing is encountered. That is, agencies or firms that are reluctant to borrow additional funds may set a maximum limit on the capital funds available in any year. Commonly, though, the projects identified as being economically desirable have capital requirements which exceed the available budget. In this case the projects must compete for the available funds. Economically, the decision rule in such cases is straightforward: implement that set of economically desirable projects which exhausts the capital budget and yields the highest total net present value.

9-5 FINANCIAL IMPLICATIONS OF RISKY INVESTMENTS

As noted in Chapter 3, the usage of particular transportation services as well as the social costs incurred may be quite uncertain for future time periods. In Chapter 7 we argued that this uncertainty can be taken explicitly into account by considering the expected benefits and costs of different facilities (and associated staging plans), given some assumption concerning the uncertainty associated with the various volume and cost predictions. The uncertainty of volume levels and costs also has implications for the service provider's deficits or profits and deserves some discussion.

Although the computations become more numerous and tedious, it is possible to calculate—at least approximately—the expected profitability of each investment alternative and staging plan given some assumption concerning the uncertainty of various levels of the demand function and costs. The procedure is identical to that described in Chapter 7, but using the revenue and private cost functions which were described above in this chapter. Basically, the expected profit of an investment alternative is the sum of the profitability under each possible condition multiplied by the (assumed) probability that the condition will occur:

$$E[TNP] = \sum_{z=1}^{m} \Pr\{\text{condition } z\} TNP_z \qquad (9\text{-}15)$$

where TNP_z is the total net profit with condition z and m is the total number of possible conditions. Investment alternatives may then be compared on the basis of their expected net profitability in the same manner as in the deterministic case analyzed earlier.

However, there is an asymmetry associated with budget targets which is not captured by this type of analysis. The consequence of falling short of a budget target (i.e., incurring a larger deficit than is anticipated) may be more severe than the benefits of realizing a budget surplus. As a result, managers might be interested in an indicator such as the chance or probability that the investment will result in budget deficits or in targets being exceeded. All other things being equal, managers would tend to prefer those projects which were less likely to have large budget deficits.

Mathematically, this indicator might be calculated by noting all the conditions under which budget deficits would result and summing the probabilities associated with these problem conditions:

$$\Pr\{\text{budget deficit}\} = \sum_{y=1}^{r} \Pr\{\text{condition } y\} \qquad (9\text{-}16)$$

where $y = 1, \ldots, r$ includes all the conditions which result in a budget deficit. Other indicators of the riskiness of a project might also be used, such as the expected amount of the deficit in cases in which deficit occurs or simply the variance of net profitability. Each of these attributes attempts to indicate the riskiness of particular investments and staging plans.

It is possible to construct a single figure which might indicate both the expected net profitability of an investment and the risk associated with the investment. For example, conditions in which budget deficits occur might be weighted twice that of conditions in which profits occur. This construction is a simple example of the general scheme of weighting for multiple-objective planning which will be described in the following chapter. The point which should be emphasized, however, is that it is perfectly rational to consider the uncertainty associated with different investments as well as the expected net profitability. As a consequence, multiple-objective planning—as described in the next chapter—is almost required in such situations.

CHAPTER 10

MULTI–OBJECTIVE AND MULTI–ATTRIBUTE PROJECT SELECTION

Most of the previous discussion was directed at the problem of identifying the investment alternative or operating policy which would result in maximizing total net benefits. In practice, decision makers are concerned with other objectives as well. For example, we discussed the impact of various alternatives on the financial profitability of transportation services in the previous chapter since profitability or deficit limitation is often an objective in undertaking new services or continuing others. Another common concern in the selection of investments pertains to the incidence of the benefits and costs, that is, who actually derives the benefits of a service and who incurs the costs, in contrast to measuring total net benefits "to whomsoever they may accrue." That is, the costs or the benefits might be disproportionally distributed to particular individuals or groups, and such differences in the incidence of benefits and costs may greatly concern decision makers.

In this chapter several techniques for dealing with multiple-objective and multiple-attribute project selection will be discussed. Cases with multiple objectives are those in which decision makers formulate more than one goal to be pursued when providing transportation services. Cases of multiple attributes arise when projects have numerous impacts and the *valuation* of these various impacts cannot be directly reduced to dollar amounts. Much of the discussion in this chapter will be concerned with the elimination of undesirable projects in light of the various objectives and attributes, rather than the selection of one "optimal" project. *As will be clear later, multidimensional project selection methods do not present any magic procedure for avoiding the difficult problems of valuing different project attributes or of making choices when there are competing objectives.*

Throughout this chapter and in conformity with the focus of this book, we shall attempt to illuminate the proper procedures for the prediction and analysis of the *economic* impacts of alternatives. Economic impacts such as total net benefits, financial considerations, lives saved, environmental degradation, and the incidence of project impacts may be only a portion of the issues of concern to decision makers. Nevertheless, political, aesthetic, social, and other concerns which may be voiced or considered by decision makers fall largely outside the scope of this work. For example, it is difficult and, we feel, inappropriate to incorporate political considerations into an analysis of the economic consequences of alternative transportation projects. Even apart from the analytical problems of formulating and analyzing objectives with respect to these noneconomic considerations, quantitative prediction of such effects is extremely difficult.

10-1 DEFINITION, MEASUREMENT, AND PRESENTATION OF PROJECT ATTRIBUTES

Previously, a single project attribute was generally used for comparing projects, namely, the total net benefits to whomsoever they might accrue. In Chapters 1 to 8 we discussed at some length the definition, composition, and measurement of total net benefits. For example, in Chapter 4 we described methods by which user costs could be identified and valued in dollar amounts. Before projects may be analyzed with respect to additional objectives or different attributes, it is necessary to undertake a similar process of definition for these additional objectives and attributes.

A number of potential objectives have already been described. In Chapter 9, for instance, we discussed the calculation of the financial profitability of services. It is also possible to analyze revenue and financial costs for any particular group in a manner similar to that used for service providers by calculating the direct costs and revenue for each group. Groups of interest might be special user groups (e.g., the elderly, minority travelers, or residents of particular areas), competing service providers, or others.

The calculation of total net benefits can also be restricted to determine the net economic benefits for any particular *group*. Such a calculation is similar to changing the unit, focus or "point of view" for analysis. Generally, benefits and costs are related to those individuals which had to risk their own resources in undertaking a project or service. By restricting the size of this analysis group, the net economic benefits to the group may be calculated in the same manner as for the overall total net benefits. As in the analysis of financial profitability, transfer payments to particular groups might be considered benefits in this analysis. The analysis of sunk and opportunity costs remain identical to the analysis for total net benefits, however.

A notable example of differences between a general and specific analysis occurs for the case of federal capital grants. Revenues for such grants are derived from taxes or user charges which are imposed nationwide. For the nation as a whole, they represent a transfer payment from taxpayers to the local operating agencies and, thus, no overall net benefit. From the viewpoint of a locality, however, these grants represent a direct benefit which can be used to offset its real resource costs of construction. Thus, a calculation of the benefits and costs of capital investments from the national and from the local viewpoints are quite different.

The discussion above has concentrated upon the calculation of attributes which might be directly related to goals or objectives, such as deficit limitation or increasing the net economic benefit to a particular local area or social-economic group. Multiple project attributes may also arise if it is impossible or inappropriate to develop dollar values for various impacts of particular projects. For example, it may be quite difficult to assign a dollar value to air pollutant emissions reduction or to the lives saved by a safety measure. In some cases the proper value to place upon a particular project impact may require a political decision, so an analyst should be reluctant to impute a particular dollar value without consulting with responsible officials. Even with only one objective (such as total net benefits), the difficulty of valuing various project impacts may make some form of multidimensional project selection analysis useful. Once again, however, such analysis requires that the various attribute measures be defined and quantitative measurements of individual project impacts made.

One additional project attribute deserves mention here, even though it is often ignored in transportation systems analysis. This attribute pertains to the risk associated with particular projects. Estimates for many inputs to the analysis process outlined above are uncertain to some degree; that is, the analyst knows that various forecasts are likely to have associated errors. In particular, estimates of travel volume over time, capital and operation costs, and technological possibilities have a substantial amount of uncertainty. Given this uncertainty, some projects may have a higher degree of flexibility or adaptiveness, so that the expected losses—in cases of detrimental outcomes—are significantly lower. These projects tend to be less risky than projects which have the possibility of large benefits in some circumstances and equally large losses in other circumstances. In general, decision makers are likely to prefer less risky projects. Measurement of project riskiness will be discussed below.

Once the various attribute measurements are defined and measured for each project alternative, the impacts of particular projects may be summarized in tabular form. For example, Table 10-1 summarizes measures of attributes of three separate projects (*A, B,* and *C*) for three separate objectives, namely, total net benefits, financial profitability of the service, and net economic benefits to elderly and handicapped individuals. Similarly, Table 10-2 is a summary of the multiple-attribute impacts of three alternative projects for which maximization of total net benefits is the only objective in project selection. In the latter case, however, the analyst has not put a dollar value on the total net benefits associated with pollution reduction and employment increases. Multiobjective and multiattri-

TABLE 10-1.   Example of a Multi–Objective Impact Summary for Three Alternatives

	Alternative		
	A	B	C
Total net benefit (in thousands)	$ 250	$ 200	$ 150
Provider profit (in thousands)	−10	1	0
Net benefit to elderly and physically handicapped individuals (in hundreds)	16	12	8

bute analysis may then proceed using the summary of project attributes contained in Tables 10-1 and 10-2.

Before discussing such analysis procedures, a few notes about the formulation of objectives and attributes should be useful. First, to the extent possible, it is important to restrict the number of objectives and attributes which are considered. Each objective and attribute which is defined requires an additional impact calculation and represents an additional dimension of analysis. Decision makers will have difficulty in analyzing impact tables having more than one objective or attribute measure. Whenever reasonably possible, objective and attribute lists should be reduced in number.

Secondly, it should be obvious that the projects which perform relatively well in the largest number of objective or attribute categories are not necessarily the most desirable projects. In many cases one objective may be of great importance, while a number of other objectives are of secondary importance. Projects which have relatively good impacts for secondary objectives may be very poor overall. For example, project C in Table 10-2 ranks first with respect to both pollution reduction and

TABLE 10-2.   Example of a Multi–Attribute Impact Summary for Three Alternatives

	A	B	C
Total net benefit[a] (millions)	$ 10	$ 5	$ −30
Air pollution reduction (kg/day)	22	10	23
Transit employment increase (hundreds)	5	5	7

[a]Excluding air pollution reduction benefits and employment increases.

employment improvement but is achieved at *very high* social cost relative to other projects. Similarly, selection rules which rank the various projects within each category and then sum these rank orders generally will not result in the most desirable project. This type of selection may be acceptable for athletic track meets, say, in which each category or event is valued equally, but this assumption is not necessarily a good one for transportation project selection, despite the fact that it has been used in practice.

10-2 ELIMINATION OF INFERIOR ALTERNATIVES

Once the impacts of each project are known for each of the various attributes, an analyst may proceed to eliminate inferior project alternatives. The previous section described the process of defining and measuring various project attributes, where a project attribute might be the value of some objective (e.g., total net benefit) or some project impact which cannot be directly valued in dollar amounts (e.g., lives saved or pollutant emission reduction). The result of the initial analysis is a table which summarizes the various measures for each project.

To simplify the discussion, we shall assume that *increases* in each measure are desirable. For example, larger total net benefits and greater provider profits are generally preferable, all other things being equal. Impact measures for which *increases* are *undesirable* must be modified for the subsequent analysis by calculating their additive or multiplicative inverse and then using the *inverse* of the impact as the attribute measure. For example, rather than defining an attribute with respect to a service provider *deficit* (for which increases are undesirable), an analyst could define the project attribute with respect to service provider *profit* which is the additive inverse of the provider deficit:

$$\text{profits} = -1 \times \text{deficits} \tag{10-1}$$

and either profit or deficit may be negative in any particular case. Similarly, the impact measure of pollutant emissions should be defined as pollutant emission *reductions* to create an attribute measure for which increases are desirable. The specific type of transformation which is used is not important, although the transformation which is used will affect the subsequent analysis of trade-offs among the various attributes. Such positive transformations are useful in avoiding analysis errors. Importantly, we do not and should not assume that the dollar value of a unit increase in each attribute measure is constant over the entire range of the attribute.

The first step in analysis is to eliminate inferior alternatives from further analysis. An inferior alternative is one for which some other feasible alternative has larger or equal values for each and every attribute measure. That is, an alternative is inferior if some other project alternative is equal or preferable for each objective or attribute measure. In Table 10-1, for example, alternative C is inferior to alternative B for each of the three objective measures and, consequently, may be eliminated from subsequent analysis. Similarly, in Table 10-2 alternative B is inferior to alternative A. The argument for eliminating inferior alternatives is straightforward: We can always do better than inferior alternatives. By adopting B rather than C in Table 10-1, we could increase each of our objective attributes: total net benefit (by \$50,000), provider profit (by \$1,000), and net benefits to the elderly (by \$400).

With only two attribute measures, inferior alternatives may be detected graphically. For example, Figure 10-1 illustrates five project alternatives (A to E) with their respective attribute measures indicated by the projection of their location onto the axes of the graph. Alternative A, for example, has a value of W_A for attribute W and V_A for attribute V. Any project which lies to the southwest of another project alternative represents an inferior alternative. Thus, in Figure 10-1, alternative C is inferior to A, and alternative E is inferior to alternative B. Mathematically, the same result may be obtained by noting that the inferior alternatives have equal or lower attribute values to some other alternative:

$$Z_i(\text{inferior}) \leq Z_i(\text{superior}) \qquad \text{for all attributes } i \qquad (10\text{-}2)$$

In the literature of multiobjective and multiattribute analysis, inferior alternatives are also called *dominated* alternatives. While the terminology may differ in particular instances, the concept is identical: an alternative can never be the most desirable if some other alternative is at least as good with respect to every desirable attribute. Note that a particular alterna-

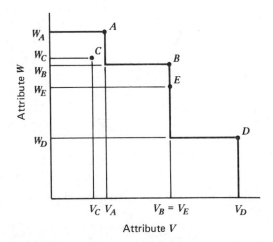

Figure 10-1. Attribute values for five project alternatives.

tive is only rejected (i.e., found inferior) if some *particular* alternative is superior. In Figure 10-1 alternative B has a lower value with respect to attribute W than does alternative A and, moreover, has a lower value of attribute V than does alternative D. However, since no one alternative is superior to alternative B with respect to both attributes, one cannot conclude that alternative B is not the best alternative; indeed, alternative B may represent the most desirable trade-off between the two attributes.

For the five alternative cases illustrated in Figure 10-1, the three alternatives A, B, and D represent the set of noninferior project alternatives which are still to be considered. These three alternatives also reveal the range of possibilities available for achieving various values of the attributes. For example, the highest achievable value for attribute W is W_A, while the highest achievable value for attribute V is V_D. The problem of project selection has been reduced to choosing among three projects, with their associated attribute measures: $A(W_A, V_A)$, $B(W_B, V_B)$, and $D(W_D, V_D)$. These three alternatives comprise the noninferior project set or frontier in this case.

With a large number of alternatives available, the number of noninferior alternatives is likely to be much larger, as in Figure 10-2. In this figure each point on the project possibility frontier represents a single alternative project, such as project P. Any alternative with attribute values lying to the southwest of some point on this curve represents an inferior and rejected alternative. The project selection problem is one of choosing some point on this noninferior project frontier.

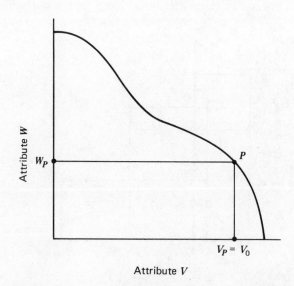

Figure 10-2.   An example of a noninferior project frontier.

To avoid excessive calculations, it is often preferable to generate the noninferior project frontier directly, rather than to compare each alternative with all others and then reject the inferior alternatives. A useful procedure for generating the noninferior project frontier is to impose a constraint on all but one attribute and then to find the project which maximizes the value of the final attribute. For example, P is the project in Figure 10-2 which has the maximum value of attribute W, given that attribute V must equal V_0. Mathematically, this procedure may be represented as

$$\text{Maximize } W_i \text{ for all projects } i \qquad (10\text{-}3)$$

subject to the constraint(s)

$$V_k = N_k \quad \text{for all other attributes } k \qquad (10\text{-}4)$$

where N_k represents the constant value of parameter k. By systematically varying the value(s) of N_k and finding the best project, the noninferior project frontier may be identified directly without comparing inferior alternatives. Mathematical details for the application of this procedure to linear problems are contained in virtually all texts describing the method of linear programming.[1]

10-3 SENSITIVITY ANALYSIS

The most common form of multiattribute analysis is a type of sensitivity analysis. In the context of multiattribute analysis, recall that an analyst is expected to define and measure various project impact attributes, as in Table 10-2. Each of these various attributes could be expressed on a single scale (such as dollar amounts) but only by virtue of assuming particular values for the attributes in dollar amounts. Sensitivity analysis may then be used to investigate how project ranking and selection would change if the dollar value of some particular attribute changed.

To perform this comparison, the analyst first defines the range of values which the dollar valuation of an attribute might assume. Using the project impact table which summarizes the attributes of the project, a single figure of net benefits may be calculated for each project using each attribute value. Project comparison with the assumed attribute value may then proceed in the same manner as for single-objective analysis described previously.

[1]See, for example, F. S. Budnick, R. Mojena, and T. Vollmann, *Principles of Operations Research for Management*, Richard Irwin, Homewood Il 1977 or T. Au, *Introduction to Systems Engineering, Deterministic Models*, Addison-Wesley, Reading, MA, 1973.

TABLE 10-3.   Attributes of Five Illustrative Projects

Project	Total Net Benefits Excluding Time Savings ($TNB_{excl.\,t}$)	Travel Time Savings (Δt)
A	200	10
B	155	30
C	120	35
D	50	40
E	20	42

To illustrate this process, suppose that five project alternatives are to be compared with respect to their total net benefit. Unfortunately, the analyst is uncertain about the value to place upon travel time savings, although the value is expected to lie somewhere between $5 and $8 per hour. Project attributes are summarized in Table 10-3, and total net benefits for any assumed value of time may be calculated as

$$TNB = TNB_{excl.\,t} + v_t[\Delta t] \tag{10-5}$$

where TNB are total net benefits, $TNB_{excl.\,t}$ are total net benefits excluding the value of travel time savings, v_t is the assumed unit value of travel time savings, and Δt is the amount of travel time savings (in hours). Total net benefits for values of travel time between $5 and $8 are shown in Table 10-4. Note that project B is preferable if the value of travel time is less than $7, while project C is preferable for values of travel time higher than $7. Projects B and C are equally preferable for a time value of $7.

This process of sensitivity analysis will not generally result in identifying a single best project. In the case illustrated in Table 10-4, the analyst or decision maker must still determine if the actual value of time lies in the range for which project B is preferable or lies in the range for which

TABLE 10-4.   Analysis of the Sensitivity of Total Net Benefit to the Value of Travel Time Savings for Five Projects

Project	Value of Time v_t ($/hour)			
	5	6	7	8
A	250	26	270	280
B	305[a]	335[a]	365[a]	395
C	295	330	365[a]	400[a]
D	250	290	330	370
E	230	272	314	356

[a] The most desirable project(s) at each value of travel time savings.

project C is desirable. More careful empirical tests—such as those discussed in Chapter 3—may be required to limit the possible range in which the value of time actually occurs. However, this preliminary analysis has revealed that projects A, D, and E may be removed from further consideration. In some cases it may also arise that one project is found to be superior throughout the expected range of variation of the attribute value; in this case the most preferable project alternative has been identified.

This type of sensitivity analysis need not be restricted to a range of values for attributes, of course. A similar sensitivity analysis may be conducted for virtually any parameter or measure of project attributes. For example, the total net benefits of projects might be calculated for various discount or interest rates and the results summarized in a table similar to Table 10-4. This type of sensitivity analysis may be particularly valuable for investigating different assumptions about input parameters such as the increase in travel volume over time (due to changes in the underlying socioeconomic situation) or the change in operating costs over time.

Analysis of different outcomes has been discussed in Chapter 9. In that discussion we assumed that the probability or chance that different outcome states (corresponding to different assumptions about input parameters or attribute values) might occur could be estimated either subjectively with historical data or through experiments. Without some estimate of occurrence probabilities, analysis can proceed no further than the construction of a summary sensitivity table (such as Table 10-4) and the determination of the project alternative which is preferable over any given range of input parameters. At this point the decision maker or analyst must assume the task of selecting a project (or selecting the do-nothing alternative) given the various possible outcomes.

A sensitivity analysis may also be performed to obtain some appreciation of the risk impact associated with different projects. Numerous measures of risk have been proposed and used in different applications. The exact nature of the measure which is used should pertain to the costs associated with different outcomes. For example, in some transportation services, deficit operation by service providers may impose severe costs and/or result in service discontinuation. In such cases the range of outcomes for which deficits occur should be the focus in evaluating the risk of different projects. In other situations the variability in the total net benefits might be appropriate, indicated by the variance of total net benefits. Each of these measures indicates the relative cost due to project attribute variability. Clearly, the first step in constructing a measure of risk is the determination of project impacts in different situations by means of a sensitivity analysis.

As a final note, some transportation studies report a somewhat different type of project sensitivity information. In the discussion above we attempted to compare the project attributes for various combinations of input parameter assumptions. It is also possible to calculate the rate of change in project attributes due to changes in particular input parameters. This may be done by using algebra or calculus, as

$$S_{zy} = z(y_{0+1}) - z(y_0) \qquad\qquad (10\text{-}6a)$$

$$\cong \frac{\partial z}{\partial y} \text{ evaluated at } y = y_0 \qquad\qquad (10\text{-}6b)$$

where S_{zy} is the rate of change of attribute z with respect to input parameter y and $\partial z/\partial y$ at $y = y_0$ is the first derivative of z with respect to y, evaluated at $y = y_0$. Computerized linear programming packages will provide this sensitivity value automatically.

The interpretation of this sensitivity measure is that changing the value of input parameter y by a small amount will result in a change in project attribute z of approximately S_{zy}. One must be careful, however, in that the value of S_{zy} is likely to change for different values of y and other input parameters. Thus, for large changes in the input parameter y or for simultaneous changes in numerous input parameters, S_{zy} might not accurately reflect the true impact of a particular project. Since the input parameters to the analysis procedures represent forecasts which may have substantial errors, an analyst must use the sensitivity measure, S_{zy}, with caution.

10-4 THE INFLUENCE OF CONSTRAINTS ON ATTRIBUTES

In many situations project alternatives may be unacceptable if they have an attribute which is valued less than some desired amount. These desired attribute values represent constraints on the range of feasible project alternatives, thereby restricting the range of the noninferior project frontier. The most common constraints of this type have already been discussed at some length, pertaining to total net benefits and provider profitability.

A common (and recommended) project requirement is that the total net benefits be positive: if no project alternative has positive total net benefits, then all projects should be rejected. Similarly, in the private sector of the economy, no project would be accepted if it would result in deficits; thus, projects are rejected if they have a negative present value after netting out revenues and private costs.

Other project constraints may arise from regulatory requirements or legislative mandates. For example, specifications for the interstate highway system were constrained by the requirement that the system must be useful for national defense purposes, and the vertical clearances must be sufficient to permit defense vehicles to pass. Other requirements exist with respect to safety, environmental degradation, and other factors.

These constraints on project alternatives are important in many situations. First, they must be explicitly considered in determining the range of possible projects. Second, they are useful in focusing attention on projects which are feasible, thereby restricting analytic efforts to a smaller range of possible projects.

10-5   PROJECT SELECTION WITH PREFERENCE SCALING OR WEIGHTING METHODS

In the previous sections we outlined the process of summarizing project attributes, eliminating inferior alternatives, and conducting sensitivity analyses. After all these calculations, it is likely that more than one project is still viable, in the sense that the noninferior project set will have more than one feasible alternative. Since some selection among these project alternatives must be made, an analyst or decision maker is still faced with the difficult problem of trading-off or balancing competing objectives and alternatives, albeit with a smaller number of alternatives than were originally considered due to the elimination of inferior projects.

Figure 10-3 illustrates the problem of project selection. In this figure three viable alternatives appear and only one can be selected. By selecting any one project, the decision maker must trade-off benefits with respect to different attributes. For example, by selecting project B rather than A in

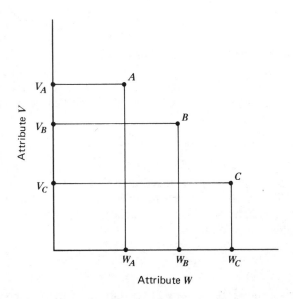

Figure 10-3.   Attributes of three project alternatives.

Figure 10-3, the decision maker is foregoing $V_A - V_B$ units of attribute V but obtaining $W_B - W_A$ units of attribute W. Similarly, selecting project B rather than project C results in an increase in attribute V of $V_B - V_C$ but a loss of attribute W of $W_C - W_B$. Thus, in choosing any particular project, the decision maker is trading-off gains and losses with respect to the various project attributes and objectives.

The process of project selection may be formalized and made explicit if weights or preferences among the various objectives and attributes are defined. For example, it may be that the decision maker would be willing to sacrifice a unit of attribute V in Figure 10-3 as long as such sacrifice would result in at least a two-unit increase in attribute W. In this case the trade-off between the two attributes would be 2 to 1. This preference may be illustrated graphically, as in Figure 10-4. The decision maker would be indifferent between each of the points along the preference lines in the figure since each point represents a trade-off of two units of attribute W for one unit of attribute V (or fractions thereof). Although the decision maker would be indifferent between points along each preference line, he would like to move outward, that is, move from line to line in Figure 10-4 as far to the northeast as possible. In the case illustrated the farthest project alternative is project B. Note that project A would be rejected since more than twice as much of attribute W would be obtained for the foregone amount of attribute V or, mathematically,

$$2V_A + W_A < 2V_B + W_B \qquad (10\text{-}7)$$

Similarly, project B is preferable to project C since

$$2V_c + W_c < 2V_B + W_B \qquad (10\text{-}8)$$

With more than three objectives or attributes, a graphical analysis is not possible. However, project selection may be done algebraically by identifying the project which maximizes the sum of the various attributes weighted by their respective preference. Mathematically, this is

$$\max A = \alpha_1 z_1 + \alpha_2 z_2 + \cdots + \alpha_n z_n = \sum_{i=1}^{n} \alpha_i z_i \qquad (10\text{-}9)$$

where α_i is the weight or preference given to attribute z_i. For the case illustrated in Figure 10-4 we can arbitrarily give attribute W a weight of one, so that the weight or preference for attribute V is equal to two, and the project selection problem is

$$\max A = W + 2V \qquad (10\text{-}10)$$

Note that this procedure is similar to that used in sensitivity analysis, although in this case the preference scale or weight in decision making is used to value each attribute, rather than an assumed attribute value such as the value of time.

By explicitly defining the trade-off or weight to be assigned to each attribute or objective, it is possible to explicitly determine the most preferable project alternative, using Equation (10-9). Unfortunately, the determination of the proper weight to assign to particular attributes or objectives is arbitrary. The weight given to different objectives is likely to be a political problem, in the sense that observers with different viewpoints or convictions would be likely to have quite different preferences among objectives. For example, a local government official is likely to value net benefits to the *locality* far more than a decision maker who is primarily concerned with the total net benefits of projects to the *nation* as a whole.

Three general approaches to obtaining appropriate weights for project selection have been used. First, explicit weights may be mandated or obtained by questioning decision makers. However, legislators and decision makers are quite reluctant to indicate preferences in the absence of project alternatives or some required decision point.

A second approach involves iterative questioning of decision makers, often called the Delphi method. An initial set of preferences is obtained from decision makers, and a sensitivity analysis is used to indicate the best project as well as the incremental changes in attribute values which are possible. The best project as well as the feasible changes are then reported to decision makers, who may then indicate changes in their preferences. The primary goals of this approach are to inform decision

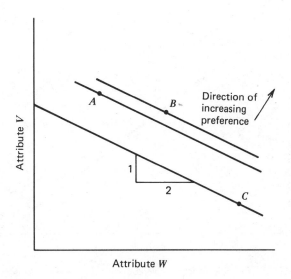

Figure 10-4.   Linear preference indifference curves with three alternatives.

makers about the consequences of their expressed preferences as well as to aid in developing a consensus within a group of decision makers who might have quite different preferences.

A third approach to the determination of preferences is to observe past choices. For example, suppose that a decision maker had chosen project B, given the choice of projects A, B, C, or D in Figure 10-5. In this case we can conclude that the decision maker's preference between attributes V and W is such that B is preferable to A and B is preferable to C. As a result, the decision maker's trade-off between the two attributes lies somewhere between the slopes of the two possible preference indifference lines which are indicated in Figure 10-5; otherwise a different alternative would have been selected. This implies that a unit of attribute V is valued at somewhere between 1.35 and 2 units of attribute W. With a large number of past selections to consider, it is possible to obtain a fairly good estimate of the decision maker's preferences as revealed by actual selections.

This third approach to preference estimation has been applied to determine the weight given to different project attributes in highway location and the weight given to income redistribution. It is an approach which must be used cautiously, however. It may be that the decision maker's preferences are changing over time, so that past decisions do not indicate the actual preferences at present. Second, the decision maker may be considering additional attributes which have not been analyzed, such as political consequences; in such cases, inferences from past decisions would be erroneous. Third, the trade-off between attributes might be nonlinear,

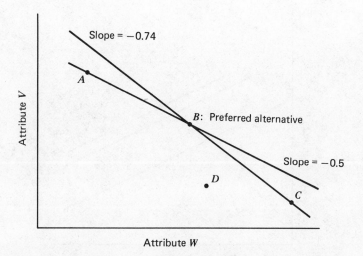

Figure 10-5.   Possible preference weights with the selection of a project B.

so that the preference between two objectives might depend upon the relative magnitude of the two attributes. Once again, a simple inference about preferences as in Figure 10-5 would be erroneous.

10-6 SUMMARY

In this chapter we have discussed a general approach to project selection under conditions of multiple-objective and multiple-project attributes for which dollar valuation is unavailable. It is expected that this type of analysis would more likely be the rule than the exception in analyzing public projects. For private projects it also is the case that attributes of financial profitability and riskiness would be worthy of analysis in a multiobjective framework. Common objectives which might be expressed for transportation projects include total net benefit, net benefit to localities or particular groups, financial profitability, and others. Common attributes for which valuation in dollars may be difficult include lives saved, the extent of progressive income redistribution, pollutant emission reduction, travel time savings (in some circumstances), project risk, and others.

Unfortunately, there is no straightforward procedure available to choose a single best project alternative unless responsible officials are willing to specify in detail their preferences among competing attributes. An analyst must typically resort to a report which summarizes the attributes of several viable alternatives and may make recommendations conditioned upon some assumptions about attribute valuation and trade-offs among competing objectives. Final project selection may be left to responsible officials.

Two general types of techniques have been outlined here for the process of multidimensional analysis. The first concerns the identification of projects which are worthy of further consideration. Undesirable projects may be eliminated in three ways: as inferior to some other alternative, as inferior within the expected range of attribute values or outcome possibilities, or as a violation of particular constraints which are imposed upon the final project selection. Techniques for eliminating alternatives on these grounds were presented in Sections 10-3, 10-4, and 10-5.

While the elimination of undesirable alternatives may seem like a roundabout method of approaching the problem of project selection, it serves to focus attention on a limited number of projects and may result in a single best alternative. The imposition of a requirement that the total net benefit of projects be positive is particularly useful in this regard, as well as providing a prudent test of economic responsibility in transportation investment planning.

The second technique for conducting multiattribute and multiobjective analysis is with the explicit incorporation of preferences or weights among the competing attributes and objectives. If decision makers mandate or indicate the appropriate weights to apply, then a single best project alternative may be determined using the process outlined in Section 10-6. Unfortunately, responsible officials are rarely amenable to quantifying their preferences in this manner.

In general, then, the result of a multidimensional analysis is likely to be a set of viable project alternatives among which responsible officials must select. The attributes of these impacts may be summarized in tabular form and, in most cases, it is desirable to indicate the variation in these attribute measures as assumptions concerning input parameters are altered by means of a sensitivity analysis.

CHAPTER 11

THE ESTIMATION AND ACCURACY OF DEMAND FUNCTIONS

Demand functions are required to forecast the usage of transportation facilities and to calculate the user benefits associated with travel. As discussed previously, a demand function relates the amount of tripmaking between two points to socioeconomic conditions and the price of travel. In any particular study an analyst must determine which socioeconomic factors are important, how to measure and value the relevant components of user cost, and what functional relationship exists between the various factors influencing the demand. In addition, some means of estimating the constant parameters associated with the demand function must be found.

While the development and use of travel demand functions is a formidable task, a great deal of effort has been expended on these problems, albeit with mixed results. The literature resulting from these studies and experiments is correspondingly large. In this chapter we shall discuss the general approaches which have been used to estimate demand functions and to develop predictions. We shall focus upon the assumptions and use of these methods, particularly with respect to the accuracy of volume forecasts. Readers who must develop and estimate demand functions on their own should probe deeper into the literature.[1]

At the outset of our discussion of demand function estimation, we should note that alternatives to estimation exist and may be preferable in many instances. Observation and experimentation may be fruitful approaches to obtain the information required for price setting or evaluation of investments. For example, it may be easier and cheaper to experiment with different prices on a toll facility than to estimate a full set of

---

[1]See, for example, P. Stopher and A. Meyburg, *Urban Transportation Modeling and Planning*, Lexington Books, Lexington, MA, 1975, and A. Kanafani, *Transportation Demand Analysis*, McGraw-Hill, New York, 1983, or the references to follow.

demand and price functions. Evaluation of results may be conducted as illustrated in Chapter 5. Similarly, experiments with novel transit services on a small scale may indicate the effects of widespread introduction of such services. Comparison of proposed facilities with experience on similar facilities in other areas may also be very useful and quite inexpensive.

However, an impetuous experimenter should be aware that straightforward empiricism has definite limitations. First, the results of particular experiments are likely to be specific to a certain location; in contrast to laboratory conditions, experiences in one location may not generalize to other situations. Second, the experiments may be expensive to perform, particularly since a sufficient period of time must be allowed during the experiment to permit individual travelers to adjust their behavior to the new travel conditions. Moreover, once such adjustments are made, it may be costly (and perhaps politically impossible) to discontinue experimental services. Finally, it is nearly always useful to analyze situations using the concepts of demand functions in conjunction with the knowledge of existing conditions and assumptions about the elasticity of demand. With relatively simple, "back-of-the-envelope" calculations, it can often be concluded that particular changes are undesirable prior to direct experimentation.

The most notable example of "back-of-the-envelope" or sketch planning analysis is to make use of measured elasticity values. These elasticities may be estimated for particular groups or components of trip price. With the use of a measured elasticity value, ϵ_x, the percentage volume change resulting from a percentage change in an attribute x is

$$\%\Delta q = 100\frac{\Delta q}{\overline{q}} = \epsilon_x 100\frac{\Delta x}{\overline{x}} \qquad (11\text{-}1)$$

where $\overline{q}$ and $\overline{x}$ are the average of before and after values. For example, with a transit fare elasticity of -0.3, a 10% increase in fare will result in about a $(-0.3)(10) = -3\%$ change in transit volume. Of course, this approach must be used cautiously since elasticity values are liable to be different over time or for different environments. Use of estimated demand functions may often be preferable. [Also, in equation (11-1), $100\Delta x/\overline{x}$ is equal to the percentage change in attribute x.]

Before discussing the process and accuracy of volume forecasting, we will first review the approaches used for demand function estimation. In Section 11-1 statistical estimation using aggregate data is discussed, while Section 11-2 considers the technique of choice model estimation using disaggregate data. Prediction with demand models is considered in Section 11-3, followed by a discussion of systematic effects which may occur and might not be captured in traditional demand models. Finally, Section 11-5 considers the accuracy which may be expected from volume forecasts.

11-1 STATISTICAL ESTIMATION WITH AGGREGATE DATA

In many instances the information available for travel demand analysis consists of aggregate observations of volumes and socioeconomic attributes for geographic areas (cities, census tracts, etc.), as well as information on travel cost (such as time, fare, etc.). Since the analyst is often interested in the total volume of travel between areas as well as the changes between them, it is natural to develop demand functions which are defined with respect to the attributes of these areas; this type of demand function uses data which are *aggregated* or characteristic of the area as a whole.

The type of data used generally falls into three categories: (1) socioeconomic attributes of the origin and the destination (population, employment, etc.), (2) travel impedance on the route or mode of interest (i.e., the components of user cost), and (3) travel impedance on alternative modes or routes. Each of these data types is then associated with a variable which appears in the demand function. For example, a typical demand function might be[2]

$$q_R = \eta w^\kappa f_R{}^\psi f_B{}^\theta f_A{}^\phi \tag{11-2}$$

where q_R is the annual number of railroad passengers carried between Boston and New York; w is real personal income per capita for the Boston and New York residents; f_R, f_B, and f_A are the one-way fares on rail, bus, and air, respectively; and η, κ, ψ, θ, and ϕ are constant parameters to be estimated. In this case f_R represents the travel impedance on the mode of interest, and f_B and f_A indicate the travel impedance on alternative modes.

Given a demand function such as Equation (11-2) and observations for the various variables for a period of years [q_R, w, f_R, f_B, and f_A in Eq. (11-2)], it is possible to estimate the values of the constant parameters (η, κ, ψ, θ, and ϕ) by the use of ordinary least-squares regression or other econometric techniques. Standard computational programs to calculate these estimates are available on virtually all computers and programmable hand calculators. Importantly, the values for the constant parameters which these programs determine are only estimates of the actual values of constant parameters. With only a small number of observations [i.e., only a few observations of w, f_R, f_B, and f_A for Eq. (11-2)] or weak relationships between the volume and a particular variable, these parameter estimates

---

[2]This functional form was used by F. Fisher and appears in "The Survival of the Passenger Train: The Demand for Railroad Passenger Transportation Between Boston and New York" in R. deNeufville and D. Marks, *Systems Planning and Design: Case Studies in Modeling, Optimization and Evaluation*, Prentice-Hall, Englewood Cliffs, NJ, 1974.

may have a substantial amount of uncertainty associated with them. Fortunately, standard statistical tests are available to indicate the degree of such uncertainty, *ceteris paribus*. These tests are discussed briefly below and in Appendix III.

Two types of observations are commonly used in the estimation of values for the constant parameters [η, κ, ψ, θ, and ϕ in Eq. (11-2)]. The first consists of observations of each variable during various time periods, such as annual data for a period of many years; these data are referred to as *time series observations*. Alternatively, a series of observations on travel impedances, volume, and socioeconomic attributes may be gathered for a number of origin–destination locations at the same time; these observations are called *cross-sectional data*. Either type of data may be used, although the different types imply different statistical problems for calculation of appropriate parameter estimates. For estimation, the analyst must assume that the demand function [such as Eq. (11-2)] is either stable over time or stable between different origin–destination locations (i.e., stable over *space*) depending upon the type of data available for estimation.

Unfortunately, it is difficult to provide firm guidelines concerning the number of variables to include and the proper form of the demand function itself. Those variables should be included which an analyst believes have important influences on travel demand and which can be measured. Generally speaking, demand functions must reflect many of the *a priori* assumptions of the analyst concerning an appropriate functional form and variables. As a result, the initial conceptualization of the problem of representing the demand function is likely to be one of the most important features in the estimation effort. In addition to the *a priori* hypotheses and assumptions of the analyst, the other determining factor of the form of demand functions is that of data availability; in most demand studies the available data are not as accurate or complete as the analyst would like.

In the case of the demand function in Equation (11-2), a modeler might conclude that additional socioeconomic and cost factors might be important in explaining tripmaking by rail. For example, changes in the population and auto availability in the two cities are likely to be important determinants of travel by train. As additional explanatory factors are included, more of the variability in travel volumes is likely to be explained. However, additional variables may lead to statistical problems in estimation and to greater inaccuracy in making forecasts of volume.

Once estimates of the various constant parameters for a demand function are developed, it is possible to calculate estimates of the volume of travel given a set of values for the explanatory variables [i.e., w, f_R, f_B, and f_A in Eq. (11-2)] as well as the implied elasticity of demand. These estimates are made by substituting the values of the socioeconomic and impedance variables into Equation (11-2) and then calculating the resulting value of q_R. In most cases, however, the user cost of travel depends upon the volume of travel, so that an equilibrium solution must be determined as described in Chapter 2. For example, parameter estimates for the model in Equation (11-2) might be

$$q_R = 25w^{1.02} f_R^{-0.3} f_B^{0.4} f_A^{0.1} \tag{11-3}$$

With $w = 8$ (in thousands of dollars), $f_R = 20$, $f_B = 22$, and $f_A = 30$, the estimated value of volume is $q_R = 25(8)^{1.02} (20)^{-0.3} (22)^{0.4} (30)^{0.1} = 411$.

Elasticity of demand with respect to the various socioeconomic and impedance attributes may be calculated as

$$\epsilon_x = \frac{\partial q}{\partial x} \frac{x}{q} \tag{11-4}$$

where x is any attribute of interest. As noted in Chapter 2, the multiplicative functional form assumed in Equation (11-2) has the characteristic that the elasticity of demand is constant throughout the entire range of volume, so a different elasticity need not be calculated for each combination of socioeconomic and impedance variables. Thus, for Equation (11-2), the elasticity of rail volume with respect to rail fare is

$$\epsilon_{f_R} = \frac{\partial q}{\partial f_R} \frac{f_R}{q} = \psi \tag{11-5}$$

which is −0.3 in Equation (11-3).

Even without detailed knowledge of the various statistical tests which are available, a user of models [such as Eq. (11-3)] can perform some simple analytical tests. First, the influence of various variables can be derived from *a priori* knowledge of demand functions; the discussion in Chapter 2 concerning travel impedance and socioeconomic influences on travel demand is relevant in this regard. For example, all other factors being constant, an increase in the price or fare charged for a facility or service is expected to decrease the usage of that service. For Equation (11-2) this observation implies that the parameter associated with the rail fare (or ψ) should be negative, so that increases in the rail fare, f_R, result in *decreases* in the volume of rail patronage, q_R. Coefficient signs which are not consistent with *a priori* assumptions of this type are worthy of close examination.

One statistic reported with nearly all estimation results is the estimated coefficient of multiple determination, r^2. (Occasionally, the square root of this value is reported as the estimated "multiple correlation coefficient," r.) This statistic represents the proportion of variability in the dependent variable (usually volume of trips) which is explained by the socioeconomic and cost variables [such as w, f_R, f_A, and f_B in Eq. (11-2)].

Values of r^2 close to one imply that the relationship between the dependent variable [usually volume of trips, as in Eq. (11-2)] and the explanatory variables [the socioeconomic and impedance variables in Eq. (11-2)] is fairly strong.

A third aspect of a demand model such as Equation (11-2) which might be checked is the degree of uncertainty associated with the estimates of the constant parameters. An indiction of this uncertainty is the t statistic associated with each parameter. A model such as Equation (11-2) is typically reported with t statistics appearing under each estimated parameter in parentheses, such as

$$q = 25 \quad w^{1.02} \quad f_R^{-0.3} \quad f_B^{0.4} \quad f_A^{0.1} \qquad r^2 = 0.38$$
$$\quad (2.4)\ (0.3)\ (-1.8)\ (0.2)\ (0.5) \qquad \text{No. of observations} = 12 \tag{11-6}$$

where, for instance, 2.4 is the t statistic associated with the estimate of the parameter $\eta = 25$, -1.8 is the t statistic associated with the estimate of the parameter $\psi = -0.3$, and so forth. These t statistics are of considerable value in assessing the statistical significance of the parameter estimates and in reaching judgments about the validity of the demand model. In general, the higher the t statistic, in absolute value, the more certain is the parameter estimate. Absolute values of t statistics higher than two generally imply that there is a probability of less than 5% that the parameter estimate is different from zero due to chance rather than in actuality. While a full-scale treatment of the subject is beyond the scope of this book, a brief overview appears in Appendix III.

11-2 FORMULATION AND ESTIMATION OF DISAGGREGATE CHOICE MODELS

In the past two decades demand models based upon individual travel choices and estimated with disaggregate data have been developed and extensively applied. Disaggregate data consist of observations of travel alternatives available to individual travelers and their choices. For example, a mode split model might use observations of a particular traveler's available travel modes, his socioeconomic situation, the impedance on the various travel modes, and the mode which the traveler actually chose.

Choice models are based upon an explicit framework which is assumed for traveler's decision making. First, the choices available to a traveler must be defined as a set of mutually exclusive, collectively exhaustive alternatives. A traveler is assumed to choose one and only one of the set of available alternatives. Second, an explicit functional form is assumed which indicates the manner in which various factors (travel impedance, socioeconomic characteristics, etc.) influence the desirability of an alternative. The functional forms used for disaggregate choice models may be similar to those used for aggregate models, although their interpretation and the estimation of parameters is somewhat different. Third, disaggregate choice models generally assume that there is some randomness associated with the desirability of various alternatives, so that the models attempt to determine the chance or probability that a particular alternative is chosen, rather than the single most likely choice. As a result, the output of a choice model is a series of probabilities or chances that particular individuals will select one or another alternative. These choice probabilities must then be aggregated or summed to determine the expected number of trips (i.e., the number of individuals who choose any particular alternative).

To illustrate the use of choice models, suppose that an analyst wished to model the choice between taking a high-speed toll facility or a toll-free but slower highway between a particular origin A and a destination B. In this situation two alternatives are available to travelers, corresponding to the two roadway routes. Among the factors which might influence the decision to take one route or the other the most important are the amount of toll, travel times on the routes, the automobile occupancy, and the income of the traveler. A functional form for the model which might be used in this situation is

$$\Pr_k\{\text{toll route}\} = \tau + v(t_{\text{toll}} - t_{\text{free}}) + \frac{\xi f_{\text{toll}}}{(n_k w_k)} \qquad (11\text{-}7)$$

where $\Pr_k\{\text{toll route}\}$ is the probability of the kth traveler choosing the toll route; t_{toll} and t_{free} are the travel times on the toll road and the freeway; w_k is the traveler's income; f_{toll} is the charge on the toll road; n_k is the number of individuals in the traveler's auto (who, it is assumed, split the toll); and τ, v, and ξ are constant parameters. (*A priori*, we would expect τ to be positive and both v and ξ to be negative.)

The functional form used in Equation (11-7) is a linear probability model, which is distinguished by having the probability of choosing a particular alternative as a linear function of a number of factors. A more complicated form for a choice model is the logit function in which the probability of the kth traveler choosing the ith of n alternatives is

$$\Pr_k\{\text{alternative } i\} = \frac{\exp(V_i)}{\sum\limits_{j=1}^{n} \exp(V_j)} \qquad (11\text{-}8)$$

where V_i is a function indicating the desirability of particular alternatives (and is often called the "utility" of alternative i), exp is the exponential function (as described in Appendix I), and n is the number of alternatives available. For the case of the roadway choice problem described above, a possible logit model formulation might be

$$\mathrm{Pr}_k\{\text{toll road}\} = \frac{\exp(V_{\text{toll}})}{\exp(V_{\text{toll}}) + \exp(V_{\text{free}})} \tag{11-9a}$$

$$= 1/[1 + \exp(V_{\text{free}} - V_{\text{toll}})] \tag{11-9b}$$

where

$$V_{\text{toll}} = \tau + v t_{\text{toll}} + \frac{\xi f_{\text{toll}}}{n_k w_k}$$

and

$$V_{\text{free}} = v t_{\text{free}}$$

which means that three parameters (τ, v, and ξ) must be estimated.

While more complicated than the linear probability model, the logit model has several statistical and conceptual advantages.[3] Most importantly, the linear probability model does not necessarily restrict forecast probabilities to lie between zero and one, as they must by the definition of a probability. The logit model does result in this restriction, in addition to possessing an often observed S-shaped form (Figure 11-1).

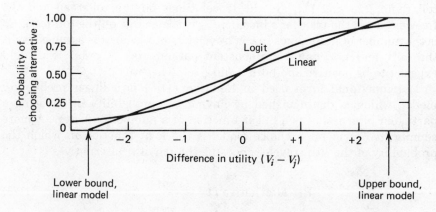

Figure 11-1.   Illustration of linear and logit discrete binary choice models.

[3]For a review, see D. Hensher and L. Johnson, *Applied Discrete-Choice Modelling*, Wiley, New York, 1981. A good introduction to binary choice models appears in S. Warner, *Binary Choice of Mode in Urban Travel*, Northwestern University Press, Chicago, 1962.

One other restriction imposed by the usual logit model may be less desirable. This is the assumption of independence of irrelevant alternatives (often abbreviated as IIA) which, in effect, assumes that random effects for different alternatives are independent. When some alternatives are similar in nature (as, e.g., carpooling and vanpooling), predictions of demand changes due to new policies may be somewhat inaccurate from the logit model without explicitly accounting for such similarities by including appropriate variables in the utility function or by using a hierarchy of choice models. For example, separate models can be estimated for the choice of mode among shared ride, transit, or drive-alone auto in urban areas, and then a choice model of shared ride modes among carpooling and vanpooling can be estimated.[4]

Other discrete choice model forms are also available for use, although they are more complicated. For example, a probit model permits a more general formulation of the random effects in the desirability of choices, but does not permit representation in a closed-form expression such as Equation (11-9).[5]

A choice model such as Equations (11-7) or (11-8) does not directly indicate the *volume* of travel on a particular alternative (such as the toll road or freeway). However, it is possible to arrive at an estimate of the overall modal split by summing or aggregating the probability of choosing a particular alternative over the entire population. For example, the number of individuals who will take the toll road can be calculated as

$$q_{\text{toll road}} = \sum_{k=1}^{N} \Pr_k\{\text{toll road}\} \qquad (11\text{-}10)$$

where N is the total number of potential travelers.

The aggregate price elasticity of travel on the toll road may be found by determining the volume of travel before and after a change, such as a toll increase, and by applying the formula for elasticity [Eq. (11-4)]. For an individual, the direct elasticity of demand for alternative i can be calculated from a logit model as[6]

$$\epsilon_{k,f}^{i} = \frac{\partial \Pr_k\{i\}}{\partial f} \frac{f}{\Pr_k\{i\}} = \xi_f f (1 - \Pr_k\{i\}) \qquad (11\text{-}11)$$

---

[4]See Hensher and Johnson, op. cit., for a discussion and examples of hierarchical models, related statistical issues, and the problem posed by the independence of irrelevant alternatives (IIA) property of the logit model.

[5]The logit model assumes independent and identically distributed random terms with a Weibull distribution. The probit model assumes a general multidimensional normal distribution for random terms. For an advanced and comprehensive review of probit models, see C. Daganzo, *Multinomial Probit*, Academic Press, New York, 1979.

[6]See Hensher and Johnson, op. cit., or Warner, op. cit.

where ξ_f is the constant factor for fare [which is $\xi/(n_k w_k)$ for the toll road model in Equation (11-7)].

Discrete choice models may also be used to indicate the relative weights which individuals place on different travel characteristics. For example, the model of Equation (11-9) suggests the desirability of the toll road might be represented as

$$V_{\text{toll}} = \tau + v t_{\text{toll}} + \frac{\xi f_{\text{toll}}}{n_k w_k} \tag{11-12}$$

This suggests that there is some *decrease* in the toll (f_{toll}) which would exactly compensate for a unit increase in travel time (t_{toll}) so that the desirability or utility of the toll road is unchanged. This decrease in fare (Δf_{toll}) could be calculated as

$$0 = v(1) + \frac{\xi(\Delta f_{\text{toll}})}{n_k w_k}$$

or

$$\Delta f_{\text{toll}} = \frac{-n_k w_k v}{\xi} \tag{11-13}$$

which depends upon the number of occupants in the car (n_k), the household income (w_k), and the two parameters v and ξ.

This method of examining the relative weights of different travel characteristics can be used to impute the value which individuals place on travel time or other characteristics. For example, Δf_{toll} represents the amount that tolls would have to decrease to compensate a traveler for a unit increase in travel time. From this manner of examining trade-offs, values of travel time are derived, as described in the next chapter.

As a numerical example, consider the choice of travel to work by transit or by automobile for an individual. For this choice an appropriate logit mode choice model might be[7]

$$\text{Pr\{transit\}} = \frac{1}{1 + \exp(V_A - V_T)} \tag{11-14}$$

---

[7]This model was used in G. Kocur and C. Hendrickson, "Design of Local Bus Service with Demand Equilibrium," *Trans. Sci.* May, 1982. Parameters are from 1978 and thus should be adjusted for inflation by converting fares from 1978 dollars in other applications.

using the model form of Equation (11-9b), with the value of the relative transit desirability ($V_T - V_A$) equal to

$$V_T - V_A = 0.38 - 0.0081 OVTT_T - 0.0033 IVTT_T$$
$$- 0.0014f + 0.0328 IVTT_A \qquad (11\text{-}15)$$

where $OVTT_T$ is out-of-vehicle transit wait and walk time (minutes), $IVTT_T$ is in-vehicle travel time on transit (minutes), f is transit fare (cents), and $IVTT_A$ is in-vehicle time on auto (minutes). With these coefficients, the value of in-vehicle transit time is $0.0033/0.0014 = 2.36$ cents/minute or \$1.41 per hour in 1978 dollars. The corresponding value of waiting time is \$3.47 per hour in 1978. With wait and walk time for transit or $OVTT_T = 10$ minutes, transit riding time or $IVTT_T = 30$ minutes, fare $f = 75$ cents, and auto riding time or $IVTT_A = 20$ minutes, the relative utility of transit choice is calculated as

$$V_T - V_A = 0.38 - 0.0081(10) - 0.0033(30) - 0.0014(75) + 0.0328(20)$$
$$= 0.75 \qquad (11\text{-}16)$$

and the probability of taking transit is

$$\Pr\{\text{transit}\} = \frac{1}{1 + \exp(-0.75)} = 0.68 \qquad (11\text{-}17)$$

so that there is a 68% chance that this individual would take transit under these conditions. Using Equation (11-11), the fare elasticity of demand is

$$\epsilon_f = (-0.0014)(75)(1 - 0.68) = -0.03 \qquad (11\text{-}18)$$

suggesting that this individual would be quite price *inelastic*.

The logit choice model also offers the possibility of directly estimating the change in net benefits to a traveler due to some environmental or policy change. This change in net benefits is calculated as[8]

$$\Delta NB = \ln\left[\sum_{j=1}^{n} \exp(V_j^{\text{new}})\right] - \ln\left[\sum_{j=1}^{n} \exp(V_j^{\text{old}})\right] \qquad (11\text{-}19)$$

in which V_j^{new} is the value of V_j after some change, V_j^{old} is the original value of V_j, ln is the natural logarithm function (described in Appendix I), and n is the total number of alternatives available. This expression

---

[8]For a derivation and discussion, see H. C. W. L. Williams, "On the Formation of Travel Demand Models and Economic Evaluation Measures of User Benefit," *Environment and Planning A* **9**(3), 285–344 (1977).

[Eq. (11-19)] simply represents a shortcut arithmetic way to evaluate the change in total benefits described in Chapter 4.

As in aggregate demand models, choice models require the use of regression or other statistical estimation techniques to obtain appropriate values for the parameters of the model [such as τ, ν, and ξ in Eq. (11-9)]. For logit models the technique of "maximum likelihood" estimation is commonly used; computer software programs are available to perform such estimations. As in the case of aggregate demand models, parameter estimates are subject to considerable uncertainty, and most computer estimation programs report t statistics which may be used in the same manner as those described in Section 11-1.[9]

In addition to statistical tests on individual parameter estimates, users of choice models should also submit the models to a scrutiny for reasonable results. For example, an analyst should expect that toll increases would reduce the volume of travel on a toll facility. In the choice model volume reductions result from reductions in the probability that the toll road alternative is chosen. Consequently, we expect that as the toll increases in Equation (11-9), then Pr{toll road} should decrease, implying that the parameter ξ should be negative. Model estimation which results in positive values of ξ for Equation (11-9) should be subjected to close examination, if not constrained to a nonpositive value for ξ.

Since choice models generally require more complicated functional forms and involve an additional step to aggregate the individual choice probabilities to obtain volumes, readers might well wonder what advantages these models offer. First, to estimate parameters for choice models using disaggregate data (which may be obtained from surveys), it is more efficient in a statistical sense to estimate a disaggregate choice model first and then find volumes, rather than to aggregate the data and then estimate an aggregate demand function. Second, it is hoped that choice models estimated with disaggregate data may be transferred over time or between areas without extensive reestimation of parameters.

11-3 PREDICTION WITH DEMAND MODELS

While the knowledge developed about travel demand and human behavior is one of the major benefits of using demand models, predictions of future volumes is the most common purpose for formulating and estimating demand models. Forecasts of volumes may be developed to investigate new

---

[9]A note of caution in this regard is in order, however. Statistical packages for estimation of discrete choice models usually rely on "maximum likelihood estimation" (MLE) procedures. With MLE, reported t statistics are only correct with a large number of observations used for the estimation. (Technically, these are termed *asymptotic t statistics*.) If the number of observations is small (say, less than 50), the use of these t statistics may be misleading. (For a discussion of this point, see Daganzo, op. cit.)

managerial strategies such as fare changes or for major investment planning studies which require forecasts many years into the future. With the use of system performance and demand functions, the general procedure for forecasting travel volumes was outlined earlier.

This forecasting procedure consists of estimating the demand function which is expected at some target date, determining the system performance function based upon a particular investment and operating strategy, and then identifying the equilibrium volume and price of travel by observing the intersection of the demand and performance functions. The future demand function will generally depend upon the expected socioeconomic data in the future period, so estimates of these factors must be prepared prior to the travel volume forecast. For example, using the model Equation (11-3), a future demand function might be

$$q_y = 25(w_y)^{1.02} (f_{R,y})^{-0.3} (f_{B,y})^{0.4} (f_{A,y})^{0.1} \qquad (11\text{-}20)$$

where w_y is the expected per capita income in year y and the f variables represent the expected fares on rail, bus, and air, respectively, in year y.

For volume forecasts for the near future, it is possible and common to assume that relevant socioeconomic variables do not change or change by only a small amount; the price of travel is likely to change more rapidly due to managerial changes or new investments. For long-term forecasts, however, it is necessary to make estimates of future population totals, employment levels, incomes, and other factors appearing in the demand model. Techniques for developing these socioeconomic forecasts will not be discussed here, although these techniques are similar in many ways to the procedure for estimating travel volume itself. In most transportation studies forecasts of relevant socioeconomic variables are obtained by extrapolating past trends into the future or from large econometric models of the national or regional economy.

Importantly, there is a great deal of uncertainty associated with these estimates of future socioeconomic factors. This comment is especially true of the estimates for per capita income and other variables representing economic activity. Even if a demand model is a completely accurate representation of travel demand, some uncertainty will arise in forecasting solely due to the uncertainty associated with forecasts of socioeconomic variables which are input to the demand function.

Analysts should also be aware of the limitations and uncertainties which may arise from the demand model itself. The uncertainty associated with estimates of constant parameters in demand models has already been discussed. In addition, it is useful to recall that demand models are calibrated on existing observations of travel volumes and conditions. Forecasts for radically different conditions would be significant extrapolations from existing conditions. As with all extrapolations, there is substantial uncertainty associated with forecasts for extreme conditions. This is particularly true for demand models since the functional form of these models is often determined from *a priori* assumptions with only limited data available for calibration and validation. Unfortunately, it is precisely for prediction in extreme cases that demand models would be most useful.

11-4 SYSTEMATIC EFFECTS

The last few sections concentrated upon estimation and interpretation of individual demand functions. It is also prudent to consider systematic effects which may be important influences on travel volumes and equilibrium prices. These systematic effects include cross-relationships between facilities or over time, effects of auto availability, interactions between series of demand functions, and constraints on travel behavior which might not be adequately represented by a demand function.

The existence of cross-relationships between facilities and over time has been mentioned in numerous places throughout this text. Briefly, if the price of travel on a facility at a particular time changes, then travel may be diverted to or from other time periods or other facilities. As a result, there are cross-relationships between the price of travel on a particular facility at different times. It is usually impossible to completely specify all the cross-relationships which exist and may be important; analysts must concentrate on the most important.

One factor in demand modeling which deserves special attention with respect to systematic effects is the availability of automobiles. Auto availability has been found to be an important short run determinant of travel demand mode choice. Since only a limited number of automobiles are available within households, the allocation of these automobiles between household members may be an important influence on the types of travel which occur. For example, it has been found that incentives for workers to use public transit and share rides can induce shifts from the drive-alone commuting alternative. However, these shifts result in greater auto availability during the day for other household members, and their travel may increase as a result. Due to the shifting auto availability, the net impact of transit and shared ride incentives on total areawide travel is less than would be expected by just examining the change in commuting trips.[10]

A second point to note is that long run automobile purchases may be sensitive to changes in the price of travel. For example, an increase in travel cost may lead to lower automobile ownership which, in turn, further reduces the amount of travel. Automobiles purchased solely for commuting purposes might fall into this category; increased tolls or improved

---

[10]See M. Ben-Akiva and T. Atherton, "Methodology for Short Range Travel Demand Predictions: Analysis of Carpooling Incentives," *Jour. of Trans. Econ. and Policy* **9**(3), 224–261 (1977), or G. Kocur and C. Hendrickson, "A Model to Assess Cost and Fuel Savings from Ride Sharing," *Trans. Res.* **17B**, 305–318 (1983).

transit service may induce a switch to transit. While this type of change in automobile ownership may be small, it does have important implications for long-term changes in travel volumes on particular facilities.

Many individuals have argued that changes in land-use patterns as a result of transportation investments or pricing strategies are likely to be quite large. However, the observed statistical relationships are quite weak between patterns of land use and most changes in the transportation infrastructure, particularly after a roadway network has been established. Even the effects on land use due to major new rapid transit systems are questionable. Therefore, analysts should be wary of assuming such relationships.

Finally, users of travel demand models and volume forecasts should be aware that most modeling efforts involve a series of demand models. A classic example of model systems is the Urban Transportation Model System (UTMS) developed by the U.S. federal government. This model system involves a series of models including separate models for trip generation from an area, destination choice, route choice, and modal split between automobile and transit. These model systems can include a wider variety of factors and cross-relationships than single-equation demand functions [such as Eq. (11-2)]. However, relationships between particular models in the system may be inconsistent and result in significant inaccuracies. For example, the UTMS has been criticized because peaking factors, trip generation, and destination choice are not functions of travel price.

11-5 ACCURACY OF FORECASTS

In previous sections and chapters we described many of the difficulties associated with developing accurate forecasts of future travel volumes and user costs. Some of these problems were related to conceptual mistakes and misapplications of the principles for demand modeling. Other problems would arise even if the existing theory and techniques for demand modeling were properly used. A summary of these problems appears below, followed by a discussion of the accuracy to be expected from particular studies.

1. *Ignoring the Elasticity of Demand with Respect to Price.*   For analytical simplicity, many planning studies assume that travel volumes are constant no matter what changes are imposed on a system. While convenient, this assumption is usually incorrect and unjustifiable.

2. *Ignoring the Equilibration of Demand and Supply.*   Demand is defined as a function of socioeconomic factors and user cost. At the same time, however, the elements of user cost are dependent upon the volume of travel on a facility, as the performance or supply function associated with a particular facility implies. Interaction of these two functions should be analyzed in order to determine the equilibrium volume and user cost of

travel. Many studies of travel demand ignore the equilibrium aspect of this problem. Often demand is assumed to be independent of price or the user cost of travel is thought to be independent of travel volume. These assumptions simplify analysis and may be approximately correct, but they will generally result in inaccurate volume forecasts. Demand functions should be explicitly defined with respect to the variables to be included and the manner in which these variables influence the travel volume.

3. *Multiple Equilibria between Demand and Supply Functions*. For certain demand and facility performance functions, the possibility exists that more than one stable equilibrium solution may occur. In these cases an analyst might validly arrive at more than one forecast of equilibrium volume and user cost. If the functions are correct, either situation may exist in reality (or the equilibria may alternate). While the existence of multiple equilibria is unusual in travel demand studies, it cannot be ruled out on either theoretical or practical grounds. The net result is that forecasts in such situations are likely to be more uncertain.

4. *Uncertainty in Supply and Performance Functions*. While we have discussed the estimation of demand functions in this chapter, analysts should remember that forecasts of future travel volumes and costs depend upon the interaction of demand and performance functions. If these performance functions are incorrect or inaccurate, then the resulting volume forecasts will also be inaccurate. Unfortunately, it is difficult to be certain that the correct variables and functions have been used in particular cases. Generally, an analyst must rely on *a priori* assumptions consistent with theory and comparisons with existing conditions to assess the relevance of particular model forms.

5. *Inappropriate Data Used for Estimation*. Data used to calibrate the parameters of a demand function should consist of numerous observations of volumes, socioeconomic variables, and user costs for the same demand function. A set of observations of this type permit estimation of the parameters of the demand function and also offer an opportunity to check the accuracy of the function. In some cases, however, a set of observations may be used which arise from different demand functions on the same or similar facilities. In these situations the observations indicate the nature of the performance or supply function of the facility. This problem is known as the identification problem in the literature of econometrics and may be overcome by gathering appropriate data.

6. *Measurement Error*. Even with appropriate data, measurement errors in the observations of volume, socioeconomic conditions, and user costs which are used for calibrating a model may lead to errors in parameter estimates and to incorrect conclusions concerning the proper form of the demand model. While better data gathering procedures can substantially reduce this problem, it is always likely to be present in demand modeling efforts.

7. *The Uncertainty of Parameter Estimates*. Virtually all demand models employ constant parameters which must be calibrated. The techniques available for estimation of these parameters are statistical in

nature, so that the resulting values for the parameters are uncertain. In Appendix III we discuss statistical tests to use to indicate the extent of uncertainty associated with any particular parameter estimate. With additional observations of actual volumes and underlying conditions as well as strong relationships between explanatory factors and travel volumes, this uncertainty tends to be reduced. However, since the parameter estimates are always uncertain to some degree, the forecasts of travel volumes are also more uncertain.

8. *Extrapolation from Existing Conditions*. Demand modeling efforts are most helpful in providing forecasts for conditions which are dissimilar to existing conditions. Unfortunately, the only validation observations which are available for demand models pertain to existing conditions, so it is precisely for the case in which models are most useful that they are likely to be the most unreliable. Clearly, a correct and complete specification of the demand function would eliminate this problem. Unfortunately, existing theory and techniques are unable to ensure complete accuracy.

9. *Uncertainty in Future Socioeconomic Factors*. Demand models usually contain variables which indicate the socioeconomic conditions which influence travel demand. For forecasts of future volumes, it is necessary to first forecast future socioeconomic conditions and then to input these forecasts into demand models. There is some evidence that inaccurate socioeconomic estimates are among the largest sources of errors in travel volume forecasts for future years.[11] While improvements in econometric models may reduce this problem, it is clear that future socioeconomic conditions will always be uncertain due to unforeseen inventions, catastrophes, and so forth.

10. *Systematic Errors*. Clearly there are interrelationships between the volume of travel on different facilities and at different times of the day. There are also interactions between the user costs of travel, personal income, and automobile purchases. Accurately representing all these interrelationships in one function or in a series of functions is likely to be difficult, if not impossible, in most instances.

As a result of these difficulties, the forecasts of travel volumes and user costs which result from modeling efforts are likely to be quite uncertain. As deNeufville expressed the situation for forecasts of air travel:

> *Whether the errors in the forecasts for new facilities are predominantly technical or not the practical result is the same: massive uncertainty pervades our estimates of the future. Until the happy day when the [analysts] have demonstrated that their estimates are consistently accurate, neither the government nor the public should place faith in forecasts.*[12]

[11]See, for example, the review in W. Ascher, *Forecasting*, The Johns Hopkins Press, Baltimore, 1978, Chapter 3.

[12]R. deNeufville, *Airport Systems Planning*, The MIT Press, Cambridge, MA, 1976, p. 55.

Before the entire procedure of quantitative demand forecasting is discarded, however, a few points should be made. First, forecasts for changes in the near future are likely to be much more accurate than are forecasts for the distant future. Fortunately, the planning horizon for many pricing policies and investments are within a five-year (or shorter) horizon. It is only major construction projects such as new airports, highways, or rapid rail transit systems which require forecasts over an extended period of time.

Second, it is possible to obtain at least some idea of the range of outcomes which are possible due to major new investments. This range might be obtained by considering different scenarios for socioeconomic and investment changes which might occur as well as the uncertainty due to inaccurate functional specification and parameter estimates. Comparisons with other systems may also indicate the range of possible travel volume outcomes. For example, new transit systems are very unlikely to achieve passenger volumes per station which exceed those attained on existing systems which serve dense urban areas. This commonsense observation is in contrast to a number of planning studies and forecasting exercises.

CHAPTER 12

ESTIMATION OF COST
AND PRICE FUNCTIONS

Cost and price functions are two of the essential tools used in pricing and investment analysis. These two functions relate the total and user costs of travel to the volume of travel between two points. The definition and composition of these functions were discussed in Chapters 2 to 4. Here we shall consider the techniques used to estimate the magnitude of cost and price components as well as some of the practical problems which arise in the use and estimation of these functions, such as accounting for inflation.[1] We should emphasize that the discussion in this chapter is meant to be illustrative of the general approaches used for cost estimation. A full treatment of this topic would require a text longer than this one, even for specific modes or facility types. Thus, our intention is to provide a convenient introduction to the techniques and problems associated with the estimation and use of cost data.

In the next section in this chapter we summarize the three most common techniques for estimating construction, operating, and external costs, namely the methods of engineering unit costs, statistical estimation, and accounting cost allocations. One or a combination of these methods is generally used in the development of standardized cost models which are widely used for transportation systems. Of course, construction and facility operating costs are only two of the components of costs which must be considered by analysts; the user costs of travel also constitute a major category. These user costs of travel include vehicle operating costs, as well as those for travel time and effort. While estimation of vehicle operating costs does not require special techniques, forecasting and valuing the travel time and effort incurred by users does require special attention. In Section 12-2 we describe the methods commonly used to estimate travel times on facilities, while in the following section we consider the problems of valuing travel time in dollar amounts.

---

[1] For some additional empirical examples, see the references listed in Chapter 3.

In the final two sections we discuss some of the difficulties which are commonly encountered in using price and cost functions. The discussion in Section 12-4 centers on the problems associated with defining the unit of time and volume for such functions, and that in Section 12-5 focuses on the impact of inflation and other problems associated with forecasting costs in future periods.

12-1 COST-ESTIMATION TECHNIQUES

Virtually all cost estimation is performed with one or some combination of the techniques of engineering unit costs, statistical cost inference, or accounting cost allocation. These three techniques are the basis for all the standardized cost models used in transportation studies. As a supplement, engineering judgment may be applied as a rough means of estimating costs, but this judgment typically relies on experience with the basic three methods.

A fourth approach makes use of the microeconomic theory of production. Economists often define an initial relationship between the output of a process (such as vehicle-miles of service) and the necessary inputs of resources such as time, labor, capital, and so on. This functional relationship is termed a *production function*. By assuming a decision process in which the various inputs are combined to produce a given output, it is possible to derive a *cost* function from the underlying production function. As a parenthetical note, it is also possible to apply this approach to the development of appropriate demand functions by considering households or individuals as units of production. This is not a common method for transportation systems analysis, however.

12-1-1 ENGINEERING OR ACCOUNTING UNIT COSTS

In principle, the use of engineering unit cost estimation is straightforward, although the application of the method is laborious. The initial step in the method is to break down or disaggregate a process (such as construction, maintenance, or facility operation) into a series of smaller subtasks or components. Collectively, these subtasks or components are required to complete or continue the overall process of construction or facility operation. Once the various components are defined, a unit cost is assigned to each and then the total cost of the process is determined by summing the costs incurred in each subtask or component.

The level of detail in dividing the process into subtasks typically depends upon the stage at which the cost estimate is being prepared. During early planning stages less is known about the prospective design, so that the level of detail in defining subtasks is quite coarse. Cost estimators often refer to three distinct stages at which such divisions might be made and engineering cost estimates prepared:

1. Conceptual estimate in the planning stage (often termed *predesign estimate* or *approximate estimate*).

2. Preliminary estimate in the design stage (often termed *budget estimate* or *definitive estimate*).

3. Detailed estimate for the final assessment of costs.

An example of the subtasks and components which might be defined for the construction of a rapid transit line is shown in Table 12-1. Construction of the rail line requires a series of purchases and specific tasks, and all of these various components must be defined in categories such as those of Table 12-1. The quantity of each purchase and the work entailed in each subtask must be estimated, usually using engineering principles, survey, or judgment. For example, soil borings are taken to help determine the underground soil and conditions to be encountered in tunneling, while route surveys are used to determine the amount of earthwork involved in laying out and preparing a roadbed, digging a tunnel, and so forth.

The breakdown in Table 12-1 might be appropriate for a preliminary planning study, for instance, while a much more detailed analysis of the labor and material requirements would be carried out during the engineering design phase (and prior to the preparation of contract bids). In the latter instance a take-off analysis would ordinarily be carried out from the blueprints in which the amount and type of each component of labor and material is enumerated (e.g., the number, type and size of reinforcing rods,

TABLE 12-1. Possible Project Components for Engineering Costing of a Rail Rapid Transit Line Construction

Components	Characteristics
Fixed factors	
Land for right of way	Area by location
Guideway	Dimensions, number of tracks, type of construction (at grade, subway, etc.), length by terrain and design standards
Terminals and stations	Number, size, design standards
Maintenance facilities	Number, capacity, design standards
Control and signaling system	Length of track, design standards
Utility relocation	Number, type, size, design standards
Rolling stock	
Vehicles	Number by type

I-bars, rivets, etc.) and then multiplied by its respective unit cost. In turn, allowances for "contingencies" are added to the accumulated cost estimates to allow for uncertainties (e.g., unexpected weather or soil conditions), inflation, and the like.

The development of cost estimates of this type requires a considerable amount of judgment to estimate the quantities of inputs. In particular, the amount of labor and time required to perform individual tasks depends upon workers' incentives and abilities, the effectiveness of management in organizing equipment, supplies and efforts, and the peculiarities of particular sites. Considering all these various factors requires considerable expertise.

Along with the various components and the quantity of each component, the unit cost of the various purchases and subtasks must be ascertained. Examples of unit costs are the cost per foot of tunneling through various types of soil or the cost per transit vehicle. Unit costs may be determined by reference to historical records, by inquiry among suppliers, by engineering judgment, or by statistical estimation. Unfortunately, unit costs may change significantly in the future or due to peculiarities at the construction site, so cost estimates will not always be accurate.

With the various purchases and subtasks defined, the quantity of each estimated, and the various unit costs determined, the total cost for constructing or operating a facility may be calculated by summing all the component quantities multiplied by their respective unit costs. Often, a contingency amount is added to this total, representing unanticipated costs due to uncertainty in defining tasks, scheduling difficulties, and so on. A difficulty with the technique of engineering unit costs is the multitude of components which must be estimated and the seemingly endless ways in which the tasks can be broken down. Each of the components listed in Table 12-1 could easily be disaggregated into smaller components or tasks. For example, it is quite important to consider the type of soil or rock through which tunnels are constructed. Similarly, purchase of right of way may depend critically on the existing uses of land and particular lot boundaries. In most applications of engineering unit cost estimation for major transportation facilities, the number of components and subtasks is large, making the process of assembling cost estimates quite laborious. Since the cost of making estimates is so high, attention is often directed to only a few alternatives and the list of components or tasks is kept small.

12-1-2   STATISTICAL COST ESTIMATION

An alternative (or supplement) to the technique of engineering unit costs is that of statistical estimation. Broadly speaking, statistical estimation of cost functions uses the same statistical techniques described in the previous chapter with respect to demand functions and reviewed in Appendix III. Cost functions developed with statistical techniques typically relate the cost of constructing or operating a facility to a few important attributes of the system. For example, the cost of operating a bus system might be assumed to be a function of the number of vehicles, total hours of operation, and miles of operation.

The role of statistical analysis is to best estimate the parameter values or constants in the assumed cost function. For example, the cost of operating a bus system might be assumed to be

$$C_o = \beta_1 V + \beta_2 H + \beta_3 B \qquad (12\text{-}1)$$

where C_o is operating cost, V is the number of vehicles, H is the annual bus hours of operation, B is the annual bus miles of operation, and β_1, β_2, and β_3 are constant parameters to be estimated. Using statistical techniques, it is possible to estimate appropriate values for the parameters β_1, β_2, and β_3 with the use of a number of observations of actual bus system operations. Thus, statistical cost estimation relies on historical data of actual operations.

The form of a cost function such as Equation (12-1) can be developed in a number of ways. By form, we mean the attributes which are included (such as V, H, and B above) and the functional relationship among the various attributes [which is linear in Eq. (12-1)]. The simplest method to determine a functional form is by assumption, based upon experience and engineering expertise. Most statistical studies of costs proceed in this manner, simply assuming that costs may be characterized by generally recognized attributes such as bus miles of operation, and so on, and that they are related in some (assumed) linear or nonlinear way.

A second approach is analysis of the actual components of a system operation or construction. This approach is similar to that of engineering unit cost estimation, although in this case "unit costs" are estimated indirectly by applying statistical techniques to system observations. Moreover, the number of components used is generally much fewer than the comparable number of components used in engineering unit cost estimation.

As an illustration of an engineering unit cost model with statistically derived estimates of unit parameter values, let us test a model of the form akin to that shown in Equation (12-1). Specifically, the parameters were estimated for all U.S. bus systems in 1980 having a fleet size between 125 and 250 vehicles.[2] (The specific data are shown in Appendix III.) The resulting expression is

$$C_o = \underset{(0.13)}{3.05}\ V + \underset{(2.79)}{22.98}\ E + \underset{(1.02)}{96.77}\ A \qquad r^2 = 0.82 \qquad (12\text{-}2)$$

---

[2]However, only those bus systems reporting their costs under the Federal Government's Section 15 Reporting System are included.

in which C_o is the annual system operating cost (in \$1,000's), V is the average weekday operating fleet size, E is the equivalent full-time employee count, and A is the average bus age (in years); the t statistics for the estimated coefficients are shown in parentheses and serve as indicators of the uncertainty of parameter estimates. Lower t statistics imply greater uncertainty in these estimates, as described below.[3]

The low t statistics for operating fleet and vehicle age coefficients might lead one to test the statistical significance of two other simpler functions, of the following general form:

$$Y = \alpha + \beta x \qquad\qquad (12\text{-}3)$$

or

$$Y = \beta x \qquad\qquad (12\text{-}4)$$

in which Y is the dependent variable (say, total annual system operating cost), x is the independent variable (say, equivalent full-time employee count), and α and β are constant parameters to be estimated using least-squares regression. Both forms were tested using the data in Appendix III, with the following results:

$$C_o = \underset{(-0.006)}{-7.83} + \underset{(7.57)}{26.44\, E} \qquad r^2 = 0.80 \qquad (12\text{-}5)$$

where C_o is the total annual system operating cost (in \$1,000's). Also,

$$C_o = \underset{(26.77)}{26.42\, E} \qquad r^2 = 0.80 \qquad (12\text{-}6)$$

In both cases much of the variation is explained by the regression and it is obvious (from the t statistics) that the estimated coefficient for the employee count is highly significant statistically (i.e., significantly different from zero). Two other issues are of importance, however. One, how accurate—probabilistically speaking—are these cost estimators (i.e., the values of C_o's)? Two, is it reasonable to conclude that the regression goes through the origin (i.e., that C_o is equal to zero when E is zero)? Each of these issues is discussed in Appendix III. More broadly, the estimates of costs from any statistical cost function such as Equations (12-2), (12-5), or (12-6) are subject to uncertainty, both as to the appropriate model form and estimate of costs (C_o).

[3] A regression was also estimated using vehicle fleet, bus miles, and bus hours—identical to the form hypothesized in Equation (12-1)—but found to have low statistical significance; specifically, the r^2 value was 0.38 and the t statistics indicated very low to fairly low statistical significance. Accordingly, the above form was felt to be more satisfying, both conceptually and statistically.

TABLE 12-2.   An illustration of an Allocated Cost Function for Turnpike Expenditures

Expenditure Item	Allocation Factor[a]	Allocated Amount (in millions)	Per Unit Amount[b]
Administration	VMT	$ 1.7	0.0011
Pavement maintenance	VMT	3.2	0.0020
	ESAL	1.1	0.0018
Other maintenance	VMT	3.2	0.0020
Services and toll collection	V	7.7	0.3182
Traffic control and safety	VMT	3.8	0.0024
Major repairs and resurfacing	VMT	7.5	0.0047
	ESAL	6.0	0.0101
Bond payments and interest	VMT	2.7	0.0017
	ESAL	10.8	0.0181
Total expenditure		47.8	

[a]VMT: annual vehicle miles of travel; ESAL: annual equivalent standard axle miles of travel; V: annual vehicle trips.

[b]Calculated as the allocated amount divided by the amount of the allocation factor, with VMT = 1583 million miles, ESAL = 595.9 million miles, and V = 24.2 million vehicle trips.

12-1-3   ACCOUNTING COST ALLOCATION

To develop a cost function for ongoing operations, allocations of cost from existing accounts may be employed. While this procedure has been used in practice, it relies upon a very restrictive assumption concerning the form of the cost function. Since this assumption is not likely to be true except as an approximation for most transportation services, allocated cost functions should be used with caution.

The basic idea in accounting cost allocations is that each expenditure item can be assigned or allocated to particular characteristics of service, such as vehicle-miles of operation or miles of pavement maintained. A possible list of such assignments for the case of a turnpike authority is shown in Table 12-2. In this list pavement maintenance expenditures are divided into components assigned or allocated to vehicle-miles of travel and the total volume of equivalent standard axle loads (ESALs) of travel on the turnpike.[4] Toll collection expenditures are assumed to vary with the number of vehicles. By dividing the total of each expenditure category by the total of the allocation factor (such as number of vehicles or ESALs), the per unit allocated cost for each expenditure category is calculated.

[4]Equivalent standard axle loads indicate the relative pavement stress due to heavier vehicle axle loads. See U.S. Congress, "Final Report of the Highway Cost Allocation Study," 87th Congress, 1961, for a discussion and example of their use in roadway cost allocation.

Ideally, the allocation factor should be causally related to the category of expenditures in an allocation process such as the one illustrated in Table 12-2. For the allocation of maintenance costs in this case, for example, statistical analysis has indicated that $1.1 million of expenditure is related to the number of *ESAL* miles of travel.[5] In many instances, however, a causal relationship between the allocation factor and the expenditure item cannot be identified or may not exist.

Once the per unit allocations to each factor are calculated as shown in Table 12-2, a total cost function may be calculated by summing up each of the per unit costs. For example, the cost function corresponding to the example in Table 12-2 would be

$$C = 0.0139\,VMT + 0.03\,ESAL + 0.3182\,V \qquad (12\text{-}7)$$

In this case the turnpike expenditures have been allocated on the basis of annual *ESAL* miles of travel (*ESAL*), the total number of vehicles (*V*), and vehicle miles of travel (*VMT*).

Note that the allocated cost function [Eq. (12-7)] assumes that the expenditure items allocated to each factor are strictly proportional to the level of each factor. That is, the function assumes that there are no economies of scale or nonlinear effects in any of the expenditure categories, such as toll collection. Thus, the cost function represents a linear approximation of what may be quite nonlinear relationships. Indeed, an increase in vehicles at toll booths with excess capacity available would be unlikely to increase toll collection costs, in contrast to the model assumptions. For this reason allocated cost functions should always be used cautiously in developing cost estimates or in estimating marginal or incremental costs. To the extent that the allocation factors are causally related to expenditure items or that a linear relationship is correct, then the allocated cost function will be an accurate representation of the true costs of operations. Unfortunately, this happy circumstance is not necessarily true.

12-2 ESTIMATING TRAVEL TIMES

Included in both the price and user cost functions are all the various costs associated with vehicle operation (gasoline, maintenance, etc.) and the user costs for the time and effort involved in travel. In addition, the price function includes the amount of any tolls, parking fees, or fares which tripmakers must pay (as described in Chapter 4). Each of these various costs must be valued in dollar amounts. In this section we shall

[5]See S. McNeil and C. Hendrickson, "Three Statistical Models of Pavement Management Based on Turnpike Data," Technical Report HCAS-81-14, Federal Highway Administration, 1981.

discuss techniques usually employed for estimating travel times over facilities. In the following section we consider the problem of valuing the estimated travel times in dollars. Both subjects are important because changes in travel times represent a major impact of many transportation investment and pricing decisions.

For existing facilities travel times may be estimated by observing actual trip times on a facility. Unfortunately, for large transportation networks direct observation of each link under all conditions would be prohibitively expensive. Moreover, observations cannot be made of conditions which will exist after a proposed investment or policy change is made. As a result, models of transportation facilities and services have been developed to estimate travel times indirectly. These models are generally called performance functions, and they relate the travel time on a particular type of facility to the characteristics of the facility, vehicle fleet mix, and the volume of travel. For some applications performance functions may be developed which estimate separate types of travel time, such as the time spent in walking, waiting, and riding for a particular trip.

An example of a performance function used for estimating the travel time on a roadway appears below:

$$t = \frac{1}{V_{\max} - \delta q} \quad \text{for } q < \frac{V_{\max}}{\delta} \tag{12-8}$$

where t is the travel time per mile over the link, $V_{\max}$ is the average speed on the link with very low volume, q is the volume actually using the link, and δ is a parameter related to the capacity of the link. The travel times indicated by Equation (12-8) for different volumes are graphed in Figure 12-1. Another commonly used model for estimating travel time on a link is

$$t = t_0 + \delta q^\rho \tag{12-9}$$

where t is the travel time, t_0 is the travel time at low volumes, q is volume, and δ and ρ are parameters specific to the roadway link.[6]

Both of these performance functions (and virtually all others) share some common characteristics. First, travel time on the facility or service is related to the travel time at very low volumes. Second, to capture the effects of congestion, each function includes the volume of travel as a variable. As the volume of travel increases, travel time increases, and this increase is generally in a nonlinear manner; at high volumes travel times may increase dramatically with a small amount of additional traffic.

[6]For a more detailed discussion of the first type of performance model, as illustrated by Equation (12-8), see A. A. Walters, *The Economics of Road User Charges*, The Johns Hopkins Press, Baltimore, 1968, pp. 172 ff. For an example of the model illustrated by Equation (12-9), see W. Vickrey, "Pricing as a Tool in Coordination of Local Transportation," *Transportation Economics*, Columbia University Press, New York, 1965, pp. 285 ff.

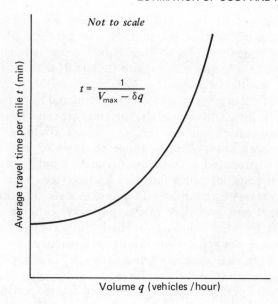

Figure 12-1.   A representative roadway performance function.

This increase is especially notable in cases in which the volume entering a facility exceeds the capacity of the facility for a period of time, leads to a shock wave, reduces facility capacity, and increases delay. In this case and others a queue forms on the roadway. This shock wave and queuing phenomenon is not captured by the steady-state model in Equation (12-8) or (12-9), but was described in Section 6-5.

Figure 12-2 illustrates the effect of queue formation. Appearing on this figure are the cumulative number of arrivals at the facility over time $[A(t)]$ and the cumulative number of departures from the facility $[D(t)]$. At any time t the queue length on the facility is given by the vertical distance between these curves, $A(t) - D(t)$. The waiting time for an arrival at time t is given by the horizontal distance to the departure curve.[7] The total waiting time in queue for all the users is given by the area between the $A(t)$ and $D(t)$ curves in Figure 12-2.

A number of modeling techniques are used to develop performance functions such as Equations (12-8) and (12-9). These techniques include statistical estimation, simulation, and analytical models. Statistical estimation is similar in nature to the use of statistical techniques for demand and cost function estimation which were described earlier. Statistical

---

[7]This assumes a discipline in which arrivals are served in turn on a first come–first served basis. For a general treatment of this type of queuing model, see G. Newell, *Applications of Queuing Theory*, Chapman and Hall, London, 1982.

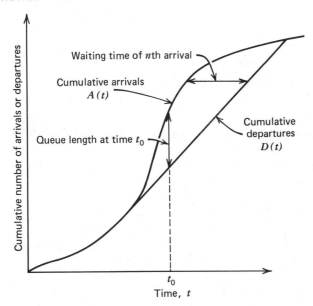

Figure 12-2. Illustration of queueing at a transportation facility.

analysis of observations of existing facilities and services can be used to infer the performance of all similar facilities and services. Simulation requires the use of a model or direct experimentation at different volume levels in order to observe the resulting travel times. The most common means of simulation involves large models formulated for manipulation by digital computers. Analytical models are based upon engineering or mathematical principles and vary substantially in their level of sophistication and accuracy. Simple analytical models involve little more than intuition, while others may employ stochastic processes and queuing theory. Finally, some of the most effective performance models are developed by using a combination of these methods.

Whichever method is used, the estimates of travel times developed from performance functions share some common features. First, the travel times are only estimates of actual times and, thus, are uncertain. As a result, the estimated costs associated with travel times will also be uncertain. Second, the actual travel times on a facility (and the estimated travel times) are likely to differ from the *perceived* travel times reported by travelers since they typically make errors in estimating their travel times. Finally, most performance functions estimate *average* travel times on a facility. Since there is likely to be considerable variation in the actual travel times, individuals may experience much shorter or much longer travel times. This variation in travel time is one aspect of the reliability of a particular transportation facility or service. Greater reliability is a desirable attribute in itself, but the estimation and valuation of system reliability is still in an embryonic stage.

12-3   VALUING TRAVEL TIME AND EFFORT

Once estimates of travel time for particular facilities or services are made, it is necessary to value these times in dollar amounts in order to construct the social cost and price functions. This problem has received a great deal of attention in the transportation literature, particularly since a major impact of most urban transportation investments is that of reduction in average travel time.

Observations of individuals in choice situations is one practical way in which estimates are made of the valuation or weight to place on different user cost components. For example, suppose that various individuals are faced with the choice between traveling on a turnpike with a toll or on a freeway which does not have a toll but is slower. In making a decision between these two alternatives, individuals must weigh the value of reaching their destination sooner (that is, a shorter travel time) against additional monetary expenses (that is, the toll charges). Illustratively, an individual might choose the tollroad if he pays only $1.00 and saves $\frac{1}{2}$ hour. At zero or very low tolls all or most travelers would be expected to choose the toll road, since their travel time would be lower. With very high tolls, travelers would be likely to choose the free road, since the extra travel time is less costly (that is, valued lower) than the cost of a (high) toll. At some intermediate toll the traveler might be indifferent between the routes since the savings in time on the toll road would be just balanced by the payment of the toll. For example, this intermediate point might occur with a toll of $1.00 and a travel time savings of 20 minutes. In this situation the analyst would conclude that the motorist would be willing to pay $1.00 to save 20 minutes of driving time. In turn, many analysts (by imputation) use such data to estimate the value of other times saved, or

$$\hat{v} = \frac{\$1.00}{(20 \text{ minutes})} = \$3.00/\text{hour} \qquad (12\text{-}10)$$

where $\hat{v}$ is the implied or estimated value of saving an hour of driving time.[8] Such imputed values should be scrutinized carefully rather than used haphazardly.

In practice, a large number of similar observations would be used to derive an estimated value or formula for the value of time using statistical techniques. At the heart of these methods, however, are the individual

[8]For a review of examples of this type of analysis and others, see D. A. Hensher, "Review of Studies Leading to Existing Values of Travel Time," *Trans. Research Record* **587**, 1976.

observations of traveler preferences when faced with competing travel choices.

A few comments may be helpful in interpreting estimates of travel time values which are derived from this type of analysis:

1.   The value of travel time is likely to vary according to the socioeconomic conditions of the tripmaker. For example, it seems plausible to assume that high-income individuals would be willing to pay more to save time than would low-income individuals. To capture this effect, the value of travel time is occasionally modeled as proportional to income, so that the individual's value of time is a constant parameter times household income. With this formulation, high-income individuals have a higher expected time value than do low-income individuals.

2.   The value of travel time is likely to vary according to the characteristics of the trip itself. For example, time spent waiting outside a vehicle is likely to be valued higher than time spent riding in a vehicle (that is, individuals would be willing to pay more to avoid waiting or walking outdoors than to spend a comparable amount of time riding in a vehicle). In fact, waiting or walking time outdoors has generally been found to be valued at roughly 2.5 to 3 times more than comparable times spent in riding vehicles. In addition to the comfort and level of effort involved in different components of the trip time, other characteristics of the trip which influence the value of time include trip purpose (work vs. recreational, etc.) and the number of individuals traveling together.

3.   The value of travel time is likely to vary according to trip duration. For very long trips it is likely that small changes in travel times have little value. For example, a 5-minute delay in a 5-day trip is not likely to influence travel choices to any great extent, but a 5-minute delay in a 10-minute trip may be quite irksome. To capture this effect, the value of travel time is occasionally modeled as inversely proportional to trip length, so that the individual's value of time is some constant parameter divided by the total trip length or time.

This observation concerning the importance of trip duration may also be applied to minor changes in travel time. It is likely that individuals place very little value on saving very small increments of time, such as a few seconds or less than a minute. Moreover, the value of 1 second is likely to be less than $\frac{1}{60}$ of the value of a minute and less than $\frac{1}{3600}$ the value of an hour. The implications of this observation for pricing and investment analysis will be considered in the next chapter.

12-4   OUTPUT UNITS AND NONHOMOGENEOUS COSTS

Specification of appropriate output units is of critical importance for cost, price, and demand functions. Determining the appropriate units becomes particularly difficult and complex as the links being analyzed for possible improvement serve the traveler for only a portion of the entire door-to-door trip and as the links are utilized by travelers from a wide variety of origin and destination zones. In the text we have generally used vehicle or person trips between specific points at a particular time, but other units may be appropriate in specific cases. Since the choice of output units does affect an investment or pricing analysis, this issue deserves some discussion.

To properly specify the output units, four aspects of travel must be accounted for: (1) the trip unit (i.e., persons, vehicles and their classification, tons, etc.); (2) the origin and destination of the trip; (3) the links over which trip is made; and (4) the time interval over which the trips are made, as well as the time of day and time period or year during which they are made.

The necessity for making the above distinctions is, of course, that cost and price–volume functions will vary from link to link and with changes in the trip unit and time interval, and that demand will vary for different origins and destination node pairs, times of day, and time periods, as well as for other factors. Determining equilibrium volumes and costs requires that the cost, price–volume, and demand functions are all consistently stated in terms of equivalent output measures accounting for these four aspects.

It is important to characterize the differences among individual travelers with respect to the way in which they perceive and evaluate certain travel costs (e.g., those for time, crowding, and discomfort) and with respect to auto purchases, car pooling, and other significant preferences and trade-offs. As noted above, there are wide variations in the manner and extent to which travelers consider and are affected by travel time and congestion, by vehicle ownership and accident payments, by inconvenience, by walking and waiting, and so forth. While it is clear that travelers whose trip value (i.e., the value of making a specific trip to some particular destination) is high will be willing to endure higher private travel prices in order to make the trip than will those with lower trip values, it cannot be assumed that those with higher trip values will necessarily regard the private inconvenience or discomfort of car pooling or of congestion as being more "costly" than will those travelers having low trip values. Thus, since the output consists of travelers having different trip values and having different travel service preferences and since the trip values and travel service preferences are only partly dependent on income level, equilibration cannot be accomplished acccurately by simply stratifying demand and price–volume functions by income level. However, one might attempt to equilibrate demand and price–volume functions stratified by income level as a first approximation for more accurate estimates (which, say, are to be determined by iterative procedures).

It appears that satisfactory treatment of these variations in travel price which are dependent both on the level of output and on the particular groups of people and goods involved in tripmaking require disaggregate forecasting models to accurately accomplish equilibration; and it would appear that iterative procedures offer the only hope for simultaneously satisfying the intricate demand and price–volume conditions. However, even these sorts of procedures may lead to multiple solutions and ambiguities.

The type of analysis which is possible in this manner has been outlined in Chapter 3. Briefly, it is possible to identify equilibrium conditions and summarize costs using a series of performance/traveler categories and separate performance functions for each link. For example, it is possible to stratify by trip purpose (as a proxy for time of day) and traveler groups, as well as travel time components such as waiting time, riding time, and reliability. Equilibration in this case requires a substantial number of iterations, which can best be performed on a computer.

Of course, in many instances the desired accuracy of forecasts may not be sufficiently high to warrant such expensive analysis procedures. For example, minor highway investments might not be expected to alter the extent of car pooling, so auto occupancy might be assumed to be constant in such cases. In other circumstances input data are so uncertain that a detailed, disaggregate analysis might not enhance the accuracy of results, so simpler analysis methods might be used, such as the illustrative diagrams used throughout this text.

12-5 FORECASTING COSTS

For the analysis of alternative investments it is essential to develop some estimate of the costs associated with the construction, operation, and use of facilities. In most cases preparing such estimates requires the use of forecasts of costs in future years. As we have emphasized in the foregoing discussion, any such forecasts of costs will be uncertain; the actual expenses may be much lower or much higher than those forecasted. This uncertainty arises from technological changes, changes in relative prices, difficulties in valuing travel time, inaccurate forecasts of underlying socio-economic conditions (which affect the volume and thus the user costs experienced), analytical errors, and other factors. While many of these factors are self-evident, a few deserve a brief discussion here.

Changes in relative prices may have substantial impacts on the costs of particular alternatives which, in turn, may affect the final choice of a project. A most dramatic example of such a change was the increase in gasoline price in the 1970s after several decades in which the relative price of gasoline had declined. This increase led to a series of important changes in the transportation industry (especially in the motor-vehicle and air sectors). Another cost component which has increased in relative price is that of construction costs, as evidenced by the increase in the construction price index compared to the consumer or wholesale goods price indices. Unfortunately, systematic changes over a long period of time for such factors are difficult to predict.

The difficulties associated with valuing travel time have already been noted above. One special problem in forecasting travel time is the effect of incomes. Generally, higher-income individuals place a higher value on travel time savings, and it is generally expected that the average income of the population will be rising over time. Whether or not the value of time will increase correspondingly is debatable.

Finally, errors in analysis also serve to introduce uncertainty into cost estimates. It is difficult, of course, to foresee all the problems which may occur in construction and operation of facilities. There is some evidence that estimates of construction and operating costs in transportation have tended to persistently understate the actual costs. This is due to the effects of greater than anticipated increases in costs, changes in design during the construction process, or overoptimism.

In this discussion of the sources of uncertainty for forecasting costs, it is important to also note the effect of equilibrium volumes and user costs. The costs associated with a particular alternative are likely to vary with the volume which is attracted, and this volume is, in turn, dependent upon the price of travel and underlying socioeconomic conditions. As we noted in the previous chapter, the socioeconomic conditions cannot be forecast with certainty, so the demand function and, consequently, the equilibrium volume and costs are also uncertain.

While forecasts of costs must be uncertain to some degree, there are a few factors which mitigate this problem. First, the use of a positive discount factor implies that costs which are incurred farther in the future are valued relatively less than costs which are incurred nearer the present. Forecasts of costs in the next few years are likely to be much more accurate, so the overall present value of costs is more accurate than it otherwise would be. Second, given that a number of alternatives are desirable (that is, have positive net present values), the analyst's problem is often one of choosing the best alternative. In this situation the comparison of the differences in costs between alternatives is important, and estimating differences in costs may be more accurate than forecasting their total.

As a final note, the effect of inflation might be mentioned. The analysis of construction, maintenance, and operating costs or of travel time costs should be performed using real or constant value dollars. This may be accomplished by always making cost estimates in real dollars (that is, values in some particular year) and then discounting them to their present value or, less preferably, by making estimates for the dollar amounts *actually* charged (that is, including inflation) and then discounting these amounts back to the base year at a discount factor which includes not only the rate of time preference (or social rate of discount) but also the rate of inflation. The former method requires fewer calculations and is generally preferable. One qualification in this procedure should be noted, however: over the course of time the price of some factors relative to all others may change. This problem was discussed above. A change in relative price may also be reflected in a differential rate of inflation, so that, for example, the rate of inflation for construction may exceed the general cost-of-living inflation. In discounting future construction costs, the specific rate of inflation might be used. Alternatively, the real increase in relative price of construction might simply be reflected in forecasts of increasing unit construction costs.

CHAPTER 13

SOME PRACTICAL PRICING PROBLEMS

Our previous discussion dealt with pricing policies under somewhat idealized conditions. It may be helpful to reexamine some of the issues, policies, and underlying assumptions in light of more reasonable expectations and actual conditions. Unfortunately, our discussion will necessarily be in abbreviated form and in rather general terms. However, our conclusions are directly relevant to pricing practice.

In the next section we shall compare four generalized pricing policies with the marginal cost pricing policy developed in Chapter 6. These policies are uniform user taxes, variable tolls or fares, a free-fare policy, and, finally, a uniform fare or toll. Each of these policies are in use for various transportation services. Following these general comparisons we shall consider in detail the problem of determining the value of time in the development of marginal cost functions. Since marginal cost or congestion pricing is often advocated, we feel that it is worth dwelling upon some of the practical problems of its implementation. Finally, we conclude with brief discussions of a few innovations which might be attempted. This final section is intended to suggest how the general concepts we have developed may be applied in practice.

13-1 A MORE PRACTICAL VIEW OF DIFFERENT PRICING POLICIES

Earlier, various pricing policies were examined under a very strict set of economic conditions which hardly correspond with the real-world situation. It was shown that for a "perfect economic world" use of a perfectly differentiated marginal cost pricing policy would maximize total net benefits.

However, it was also noted that the general theory of second best (alone) weakens the validity of this conclusion and merits consideration of other pricing options before reaching any hard and fast decision about *the best* pricing policy. Moreover, there are three other major reasons which undermine the insistence on adopting marginal cost pricing as the only proper pricing policy. First, to adopt perfectly differentiated marginal cost pricing would lead to the existence of different prices during each hour of the day, day of the week, month of the year, and so forth. Thus, as a practical matter, one would probably have to back away from a pricing mechanism in which prices necessarily varied whenever there were changes in variable costs or demand. Second, none of the discussion thus far has taken into account the very real and perhaps high costs required to implement a practical marginal cost price system, to include the delays and discomforts which people would face while standing in line or queues to pay fares or tolls. Finally, the formulation of appropriate marginal cost functions is difficult due to the problem of valuing very small changes in travel times (as will be discussed in Section 13-2). While this final problem may someday be overcome by more extensive analysis, the difficulty does limit the applicability of marginal cost pricing.

Accordingly, less than "perfectly" differentiated pricing policies probably will be selected, both for practical and real-world economic conditions. Among other possibilities, these can include uniform taxes, uniform fares or tolls, simple peak and off-peak differential fares or tolls, or more highly differentiated rate structures with fares or tolls varying during, say, three or four periods of the day and from season to season. Invariably, each of these pricing schemes involves price discrimination or subsidy of one sort or another and necessitates departure from the idealized conditions under which maximum efficiency can generally be anticipated. Thus the benefits and costs of these pricing possibilities will have to be estimated and compared in order to make any statements regarding the "best" pricing policy.

For the analyses and comparisons in this discussion, let us assume that demand can be fully represented by a pair of peak and off-peak demand functions and that no other daily, seasonal, or year-to-year fluctuations occur. Also, it will be assumed that privately perceived travel costs are equal to the short-run average variable costs, *exclusive* of any user taxes, fares, or tolls. It is important to recognize that the representation of demand by only two demand functions (one for peak hours and another for off-peak) as illustrated in Figure 13-1 is unrealistic in two ways: (1) it assumes the equilibrium flow or hourly volume will be at one level during each hour of the peak period and at another level during each off-peak hour, when in fact we know that hour-to-hour flow varies considerably more for transportation facilities and (2) it assumes away the shifting peak problem by failing to include time-of-day cross-relations. We consider these aspects below.

First, the simple demand functions illustrated in Figure 13-1 are of the following form:

$$q_p = \alpha_p - \beta_p p_p \tag{13-1}$$

$$q_o = \alpha_o - \beta_o p_o \tag{13-2}$$

where q_h is the hourly demand during the hth time-of-day period and p_h is the trip price during the hth time-of-day period. For simplicity, we assume that the functions are linear. With only two time-of-day periods (i.e., peak and off-peak) the end result after equilibrating the above two demand functions (q_p and q_o) with the corresponding price functions (for p_p and p_o) will be equal hourly volumes of q_p during each hour of the peak period and of q_o during the off-peak period. More realistically, though, the demand throughout the day would be better represented by using a separate demand function for *each* time-of-day period, or, say, hour, as follows:

$$q_h = \alpha_h - \beta_h p_h \qquad \text{for } h = 1, 2, \ldots, 24 \tag{13-3}$$

in which q_h is hourly quantity of tripmaking to be demanded during the hth time-of-day period. Importantly, however, the use of a simple peak and off-period rather than a more stratified representation of demand will not affect the generality of the results to follow. Thus, it seems preferable to use the two-period model for discussion.

Second, the demand functions in Equations (13-1), (13-2), and (13-3) assume that the time-of-day cross-elasticities are zero. That is, they assume that price changes in one time-of-day period do not affect the demand in other times of day, and thus that shifting peaks would not occur. Contrarily, it is more realistic to expect that price changes in one time-of-day period would more often than not affect the demand in at least one other time-of-day period. In short, the hourly demand during the hth time-of-day period should be represented as follows:

$$q_h = \alpha_h - \beta_{h,1} p_1 - \beta_{h,2} p_2 - \cdots - \beta_{h,t} p_t - \cdots - \beta_{h,r} p_r \tag{13-4}$$

in which $h = 1, 2, \ldots, r$. (In other words, there would be r time-of-day periods and r separate demand functions.) Use of this type of demand function with cross-elasticities was illustrated in Chapter 3.

While it is certainly more realistic to incorporate both direct and cross demand relations within our demand functions, it would also seriously complicate the analytical and graphical presentations and thus cloud our discussion. It is for these reasons that we have excluded these more realistic conditions in the remainder of the discussion on the practicalities of various pricing policies.

To examine the effects of instituting different pricing policies, the circumstances will be explored in detail for four cases, one in which a uniform user tax is imposed, a second in which differential or marginal cost fares or tolls are employed, a third in which there is no fare or toll, and a fourth in which uniform fares or tolls are used. The first applies only to public highways, while the last three apply with equal validity to public transit and highway facilities, as well as other transport situations.

Essentially, the purpose in this analysis is to determine the total net benefits which result from the implementation of these four different pricing policies, *but while also considering the extra costs and benefits of administering and implementing each of the policies.* The mechanism which will be used to compare each of the four pricing policies will be a simple but still valid one; it will be to compare the benefit and cost totals for each policy with those for *costless* marginal cost pricing and thus to determine for each the loss in total net benefits which stems from considering the extra implementation costs. In turn, the pricing policy which brings about the lowest loss in total net benefits—relative to costless marginal cost pricing—can then be regarded as the best policy from an economic welfare point of view.

Throughout this discussion the short-run marginal cost function $srmc_z(q)$ will be identical to that discussed previously in Chapters 2 and 3, representing the conditions for *costless* marginal cost pricing. This policy will be the base for our pairwise comparisons. That is, no implementation costs will be included in the base alternative. On the other hand, the $srmc'_z(q)$ function—that is, that with a "prime"—will represent the actual marginal costs for the actual pricing policy being tested, *to include any and all extra administration and implementation costs*. Similarly, $sravc'_z(q)$ represents the actual variable costs faced by users for all but the user tax pricing policy. Also, and as before, the total net benefits for costless marginal cost pricing will be maximized when $p(q) = srmc_z(q) = mb(q)$. The resulting total net benefits when compared to the total net benefits resulting from each of the four policies to be tested will permit determination of the loss in total net benefits [relative to costless $srmc_z(q)$ pricing] for each policy.

When comparing each of the four pricing policies to the *costless* marginal cost policy, the total (daily) net benefits for the base or costless $srmc_z(q)$ case will be as follows:

$$TNB_{z,\text{costless}} = n_p \sum_{q=1}^{q_p} [mb_p(q) - srmc_z(q)]$$

$$+ n_o \sum_{q=1}^{q_o} [mb_o(q) - srmc_z(q)] - F_{z,\text{costless}} \qquad (13\text{-}5)$$

where n_p is the number of hours in the peak period, n_o is the number of hours in the off-peak period, q_p is the equilibrium hourly volume during the peak period, q_o is the equilibrium hourly volume during the off-peak period, $mb_p(q)$ is the marginal benefit during the peak period at a flow rate of q, $mb_o(q)$ is the marginal benefit during the off-peak period at a flow rate of q, and $F_{z,\text{costless}}$ are the facility z fixed costs for costless marginal cost pricing.

13-1-1   UNIFORM USER TAX PRICING FOR HIGHWAYS

For analyzing the consequence of imposing uniform user taxes, a pricing practice common for public highways, the demand cost and price relationships might be as shown in Figure 13-1 (for some facility z). First, the $srmc_z(q)$ and $sravc_z(q)$ curves are as described previously and include all costs for the facility and vehicles operating on the roadway, as well as all personal travel time and effort costs, exclusive of any user tax or toll. However, for this pricing policy these cost functions not only apply to the costless marginal cost situation but also to the actual circumstances for a uniform user tax pricing policy. That is, the variable implementation and collection costs for employing uniform user taxes are extremely small, negligible for all intents and purposes, since travelers experience no extra

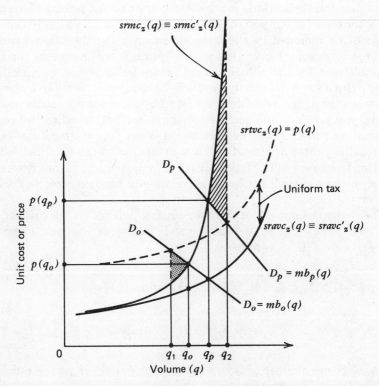

Figure 13-1.   Cost and price functions for uniform user tax pricing for public highways.

delays or running costs while paying them and since additional variable costs are not incurred (other than to a minor extent) in the process of collecting the user taxes. For example, the delays and costs associated with buying motor vehicle fuel would be virtually identical with or without local, state, or federal fuel taxes. This statement is reasonable at present and for internal combustion engines, but may not be true for large-scale adoption of battery-operated or electric automobiles. With the advent of battery-operated automobiles, a more complex pricing scheme would be required. This ease of collection is an important virtue of this pricing policy. Accordingly, for this pricing policy the $srmc_z'(q)$ function is defined as being identical to the $srmc_z(q)$ function, and $sravc_z(q)$ is equal to $sravc_z'(q)$.

Second, the $srtvc_z(q)$ curve is equal to the privately perceived travel costs *including* uniform taxes and thus is equal to $sravc_z(q)$ *plus* the uniform user tax. Also, the $srtvc_z(q)$ curve is the appropriate price function for highway user tax pricing.

For highways with these conditions and uniform user tax pricing, the equilibrium hourly flow would be equal to q_2 during the peak period and to q_1 during the off-peak period. The former results from the intersection of the D_p and $srtvc_z(q)$ functions and the latter from the D_o and $srtvc_z(q)$ functions. Note first that this pricing policy—relative to a costless marginal cost policy—usually leads to overutilization during peak hours and to underutilization during off-peak hours. The total (daily) net benefits for the uniform user tax pricing policy and equilibrium flows of q_2 and q_1 would be as follows:

$$TNB_{z,\text{user tax}} = n_p \sum_{q=1}^{q_2} [mb_p(q) - srmc_z(q)]$$

$$+ n_o \sum_{q=1}^{q_1} [mb_o(q) - srmc_z(q)] - F_{z,\text{user tax}}$$

$$- \text{user tax collection costs} \qquad (13\text{-}6)$$

where $F_{z,\text{user tax}}$ are the facility fixed costs for user tax pricing.

In turn, we can compute the daily loss in total net benefits for user tax pricing relative to costless marginal cost pricing by subtracting the results in Equation (13-6) from those in Equation (13-5), the difference being as follows:

$$\text{Relative } user \ tax \text{ loss in } TNB = n_p \sum_{q=q_p}^{q_2} [srmc_z(q) - mb_p(q)]$$

$$+ n_o \sum_{q=q_1}^{q_o} [mb_o(q) - srmc_z(q)]$$

$$+ [F_{z,\text{user tax}} - F_{z,\text{costless}}]$$

$$+ \text{user tax collection costs} \qquad (13\text{-}7)$$

The loss in total net benefits for user tax pricing relative to costless marginal cost pricing can also be depicted graphically, as in Figure 13-1. The hourly loss during the peak period would be indicated by the crosshatched area in Figure 13-1, and that during the off-peak period by the dotted area, plus, of course, any extra fixed or user tax collection costs. While it is clear that some loss in total net benefits relative to costless $srmc_z(q)$ pricing would occur, it is not possible to state *a priori* what level of user tax would minimize the relative loss. To determine that level would require full knowledge of the demand and cost functions.

13-1-2   NONCOSTLESS MARGINAL COST PRICING FOR HIGHWAYS AND TRANSIT

The problem of analyzing relative total net benefit losses is not so straightforward with respect to the implementation of a noncostless marginal cost pricing policy in which prices differ as marginal costs vary. First, there are a wide number of possible mechanisms and devices which can be used to implement such a policy. For highways they can vary from taxes imposed at the destination end of the trip, to parking surcharges, to vehicle meters, to electronic devices, to special licenses, to tollgates, and so forth.[1] For transit there can be on-board or centralized fare collection, manual or automated collection, and so forth. Second, for these sorts of situations it is vital to consider the collection cost possibilities over the long run. This would be particularly important in centralized fare or tollgate situations, since in the short run increased input volume can substantially increase waiting or congestion at the collection center or tollgates. Over the long run, of course, more toll booths, turnstiles, or gatekeepers can be added in those cases where the reduction in congestion costs will be more than off-setting. Of course, long-run circumstances will vary from one pricing system to another, but the principles for planning purposes will remain the same.

In Figure 13-2 the cost and price functions are shown for a normal transit fare collection system or a highway tollgate type of operation which in the short run may seem to be the most costly type of system, but is not necessarily so in the long run. For example, vehicle meters or electronic monitoring devices may have quite low short-run marginal and average variable costs, but over the long run may have capital and maintenance costs (etc.) which exceed those for this seemingly more expensive technology. Also, let us assume that the number of fare booths, tollgates, or gatekeepers (etc.) being utilized represents the "optimum" for the demand and cost conditions portrayed. The $srmc_z'(q)$ and $sravc_z'(q)$

---

[1]For a fairly complete review of the alternatives, see "Road Pricing: The Economical and Technical Possibilities," Ministry of Transport, London, 1963.

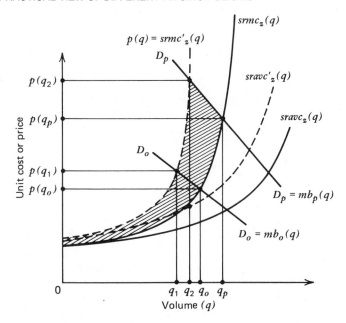

Figure 13-2. Cost and price functions for noncostless marginal cost pricing for public highways or transit. D_p = Demand function for *hourly* flow during *peak periods*; D_o = demand function for *hourly* flow during *off-peak periods*.

curves, respectively, are the actual short-run marginal cost and short-run average variable cost functions for facility z *including* all the extra variable fare or toll collection costs *and* traveler delays which result from using differential tolls to implement a marginal cost pricing policy. The appropriate price function is equal to $srmc'_z(q)$. Accordingly, the equilibrium hourly volume during peak hours will be q_2 and that during off-peak hours will be q_1.

In mathematical terms the total (daily) net benefits for a marginal cost pricing policy and equilibrium flows of q_2 and q_1 will be as follows:

$$TNB_{z,\text{marginal cost}} = n_p \sum_{q=1}^{q_2} [mb_p(q) - srmc'_z(q)]$$

$$+ n_o \sum_{q=1}^{q_1} [mb_o(q) - srmc'_z(q)]$$

$$- F_{z,\text{marginal cost}} \tag{13-8}$$

where $F_{z,\text{marginal cost}}$ are the fixed facility costs incurred for implementing marginal cost pricing.

In turn, we can compute the daily loss in total net benefits for marginal cost pricing relative to *costless* marginal cost pricing by subtracting the results in Equation (13-8) from those in Equation (13-5), the difference being as follows:

$$\text{Relative } marginal \ cost \text{ loss in } TNB = n_o \sum_{q=1}^{q_1} [srmc'_z(q) - srmc_z(q)]$$

$$+ n_o \sum_{q=q_1}^{q_o} [mb_o(q) - srmc_z(q)]$$

$$+ n_p \sum_{q=1}^{q_2} [srmc'_z(q) - srmc_z(q)]$$

$$+ n_p \sum_{q=q_2}^{q_p} [mb_p(q) - srmc_z(q)]$$

$$+ [F_{z,\text{marginal cost}} - F_{z,\text{costless}}] \qquad (13\text{-}9)$$

Also, the relative hourly loss in total net benefit during peak hours will be equal to the entire hatched area shown in Figure 13-2 and that during off-peak hours will be equal to the hatched area lying below D_o, the off-peak demand function.

Importantly, if you compare the graphic results in Figure 13-1 and 13-2 or those in Equations (13-7) and (13-9), you can see that the relative loss in net benefit from using differential tolls to implement marginal cost pricing is *not necessarily* less than the relative loss from using uniform user tax pricing.[2] In some cases marginal cost pricing will result in reducing the net benefit losses (everything else being equal) and in improving economic efficiency more than uniform tax pricing and in other cases less. Thus, in contrast to the usual "pure theory" recommendations described in Chapter 6, it must be concluded that no *a priori* judgment can be made with respect to the "best" pricing policy for highways, *at least between these two options*.

13-1-3   FREE-FARE PRICING FOR HIGHWAYS AND TRANSIT

Figure 13-3 illustrates those cases in which no toll or fare is charged and thus $sravc_z(q)$ is the appropriate price function. In turn, for either zero

---

[2]To compare the results in Equations (13-7) and (13-9), some caution must be taken since the equilibrium hourly volumes during the peak and off-peak hours (q_1 and q_2, respectively) will have different values for each different pricing policy. That is, the values of q_1 and q_2 for user tax pricing will be different than the values of q_1 and q_2 for marginal cost pricing.

fare transit service or toll-free *and* taxless highways, the total net benefit would be as follows:

$$TNB_{z,\text{free fare}} = n_p \sum_{q=1}^{q_2} [mb_p(q) - srmc_z(q)]$$

$$+ n_o \sum_{q=1}^{q_1} [mb_o(q) - srmc_z(q)] - F_{z,\text{costless}} \quad (13\text{-}10)$$

Note that the fixed costs for this pricing policy would be identical to those for costless marginal cost pricing. In turn, by subtracting the results in Equation (13-10) from those in Equation (13-5), we can obtain the loss in total net benefits for a free pricing policy, relative to costless marginal cost pricing. Thus,

$$\text{Relative } free\text{-}fare \text{ loss in } TNB = n_o \sum_{q=q_o}^{q_1} [srmc_z(q) - mb_o(q)]$$

$$+ n_p \sum_{q=q_p}^{q_2} [srmc_z(q) - mb_p(q)] \ (13\text{-}11)$$

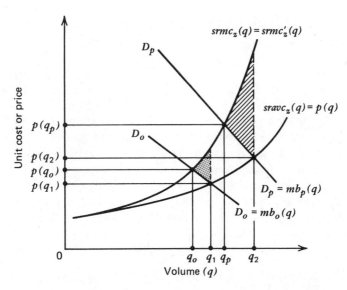

Figure 13-3. Cost and price functions for free transit service or toll-free and taxless highways.

Graphically, the hourly loss in total net benefits during off-peak hours, relative to costless marginal cost pricing, would be equal to the dotted area in Figure 13-3 and the hourly loss during peak hours would be equal to the hatched area.

Two important conclusions emerge. First, comparison of the relative losses in total net benefit for a free-fare policy (i.e., zero fare for transit and no taxes *or* tolls for highways) to those for marginal cost pricing will show that marginal cost pricing in practice will not necessarily be best, at least not on *a priori* grounds. While marginal cost pricing may turn out to be more efficient, such a conclusion must stem from a full-scale analysis of actual cost and benefit circumstances rather than pure theory. Second, for highways (but not transit) it can be shown that the relative losses for user tax pricing, or $p(q) = srtvc(q)$, will be less than those for toll-free and taxless pricing. Put differently, it can be seen that the shaded areas (which represent the relative losses in total net benefit) in Figure 13-1 will be less than those in Figure 13-3. Since the user tax is virtually costless to administer and implement, to add a small tax onto the short-run average variable cost or $sravc_z(q)$ in Figure 13-3 will lead to a reduction in both peak and off-peak volume and to a reduction in both the peak and off-peak relative losses in total net benefits. To convince oneself of this, in Figure 13-3 simply add a uniform tax equal to $mb_o(q_o) - sravc_z(q_o)$. Then the equilibrium flow during off-peak hours would fall from q_1 to q_o, thus eliminating all the relative losses during off-peak hours; flow during peak hours, as well as relative losses, will also be reduced.

13-1-4   UNIFORM FARE OR TOLL PRICING FOR TRANSIT OR HIGHWAYS

The cost and price functions in Figure 13-4 represent the situation in which a uniform daily fare is charged for transit or a uniform daily toll for highways. In this case the appropriate price function is $srfvc_z(q)$. For highways the difference between this case and that for uniform highway user taxes is that tolls, unlike user taxes, are not costless to administer and, in addition, delay the users. The difference is reflected in the fact that the appropriate *cost* function for the uniform user tax case is the $srmc_z(q)$ curve and for the toll case is the $srmc_z'(q)$ curve. (For transit there is no costless way to impose taxes or tolls on its users.) Given uniform fare or toll pricing for transit or highways, the total net benefits will be as follows:

$$TNB_{z,\text{uniform fare}} = n_p \sum_{q=1}^{q_2} [mb_p(q) - srmc_z'(q)]$$

$$+ n_o \sum_{q=1}^{q_1} [mb_o(q) - srmc_z'(q)] - F_{z,\text{uniform fare}} \quad (13\text{-}12)$$

And, in turn, the loss in total net benefits for uniform fare or toll pricing relative to costless marginal cost pricing will be equal to the difference between the totals in Equations (13-5) and (13-12), as follows:

$$\text{Relative } \textit{uniform fare} \text{ loss in } TNB = n_o \sum_{q=1}^{q_1} [srmc'_z(q) - srmc_z(q)]$$

$$+ n_o \sum_{q=q_1}^{q_o} [mb_o(q) - srmc_z(q)]$$

$$+ n_p \sum_{q=1}^{q_2} [srmc'_z(q) - srmc_z(q)]$$

$$+ n_p \sum_{q=q_2}^{q_p} [mb_p(q) - srmc_z(q)]$$

$$+ [F_{z,\text{uniform fare}} - F_{z,\text{costless}}] \qquad (13\text{-}13)$$

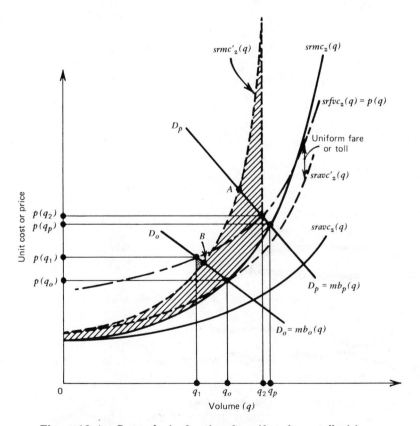

Figure 13-4.   Cost and price functions for uniform fare or toll pricing.

Also, for uniform daily fare or toll pricing, the loss in total net benefits relative to "costless" marginal cost pricing will be equal to the entire *hatched* area during each peak hour, as shown in Figure 13-4, while the loss during each off-peak hour will be equal to hatched area lying below the off-peak demand function (D_o) *plus* the *dotted* "triangular"-shaped area to the left of point B in the figure.

One very important conclusion can be drawn, both for highway and transit facilities. If *some* fare or toll *is* to be charged (for whatever reasons), then it will be better to use differential tolls or fares (e.g., those resulting from marginal cost pricing as shown in Figure 13-2) than uniform daily fares or tolls. Visually, this can be seen simply by comparing the shaded areas (which represent the relative losses in total net benefit) in Figures 13-2 and 13-4; it should be apparent that those in the latter are larger, thus indicating the economic desirability of marginal cost pricing in preference to uniform fares or tolls. Specifically, and referring to Figure 13-4, if the peak period price of $p(q_2)$ were raised to the level of A, then the relative losses lying above the peak period demand function (D_p) would be eliminated. And if the off-peak price of $p(q_1)$ were reduced to the level of B, then the losses included in the dotted area would be eliminated during off-peak hours. However, the conclusion that the use of peak and off-peak marginal cost prices is better than the use of uniform daily fares or tolls does rest on one relatively minor assumption, to wit: Implementation costs (including delays to users) for marginal cost pricing and uniform toll or fare pricing are virtually identical.

13-1-5 COMPARISON OF DIFFERENT PRICING POLICIES: A SUMMARY

Among the four pricing policies examined, the following conclusions are obtained (again, in terms of maximizing total net benefits):

1. For *transit* systems: (a) it is not clear whether a free-transit policy or a peak and off-peak differential or marginal cost price policy is best and (b) if *some* fare is to be charged for transit use (for whatever reasons), then it will be better to use a peak and off-peak marginal cost price policy than a uniform fare policy.

2. For *highway* facilities: (a) it is not clear whether a highway user tax policy or a peak and off-peak marginal cost price policy is best; (b) a highway user tax policy is better than a taxless and toll-free policy; and (c) if *some* toll is to be charged for use of facilities (for whatever reasons), then it will be better to use a peak and off-peak marginal cost price policy than a uniform toll policy.

Finally, if we extend the previous two-period (peak and off-peak) demand case, which consisted of only two demand functions, to a more realistic demand representation, as many as 24 time-of-day demand functions can be required (if the time interval for output were 1 hour and if it seems reasonable to ignore the differences in minute-to-minute flow rates and travel costs within the hourly period). Thus, as many as 24 hourly toll rates would be required if more "perfect" price differentiation and marginal cost pricing is to be employed. An even more complex set of prices would result if the directional characteristics were taken into account (and thus if 48 different demand functions and fares or toll rates were employed). Also, the information needs and analysis required to fully characterize the 48 demand functions and to properly determine rates by hour and by direction may be so costly (in terms of data gathering, processing, and analysis) and the resulting rate and flow conditions so complex as to suggest the "desirability" of less than "perfectly differentiated" pricing. That is, for the above reasons, it may be appropriate to use simple peak and off-peak prices or, at most, only three or four fare or toll rates during the 24-hour day.

In addition, some analysts have expressed concern with respect to the year-to-year fluctuation of fares or toll rates which results either from changes in facility size at various stages of development or from changes in demand or technological conditions. On this matter, Boiteux has summarized the issues in the following way:[3]

> *Plant may be of unsuitable capacity for various reasons—unintentional over-equipment through erroneous forecasting, unintentional lag in equipment through underestimating the anticipated expansion of demand or owing to shortages of materials, or deliberate overequipment in anticipation of a subsequent development of demand. Under the marginal theory it would be necessary to fix rates at the differential cost all the time [that is, the rate would be equal to the short-run marginal cost of the particular plant in existence at each point in time], so that the optimum use is made of the plant as it stands. But the need to keep rates steady (which has nothing to do with the marginal theory) makes long-term policy preferable to the* instantaneous *optimum use of investment; the underlying principle of this is* to fix rates equivalent to what the differential [or short-run marginal] costs would be if the plant were constantly at correct capacity, *that is, rates equivalent to the development [or long-run marginal]* costs.

As a final note, we should comment upon the financial implications of different pricing schemes. Due to financial restrictions for some facilities and services, sufficient revenue must often be raised from toll and fare charges in order to cover operating expenses plus repayment of construction funds. In these cases uniform or time-of-day differentiated tolls and fares must be set sufficiently high so as to generate the necessary level of revenue. For situations in which it is desired to have the toll and fare

[3]M. Boiteux, "Peak-Load Pricing," *Journal of Business*, **33**(2), 166 (1960). Reprinted by permission of the University of Chicago Press.

revenues just equal the costs in total, then the most efficient policy to adopt is the "inverse elasticity" pricing rule described in Chapter 9. In this case fares for time periods or groups with low elasticity of demand are set higher than the charges for groups or periods with more elastic demand. This type of deviation is appropriate for each of the pricing schemes discussed above. Of course, some concern for the practicality of differentiating charges or for the distributional impact upon different groups may provide reasons not to differentiate tolls in this manner but to rely upon uniform increases in charges. Unfortunately, this type of modification results in higher social costs than would otherwise occur.

13-2   DEVELOPMENT OF SUITABLE MARGINAL COST FUNCTIONS FOR CONGESTION PRICING

For decades marginal cost pricing has been discussed as a potential tool for bringing rationality to congested roadways and transit facilities. By and large, the discussion has centered around the theoretical aspects of marginal cost pricing and dealt far too little with the practical problems of implementing such a pricing policy. Moreover, if we adhere strictly to the pure theory and attempt to use the short-run marginal cost function *as normally derived*, some doubt must be cast on the validity of the outcome even without considering the political difficulties in implementation. (See Section 6-4.) Part of the problem involves the analytical construct and part involves implicit assumptions with respect to the value of time savings.

13-2-1   ROLE OF VALUE OF TIME IN MARGINAL COST PRICING

The "value of time" issue arises when analysts consider the efficacy of various pricing policies, especially marginal cost pricing (or congestion cost pricing). For the relationships shown in Figure 13-5, marginal cost pricing would result in q_1 users facing a price of $p_1(q_1)$ which is just equal to $srmc_x(q_1)$. Broadly speaking, users or tripmakers *aside from any toll or fare surcharges* are faced only with the average variable costs for traveling, operating vehicles, and fighting congestion (or approximately so); thus, they usually consider and perceive only (or mainly) the average payments for vehicle operation and for the time and effort involved. As a consequence, users of most public highways and transit systems would tend to pay average variable costs in the absence of marginal cost pricing. Without congestion tolls or fare surcharges, then, q_2 users would travel and pay a price equal to $sravc_x(q_2)$. In a sense this is to allow average congestion and average operating costs to "govern" flow and would be tantamount to invoking average variable cost pricing. By contrast, in order to invoke marginal cost pricing, it would be necessary to impose a marginal cost toll equal to $srmc_x(q_1) - sravc_x(q_1)$ since, aside from a toll, travelers only perceive their average payments for operation, maintenance, time, and effort.

To implement marginal cost pricing, the value of time becomes a necessary ingredient in two ways. First, it is one of the components of the average variable cost function. Thus, when the flow is q_1, how long does the trip take, how congested is it, and what is the disutility of the travel time and effort? This value, together with other money and nonmoney payments, permits the determination of $sravc_x(q_1)$. Second, the value of time—or, more specifically, the disutility of extra time and effort—is imbedded within the marginal cost figure used to determine the marginal cost toll. Essentially, the marginal cost represents the aggregate disutility of extra time and effort (and of other such payments) which is experienced by all q tripmakers when the flow is increased by one unit from $q - 1$ to q trips per hour. Stated in other terms, when the flow rate is increased from $q - 1$ to q trips per hour, travel time and congestion is increased ever so slightly for all tripmakers and the average variable cost rises from $sravc_x(q - 1)$ to $sravc_x(q)$. While the qth tripmaker (aside from the toll) experiences a trip cost of $sravc_x(q)$ when the flow rate increases one unit from $q - 1$ to q, the other $q - 1$ tripmakers each experience only a slight increase in congestion and travel time, an increase whose disutility to each tripmaker is represented by $sravc_x(q) - sravc_x(q - 1)$. The aggregate of these $(sravc_x(q) + (q - 1)[sravc_x(q) - sravc_x(q - 1)])$ is equal to the marginal cost at flow level q. Thus, the analyst needs to know the aggregate disutility of these slight increases in travel time and effort. That is, to

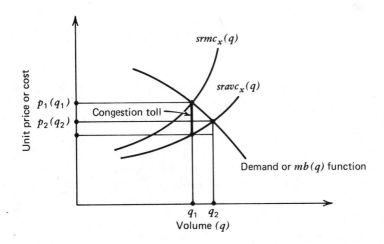

Figure 13-5. Illustration of marginal cost pricing. $sravc_x(q)$ = short-run average variable cost at a volume of q trips per hour; $SRVC_x(q)$ = total (short-run) variable costs at a volume of q trips per hour = $q\ sravc_x(q)$; $srmc_x(q)$ = short-run marginal cost at a volume of q trips per hour = $\partial SRVC_x(q)/\partial q$ or $\Delta SRVC_x(q)/\Delta q$.

deal with pricing problems of this sort, it becomes necessary to know the overall value of the trip time and effort as well as the value of small increments in trip time and effort.

13-2-2 DEVELOPMENT OF MARGINAL COST FUNCTION IN PRACTICE

Most discussions of marginal cost pricing employ fairly simple travel time and cost models as described in Chapter 12, with the most usual being one of the following two forms:[4]

1. $sravc_x(q) = \tau_x + \dfrac{v}{(V_x - \delta_x q)} = \tau_x + \dfrac{v}{v_x(q)}$ for $v_x(q) > 0$ (13-14)

in which

$\quad sravc_x(q) =$ average variable cost to user (in time, effort, and money) for a volume of q on facility x, in cents per vehicle mile

$\quad \tau_x =$ portion of average variable cost which is invariant with speed

$\quad V_x =$ average speed on facility x at low or near-zero levels of volume, in mph

$\quad \delta_x =$ speed reduction parameter for facility x

$\quad v =$ value of travel time and effort, in cents per vehicle-hour

$\quad q =$ flow rate or volume on facility x, in vph

$\quad v_x(q) = V_x - \delta_x q =$ average speed on facility x for a volume of q, in mph

or, alternatively,

2. $sravc_x(q) = \tau_x + v\delta_x q^\rho$ (13-15)

in which the terms are defined as before, except for ρ which is a speed reduction parameter. These functions are almost identical to those discussed in Chapter 12.

For the cost functions shown in Equations (13-14) and (13-15), the average variable cost (per mile) varies directly with the average travel time or $t_x(q)$, which is the inverse of the average speed or $v_x(q)$.

In both models it can be shown that the disutility of an extra minute of time and effort is assumed to be constant for all congestion levels and all trip lengths. Thus, an extra 5 minutes of time and effort is assumed to be five times more costly than 1 extra minute of time and effort, whether the

---

[4]For more details of the first model, see A. A. Walters, *The Economics of Road User Charges*, The Johns Hopkins Press, Baltimore, 1968, pp. 172 ff. For an example of the second model, see W. Vickrey, "Pricing as a Tool in Coordination of Local Transportation," in *Transportation Economics*, Columbia University Press, New York 1965, pp. 285 ff.

overall trip time is 10 minutes, 20 minutes, 60 minutes, or whatever. More realistically, we would expect the value of extra increments of time and effort to be a function of both the size of the increment *and* the overall trip length. Also, it seems apparent that one should consider the *nature* of the extra time and effort; that is, what is the value of an extra minute of *walking* time and effort as opposed to that spent driving on congested freeways, or that spent driving on congested streets with signals, or that spent standing on a bus, and so forth? For convenience, however, let us assume the validity of the assumption that v is constant; stated differently, assume that the marginal utility of time is constant.[5]

Given the above, what else is implied by using these cost models in marginal cost pricing? To answer this, and for illustrative purposes, the first form of cost model, that shown in Equation (13-14), will be used, along with the following specific parameter values:[6]

$$srauc_1(q) = \tau_1 + \frac{v}{(V_1 - \delta_1 q)} \tag{13-16}$$

$$= 6.2 + \frac{350}{(28 - 0.008q)} \quad \text{in cents per vehicle-mile} \tag{13-17}$$

In turn, the accompanying marginal cost function or $srmc_1(q)$ can be determined as follows:

$$srmc_1(q) = \frac{\partial(\text{total var. costs for } q)}{\partial q} = \frac{\partial q \cdot srauc_1(q)}{\partial q} \tag{13-18}$$

$$= \tau_1 + \frac{v}{(V_1 - \delta_1 q)} + \frac{v\delta_1 q}{(V_1 - \delta_1 q)^2} \tag{13-19}$$

$$= \tau_1 + \frac{v V_1}{(V_1 - \delta_1 q)^2} \tag{13-20}$$

$$= 6.2 + \frac{9800}{(28 - 0.008q)^2} \tag{13-21}$$

or

$$srmc_1(q) = srauc_1(q) + \frac{v\delta_1 q}{(V_1 - \delta_1 q)^2} \tag{13-22}$$

---

[5]Mathematically, this means that
$$\frac{\partial srauc_x(q)}{\partial t_x(q)} = v = \text{constant}$$
since $t_x(q)$ is the average trip time per mile when the flow is q on facility x and is equal to 1 divided by $v_x(q)$.

[6]This model applies to 1-mile trips on Central London roadways and is based on the previous work of J. M. Thomson and R. F. F. Dawson; for details see M. Wohl and B. V. Martin, *Traffic System Analysis*, McGraw-Hill, New York, 1967, Section 10.2.1.

Again, the average variable cost function or $sravc_1(q)$ expresses the average user cost in time, effort, and money which an individual tripmaker perceives and pays aside from any congestion toll. It is the private or internal cost to any individual tripmaker in a flow of q. Also, it is assumed that each of the q tripmakers experience the same cost or $sravc_1(q)$. However, to charge marginal cost prices, the average variable cost price would have to be increased by a "surcharge" or congestion toll equal to the difference between $srmc_1(q)$ and $sravc_1(q)$; this difference is equal to the second term in Equation (13-22). Essentially, this surcharge reflects the disutility of the extra congestion, time, and effort which was experienced by each of the $q - 1$ tripmakers when the flow rate was increased from $q - 1$ to q. Put differently, if the flow rate were to increase from $q - 1$ to q, the congestion, average travel time, and effort would increase ever so slightly, and the qth extra tripmaker (whomever he may be), if left to his own devices, would surely only consider *his* average travel time and effort and thus *his* average variable cost, thus ignoring the extra congestion which would be imposed on others. By contrast, the marginal cost price is intended to insure that the extra delays to others also would be considered.

The legitimacy of the analytical structure and concepts is unquestioned. But the application is less than satisfying. For instance, when the flow rate is increased from 1999 to 2000 trips per hour, users will certainly experience *some* increase in (the average) travel time. The average amount of increase can be determined from Equations (13-17) and (13-21) since

$$v_1(q) = 28 - 0.008q \qquad (13\text{-}23)$$

and therefore

$$t_1(q) = \frac{60}{v_1(q)} \qquad (13\text{-}24)$$

in which $t_1(q)$ is the average travel time in minutes for a 1-mile trip on facilities of this sort. Specifically, it can be shown that *for a 5-mile trip* the average travel time for each tripmaker will increase only *1 second* (i.e., 1500 − 1499 seconds) as the hourly flow rate, or q, increases from 1999 to 2000. (See Table 13-1.) That the travel time will increase, even for such small increments in the flow rate, is not only obvious but measurable. But to make the next step and to assume, albeit implicitly, that this small increase in travel time increased the trip disutility of the first 1999 tripmakers by 194 cents, in total, is somewhat questionable.[7] Stated in other

---

[7]External cost *per mile* = $srmc_1(2000) - srvc_1(2000) = 38.89$ cents and thus the 5-mile external costs = 5(38.89 cents) = 194 cents (approximately). See Table 13-1.

TABLE 13-1. Approximate Trip Costs and Times for 5-Mile Trips[a]

q	$sravc_1(q)$	$srmc_1(q)$	$t_1(q)$
Flow Rate in Trips per Hour	Average Variable Cost (Cents)	Marginal Cost (Cents)	Average Travel Time (Seconds)
1999	176.7	370.8	1499
2000	176.8	371.3	1500[b]
2399	229.7	662.6	2043.6
2400	229.9	663.8	2045.5[c]

[a]Costs were derived from Equations (13-17) and (13-21). Times were derived from Equations (13-23) and (13-24). Unit costs and times were then multiplied by five.

[b]25 minutes.

[c]34 minutes.

terms, would the average tripmaker pay anything to save *only 1 second* if his total trip time was about 25 minutes? Or, if the volume and congestion were considerably higher, say, about 2400 trips per hour for this sort of facility, would the average tripmaker pay anything to save about 2 seconds per trip (i.e., 2045.5 − 2043.6) if the average trip time were about 34 minutes?

The validity of marginal cost pricing as commonly applied to highways and transit facilities *requires* one to make the assumption that such small increases in travel time and effort (as opposed to increases in other resources consumed) *do* have value and can be determined in the straightforward fashion indicated. On the other hand, if one rejects the assumption that such small increases in travel time and effort do have value, and therefore assumes that such negligible increases would have negligible value, this is tantamount to saying that the average variable cost and marginal cost functions are identical and that the marginal cost toll is zero. But some algebraic manipulations will show that this conclusion is mathematically inconsistent with a monotonically increasing average variable cost function. That is, by assuming the equivalence of average variable and marginal costs, it is implied that the average variable cost is constant.

Clearly, though, the average variable cost does increase with increases in flow, travel time, and congestion. As a consequence, it is necessary to understand the dilemma and to probe deeper. In simplest terms the problems stem (partially) from the initial assumption about constant marginal utility of time. On the one hand to accept that assumption leads to the questionable result that even very small increases in travel time and effort have disutility and can be aggregated as shown to determine marginal cost tolls. On the other hand to reject it means that an expression relating the disutility of increased time to the amount of the increase is required.

To give this more meaning, let us assume that the demand or marginal benefit function for 5-mile trips is linear, as follows:

$$q = 3060 - 2.857p(q) \qquad (13\text{-}25)$$

or, when inverted,

$$p(q) = mb(q) = 1071 - 0.35q \qquad (13\text{-}26)$$

In this case, for marginal cost pricing, it becomes necessary to determine the flow and price when $p(q) = mb(q) = srmc_1(q)$. Equating Equations (13-21) and (13-26) after multiplying the former times 5, it can be determined that for a 5-mile trip the resultant marginal cost price is 371 cents and the accompanying flow is 2000 trips per hour. Also, at this volume level the average variable cost is 177 cents, the requisite marginal cost toll is 194 cents, and the average travel time will be 25 minutes.

However, for average variable cost pricing, the average variable cost price will be about 230 cents and the accompanying flow will be 2400 trips per hour.

The above two cases are illustrated in Figure 13-6, while their data are summarized in Table 13-1.

Two points deserve emphasis, the first involving the result of *marginal* changes in flow rates and the second involving the result of *incremental* changes in flow rates.

First, *marginal* or unit changes in flow rates lead to almost insignificant increases in travel time (i.e., only 1 extra *second* per trip at a flow rate of 2000 vph and about 2 extra seconds at 2400 vph) yet, when accumulated, these miniscule time changes account for the external congestion costs being valued at 194 and 434 cents, respectively, for the 2000 and 2400 flow rate cases. Put differently, does it *really* seem reasonable to think that just 1 second added to the trip time for 1999 tripmakers is actually valued at 194 cents, especially given that the average trip time is 25 minutes? While it is clear that the analytical construct requires a positive answer—if one accepts the validity of the average variable cost function— one at least must wonder about the large values associated with the accumulation of such small time changes.

Second, for *incremental* changes in flow rate—such as that from 2000 to 24000 vph—the results seem *more* plausible. For this change, about 9 minutes were added to the initial 25-minute trip and the average trip cost increased from 177 to 230 cents. Thus, it is implied that tripmakers on the average would be willing to pay 53 cents (i.e., 230 − 177) in order to avoid adding an extra 9 minutes to the 25-minute trip. Importantly, if differential disutilities are valid for fairly large increments in travel time, then

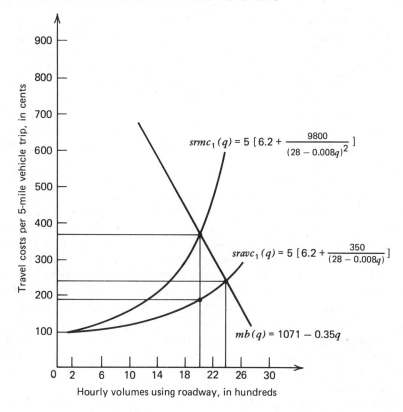

Figure 13-6. Travel cost and demand functions for 5-mile trips.

also implied, mathematically, is the existence of measurable utilities for very small or marginal increments in travel time.[8] That is, if the average variable costs increase, it can be shown (again, mathematically) that the marginal costs must exist and are higher than the average variable costs (for at least some of the intervening flow levels). And it is difficult not to argue that also implied is constant marginal utility of time, although nothing is explicitly assumed on that score.

It seems that, in a sense, we are allowing the mathematical relationships and niceties to overrule common sense if we accept the above inferences. For instance, why must or should we be willing to assume that a 1-second time increase experienced by 2000 travelers is really no different in

[8]Specifically, the following mathematical equivalence can be shown:

$$2400 \, sravc_1(2400) - 2000 \, sravc_1(2000) = \sum_{q=2000}^{2400} srmc_1(q)$$

value than a 400-second time increase experienced by 5 travelers? Admittedly, it is necessary to do so if we are to develop marginal cost functions and use them to determine marginal cost prices and tolls, as indicated before and in Figure 13-6. Also, the validity of marginal cost functions and marginal cost is clear-cut when one is dealing with small increases in gasoline or tire wear or other such resources consumed when output is increased by one unit, but it is not so straightforward when dealing with small increases in congestion, or crowding, or the like. The distinction is simple: the former can be easily valued, while the latter are difficult to value and may have no value at all.

Stated somewhat differently, it is considerably easier to accept the validity of the average variable cost function, especially when dealing with fairly large increments in flow rate, than it is to accept and apply the marginal cost function to marginal changes.

Obviously, one should ask: How should we determine the appropriate "congestion toll" in the absence of a marginal cost function (that is, if we deny its existence, *at least as determined by taking the derivative of the total variable cost function)?* First, let us not forget that the objective of imposing a congestion toll is simply to insure that trips whose value is less than their contribution to congestion are not made. Thus, with respect to the results taking place with average variable cost pricing, set the congestion toll so as to maximize the difference between the savings in total variable costs and losses in total benefits which stem from adding a congestion toll.

The above implies that for the situation depicted in Figure 13-7, the optimum flow and price, or q_{opt} and $p(q_{opt})$, respectively, occur when the following difference is maximized:

$$\max[\text{Cost savings} - \text{Benefit losses}] =$$

$$[q_{avc}\, sravc_x(q_{avc})] - [q_{opt}\, sravc_x(q_{opt})] - \sum_{q=q_{opt}}^{q_{avc}} mb(q) \qquad (13\text{-}27)$$

Moreover, rather than specify an explicit average variable cost function, it would seem wiser to deal incrementally with isolated points and their average trip times and costs. For instance, and referring to Figure 13-7, suppose that some facility operating without congestion tolls had a usage level of q_{avc} and an associated average travel time of $t_x(q_{avc})$. In turn, it would be necessary to estimate the average variable cost or $sravc_x(q_{avc})$ stemming from this travel time. Following this, a series of iterations would be required in order to determine the optimum flow rate, or q_{opt}, which would lower average travel time such that the difference in Equation (13-27) was maximized. Obviously, one would have to estimate not only the average travel time and cost for a flow rate of q_{opt}, but also the loss in trip benefits stemming from the reduction in flow. Finally, then, an estimate must be made of the congestion toll which would clear the market at that flow rate.

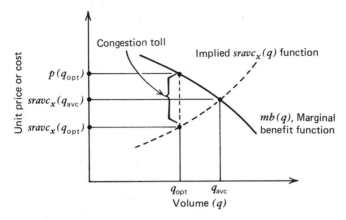

Figure 13-7. Congestion toll with implied unit cost function.

Such an iterative procedure, and one which deals with large increments in travel time and flow, may seem more sensible than one which accepts without question the validity of the marginal cost function derived simply by taking the partial derivative of the total variable cost function, as described by Equation (13-18).

13-3 SOME INNOVATIVE PRICING POSSIBILITIES FOR ROADWAYS

Our intent in this section is to discuss some possible innovations in the area of user charges for transportation services. We shall include suggestions for specific innovations in the areas of roadway charges, taxi regulations, and transit fares. We use the term *innovative* for these possibilities with the realization that our suggestions have been both proposed and implemented on occasion. However, few have been widely considered or implemented, even though many seem to us to be improvements on present practices.

Rather than prepare an exhaustive analysis of one or a few pricing possibilities, we have chosen to consider briefly a wide range of possibilities. Certainly, our suggestions should not be adopted without more extensive analysis and/or some consideration of the peculiarities of specific areas and services. Our main objective is to suggest that pricing innovations *can* be undertaken and *can* be beneficial. Also, we believe that the mere *existence* of a pricing policy is no argument for its continuation (nor should it be a *guarantee* of its continuation).

The innovations we shall discuss have been divided broadly into applications to roadways, taxi fare regulation, and transit pricing policies. With the first category, we shall consider one-way tolls on facilities, a late-night honor system for toll collection, and indexing of gasoline taxes. For taxi regulation, we consider the desirability of zone fare systems, surcharges on flag drops, and the relative levels of mileage and time charges. For transit, we consider the use of monthly and weekly passes, major fare increases, and peak hour surcharges.

Prior to detailed discussions, we should ask "Why haven't such ideas been adopted more widely?" Apart from the question of the desirability of any one policy, we believe that oversight and neglect are the most important reasons. The theoretical literature concerning pricing in public transportation has tended to concentrate upon the virtues of marginal or variable cost pricing for peak hours. With this focused attention, numerous innovations have been overlooked which could improve resource allocation but are not "optimal" or "first best" in an economic sense. While the theoretical literature has tended to be one-sighted, the practice of formulating pricing policies has been *other-sighted*. Agencies generally devise pricing policies which are politically and legally acceptable. Improved resource allocation has not been a notable concern of most of the fare and price setting agencies.

Of course, we should not denigrate the importance of political and financial considerations in formulating pricing policies. Any innovation must be acceptable on these grounds. For example, the lack of attention to the political implications of congestion pricing has probably been the major factor in the almost universal failure to implement such schemes. Attention to financial acceptability is the first and most important consideration for insuring the continued availability of transportation services. In what follows, we hope to suggest pricing innovations which are politically acceptable, financially possible, and economically advantageous.

13-3-1   ONE-WAY FACILITY TOLLS

Introducing a free direction on toll facilities is probably the most widespread and successful of all transportation pricing innovations made in the last 20 years. (Since the evidence is not yet in, we shall not compare this innovation to the fare deregulation for airlines and freight carriers.) Still, many toll bridges and tunnels have not adopted this pricing policy.

One-way facility tolls consist of removing the toll charge for one direction of travel on a facility. Usually, the toll in the other direction is increased to twice the level of the original toll, so that travelers making a round-trip over the facility still pay the same amount in total but need make only one stop to pay the toll charge.

The advantage of introducing this innovation is that toll collections are eliminated in the free direction of travel. The demand for toll collection space, personnel, and equipment is thereby reduced. Moreover, the congestion and queues in one direction of travel, which would have been caused by the toll collection stops, are eliminated. In addition, a shift from two-way to one-way toll collection will usually lead to an increase in the number of toll booths available for toll collection, thereby leading to a reduction in congestion and queueing for the one-way toll payers. Suppose, for instance, that a two-way toll plaza currently has space for 10 toll booths, and that during morning peak hours 6 booths are used for the inbound flow and 4 for the outbound flow. Since a toll booth can handle only 500 to 600 vph, the two-way system has the capacity to handle (at most) about 3600 vehicles inbound and 2400 outbound. However, a switch to a one-way system would mean that only two outbound noncollection lanes would be needed, thus leaving 8 toll booths to handle the inbound flow and reducing the inbound congestion and queues. In the afternoon the plaza presumably could operate with four (or more) inbound toll collection booths and six (or less) outbound noncollection lanes.[9]

Also, by having one-way tolls, traffic queueing at the toll plazas will be limited to one direction of travel, thus avoiding the possibility of blocking other critical streets and intersections in the vicinity. (Since many, if not most, toll plazas are on roadways heading to or located near downtown and other such congested areas, it would seem wise to collect the one-way toll in the inbound rather than outbound direction.) These considerations did indeed lead the Division of Bay Toll Crossings in the San Francisco area and the Port of New York Authority to invoke such a practice more than a decade ago. One can only wonder why most toll facilities, bridges, and tunnels in the heart of large cities have not also been converted.

The losses or costs of introducing one-way facility tolls are of four kinds, although two of these categories may be quickly rejected. First, most toll facilities will require some minor modifications to the toll collection booths for implementation. Some authorities which have introduced one-way tolls simply keep the booths in place, but this is at the cost of requiring vehicles to slow down in order to safely pass the constricted width of a toll booth. In any case modification costs are likely to be minor, and savings may even be made in some cases by eliminating some of the land required for extra toll booths. Second, some motorists may have an adverse psychological reaction to paying a double toll in one lump sum, rather than in two installments. We suspect that most motorists are not so naive that they cannot add up the total of the two separate toll payments.

A third concern may arise if there is an alternative, cheaper route that motorists may take and thereby avoid the payment of the double toll in one direction. Presumably, these motorists would use the facility in the free direction and then use the alternative route for the return trip. Strictly speaking, this shift in route choice does not represent an economic cost (that is, an irreversible use of resources) except to the extent that the use of the alternative route is more expensive than the toll facility

---

[9]For an empirical discussion of toll booth congestion, see L. C. Edie, "Traffic Delays at Toll Booths," *J. Oper. Res. Soc. Amer.* **2**(2), 107–138 (1954).

in terms of time and vehicle operating expenses. However, since these diversions represent a loss of revenue, they do present a financial burden to the toll authority.

To analyze this last point, an initial step would be to estimate the amount of diversion which would likely occur due to the toll increase. Only those motorists who value the extra costs of the alternative route *less* than the *extra* toll charge would be expected to alter their routes. In this calculation the level of the toll and the extra costs of the alternative route(s) are clearly important. Fairly good estimates of the amount of diversion could be prepared by experimentation or using the techniques of travel demand analysis (with the possible aid of a small roadside survey). Disaggregate mode split and route choice models as discussed in Chapter 11 are an obvious technique for application here.

While motorists who are diverted represent a loss of revenue, elimination of tolls in one direction should result in savings in toll collection equipment and personnel, perhaps a significant savings. In addition, even though toll authorities might have a net loss, it is important to note that motorists as a whole would be better off.

Finally, it might be argued that one-way tolls are unfair to motorists who are passing through. But, by the same token, it may be argued that it is equally unfair for motorists passing through in the opposite direction to pay no toll. To the extent that the two groups are roughly equal or that individual travelers will return over the course of some years (barring motorists who are migrating), any inequity will be equalized over time.

13-3-2   LATE-NIGHT HONOR SYSTEM FOR TOLL COLLECTIONS

During late-night shifts (such as 10:00 PM to 6:00 AM), the number of tolls collected at many booths is very low. In many cases it may be desirable to collect tolls on the honor system, thereby saving the cost of manning collection booths during the inconvenient low-volume and crime-prone late-night hours.

An honor system for collecting tolls relies upon motorists to deposit the appropriate toll without manual supervision. It is possible to place sirens and other devices to identify cheaters, but it would likely be ineffective (if not too costly) to place easily broken barriers, such as wooden arms, in the path of cheaters. To facilitate toll payment, it would be desirable to introduce simplified toll structures, automatic change machines, envelopes for later payment, or tokens (which might be sold at rest areas and during daytime hours).

Against the cost savings from eliminating late-night attendants, toll authorities might lose some revenue with this policy due to cheaters. To some extent, roving police patrols authorized to stop cheaters could reduce the amount of this revenue loss. However, for some low-volume toll facilities (such as at rural turnpike exits), it might well be that even a 100%

proportion of cheaters might still result in savings, since full collection of tolls can be insufficient to cover the expense of manning the toll booths for the late-night shift. In this case eliminating late-night tolls might be desirable (though possibly unfair). Thus, the criteria which should be examined in assessing a late-night honor system include the amount of savings realized by reducing manning levels, the amount of tolls now taken, and the proportion of cheaters expected. Algebraically, the late-night honor scheme at a particular facility will be financially desirable if

$$S > pqf \qquad\qquad (13\text{-}28)$$

where S is the amount of savings realized, p is the proportion of cheaters, q is the volume of vehicles during the late-night shift, and f is the average toll amount.

13-3-3 INDEXING GASOLINE TAXES

At both the federal and state levels gasoline taxes are set as a surcharge on each gallon, such as 10 cents per gallon. An alternative procedure would be to collect gasoline taxes as a *proportion* of the basic cost per gallon (but rounded down to the closest cents per gallon) or, alternatively, increase the tax rate periodically in proportion to the increase in the cost of maintaining roads.

The existing practice has substantial political and financial drawbacks. With annual gasoline sales expected to be constant (or only slightly increasing) in the next decade, the revenue from gasoline taxes will be declining in real dollars (that is, after correcting for inflationary increases in costs). Without tax increases or other revenue road deterioration is a likely (though not necessary) result. With deterioration motorists could incur extra costs from more frequent accidents, longer travel times and increased vehicle repairs. Politically, legislative bodies are faced with a continuing series of requests to increase gas taxes in order to continue adequate levels of maintenance, and increased taxes are always difficult to vote for. Faced with declining revenues and periodic requests to legislatures, transportation agencies understandably have a difficult time in planning maintenance and rehabilitation expenditures rationally.

Economically, it is desirable to impose a charge on drivers which is equal to the roadway wear and tear caused by their vehicles. (It may also be desirable to impose a charge for the external costs of congestion, but as noted earlier, this is generally politically unacceptable and also may incur more costs due to collection expenses than benefits.) This charge would be directly proportional to the amount of wear and tear caused by individual vehicles and, by and large, taxes on gasoline serve as a rough and practical means of imposing this charge. Thus, motorists pay gasoline taxes which are roughly equal to the average variable costs of maintaining the roadway system. (This argument does not imply that the capital costs of new construction should also be obtained from gasoline taxes or tolls, however. This is a financing mechanism which may unduly restrict the amount of tripmaking in some cases.) If gas tax revenue declines over time (again in inflation-adjusted dollars), motorists may end up paying less than the costs which they impose on the roadway system. Thus, indexing the amount of gasoline taxes can insure that charges remain commensurate with actual costs.

Legislation can be introduced to make gasoline taxes a proportion of purchase price, just as sales taxes are imposed. It would be better to set gas taxes with respect to the actual costs of maintenance and rehabilitation of the roadway system by means of automatic tax increases as these costs increase. (However, a caveat is due here: with automatic tax increases to cover costs, there is no managerial incentive to hold costs down. For this reason the use of a more general price index—such as the wholesale price index or gas prices—might be appropriate.) For implementation, a minor difficulty arises from a limitation of gas pumps: often, meters only allow the collection of taxes as a surcharge on volume, such as 10 cents per gallon.

In sum, with the introduction of gas indexes, legislatures would avoid the need to periodically impose higher taxes, transportation agencies would have a dependable funding source, motorists would face charges commensurate with their use of roadways, and hopefully we would all benefit from a roadway system in good condition.

13-4   SOME POSSIBLE INNOVATIONS FOR TAXI FARE SETTING

13-4-1   ZONE SYSTEMS VERSUS METERED FARE CHARGES

In most major metropolitan areas taxicabs are required to have a meter, and fares for a ride are set by a combination of the trip time and distance plus a fixed "flag drop" charge. However, there are a number of reasons that fares based upon a zonal system might be more desirable. A zone-based fare system divides a metropolitan area into numerous distinct districts or zones. A distinct fare is set in advance for trips entirely within a zone or between each pair of zones. Fixed surcharges may be added for specific time periods, such as peak hour service. Extra charges may be imposed for waiting time, additional passengers, baggage, and so on.

Discussions of zone- and meter-based pricing policies have occasionally appeared in the literature.[10] Washington, D.C., has provided a highly visible example of the practicality of zone fare systems. Here we shall briefly consider some economic issues relevant to determining the desira-

---

[10]See R. Kirby et al., (1974), *Paratransit*, The Urban Institute, Washington, D.C., for a review.

bility of one or the other fare system. We shall not discuss the political implications of metered versus zonal fares.

First, some individuals have argued that a zonal fare system is unfair. For example, trips with identical destinations but originating close to one another (e.g., across a street) may have different fare charges if a zonal boundary is between the origins. In this case one trip might be an intra-zonal fare charge while the other is an interzonal (and presumably higher) fare. While some bias of this nature is inevitable in a zone fare system, it can be reduced to very small amounts by simply making zones smaller.

Second, meter-based fares impose the costs of unexpected congestion delays on patrons rather than on taxi operators. With unusual congestion delays, meter-based systems will automatically impose higher fares, whereas zone-based systems are insensitive to extraordinary congestion delays on a particular trip. The issue here is not one of insuring adequate compensation to taxicabs: over the course of time both zone- and meter-based fare structures must return compensation which is adequate to insure taxicab profitability. To compensate for daily peak period congestion (which, after all, is expected and hardly extraordinary), it is possible to impose a surcharge or separate (and higher) interzonal fares during peak periods within a zonal fare system, as is the case in Washington, D.C. Thus, the question is whether or not taxis or patrons should assume the risks of *extraordinary* delays. Retailers in other fields ordinarily assume extra costs of this nature, and we shall argue below that there are several good reasons for this practice.

One such reason is the greater predictability of fares under a zonal system. Regular (and perhaps irregular) users of taxicabs know exactly what fare will be charged under the zonal system, whereas meter fares may vary considerably. This reliability is analogous to retailer's practice of uniform price setting and serves to increase the overall demand. Since many taxi patrons come from low-income households who undoubtedly have low capital reserves, predictability of fares may be quite important for these patrons. In 1977 one-third of all taxi patrons came from households with incomes less than $10,000 as indicated by the Nationwide Personal Transportation Study.

Another problem with fares based upon actual distance and times is that cabdrivers have an incentive to adopt circuitous routes. Newcomers to a city are often (unwittingly) provided with a lengthy tour rather than a direct trip, solely as a means to increase the ultimate fare (we presume, of course, that the touring benefits of such circuitous routes do not compensate for the extra charge). This wasteful incentive is eliminated with a zone fare system, in which cabdrivers receive no extra compensation for detours. (As a parenthetical note, the zone fare system might encourage cabdrivers to break traffic regulations or drive at unsafe speeds in order to reduce the required trip time. This phenomenon also exists in meter-based systems. Stricter enforcement of traffic codes is called for in these situations.)

In several areas zone fare systems can have distinct and unambiguous advantages over meter-based systems. First, the costs of providing taxi service vary with the density of demand due to the reductions in dead-heading. With meter-based systems cabdrivers are often reluctant to undertake trips to distant suburbs since they usually involve deadheading empty and unprofitably in one direction and since the density of demand cannot be reflected in the fares. This phenomenon is one cause of the problem of service refusal. In setting up the table of fares between specific zones, it would be possible to have fares reflect the higher unit costs for trips to or from areas of low-demand density.

Zone fare systems are also more easily adapted to the practice of shared-ride taxi service in which more than one patron group is serviced at a time. We suspect that the increase in subsidized taxi trips (assisted by social service agencies) and continuing financial troubles in the taxi industry will lead to more shared-ride service (of course, service reduction or discontinuation is also a possibility). Taxi meters would require extensive modification to permit differential charges for shared-ride service.

Finally, zonal fare systems eliminate the need and thus the costs associated with purchasing and maintaining taxi meters themselves. These meters cost in the range of $300 to $400 apiece in 1973, whereas zonal systems require only a city map and placard indicating interzonal fares. Taxi meters modified for use in shared-ride service would be even more expensive.[11] Reducing the capital charges associated with operating a taxi may have an important effect on the availability of taxis in the event of entry controls relaxation. In Washington, D.C., the cost of entering taxi service is low, so many part-time drivers enter the industry with vehicles also used for private purposes. As a partial result, Washington has more per capita cab and taxi service available than any other American city.[12]

13-4-2   THE FIXED CHARGE IN METERED TAXI FARES

Given that a policy of metered taxi fares is established, the level at which the various charges are set is an important policy question. In this section we argue that rate increases should not be concentrated upon the fixed or "flag drop" charge for service. We will assume that in the long run the overall compensation to taxi operators must be sufficient to cover costs and a normal rate of profitability; otherwise, the operators will discontinue service. The issue we address here is the proper ratio between the fixed charge and charges associated with time or mileage. Since we con-

[11]See D. Baumann and T. Au, "Ride-Shared Vehicle Paratransit System," Report to USDOT, DOT-TST-77-86, 1978 for a description of a computer-based, shared-ride taxi meter.

[12]Kirby et al., op. cit., p. 77.

sider the relationship between time and mileage rates in the next section, we shall simplify the discussion here by comparing only the fixed flag drop and the mileage drop.

Requests for rate increases have often concentrated upon increases in the flag drop charge. For example, New York City approved a 15-cent increase in the flag drop charge as a temporary increase to compensate for increased fuel charges.[13]

If a regulatory commission is interested in setting fares based upon cost, then it is relevant to consider the extent to which taxicab costs should be reflected in initial charges or in variable charges. On these grounds the New York City flag drop surcharge to compensate for increased gas charges is peculiar: long trips use more gasoline than do short trips, and so these longer trips should bear a higher burden of the increased gasoline costs. Thus, a gasoline surcharge should be placed upon the per mile taxi rate.

After some consideration, we can justify only two costs directly attributable to taxi trips as contrasted with trip durations. These are the costs of dispatching services and the time spent in boarding and unloading patrons which is not included in metered time. We suspect that these two costs are below the average initial charge of 50 cents in 1973, which represents roughly 25% of all taxi revenue.[14] One might also argue about the allocation of the costs of deadheading to collect patrons. However, time spent in deadheading is not incurred by all trips and, moreover, tends to vary with the length of trips (as well as the origin and destination location). To include deadheading costs, a special surcharge for radio dispatching might be introduced (as occurs in Washington, D.C.).

There also exists, however, a relatively large sum of expenses which cannot be directly attributed to trips or trip durations. These expenses include time spent waiting or cruising for additional new patrons and capital charges associated with taxi ownership (including registration fees, chauffer's license fees, medallions). It is not at all clear whether these various fixed expenses should be allocated on a per passenger basis (and thus included in the flag drop charge) or on a per mile basis (and thus included in the mileage or time charge).

The difference in these allocations is simply this: should patrons making long trips pay a higher proportion of fixed costs than patrons making short trips? Lower flag drops will clearly favor patrons with shorter trips.

---

[13]M. Carrol, "Taxi Fares to Rise by $.15 Temporarily to Offset Gas Costs," *New York Times,* July 12, 1979, p. A1.

[14]Wells ("An Analysis of Taxicab Operating Characteristics," Report to USDOT, 1975) reports a typical flag drop charge of $0.60 for the first $\frac{1}{5}$ mile and an additional mileage charge of $0.10 per $\frac{1}{5}$ mile. Hence, the initial fixed charge is $60 - 10 = \$0.50$. Wells and Selover ("Characteristics of the Urban Taxicab Transit Industry," Report to USDOT, 1972) report an average fare of $2.00, so the initial charge is $\frac{0.50}{2} = 25\%$ of revenue.

An assumption that the taxi patronage volume is fixed suggests one reason to concentrate fare increases on flag drop charges. In this case the extra revenue from a surcharge is relatively simple to calculate as the product of volume and the amount of the fare increase. However, there is considerable evidence that taxi volume is not invariant with respect to fare, so this analytical simplicity is a pipedream. A few other aspects of this question deserve mention.

First, although the data are rather sketchy, it seems to be the case that long-distance taxi trips are concentrated among individuals with higher incomes than other taxi passengers. As a result, higher flag drop charges are slightly regressive, distributing money from poorer to richer patrons. Second, patrons taking shorter trips tend to have a ready substitute in the form of walking. As a result, the elasticity of demand for shorter taxi trips is probably larger than the corresponding elasticity for long taxi trips. To maximize revenue and ridership, it would be advantageous in this case to charge longer trips relatively more than short trips. Third, long taxi trips often have an origin or a destination in areas with a relatively low demand density, thereby requiring more deadheading by cabs and occasionally higher costs. For these reasons fare increases should not be concentrated in the flag drop charge.

13-4-3 MILEAGE AND TIME CHARGES FOR METERED TAXI FARES

In this section we suggest that the time charge may be set too low in many metered taxi fares. The amount charged per taxi trip using a meter is a combination of a fixed "flag drop" charge, a mileage-based charge (accumulated during periods in which the taxi exceeds a set speed such as 10 mph), and a time charge (accumulated during periods in which the cab travels at less than a specified speed, such as 10 mph). Algebraically, the total fare is roughly[15]

$$F = F_0 + aX + bT \tag{13-29}$$

where F is the fare, F_0 is the flag drop charge, X is the total distance traveled, T is the total time traveled, and a and b are constants that depend upon the distance and time fare rates (generally known as the additional mileage and traffic delay or waiting time charges, respectively). Equation (13-29) is somewhat misleading, however, in implying that time and distance charges accrue simultaneously. In fact, taxi meters work on the principle that the higher of the mileage rate or of the time rate is charged at any time. As a result, there is a critical speed (such as the 10

---

[15]See D. Ghahraman, T. Au, and D. Baumann, "Analysis of Metered Taxi Fares," *Trans. Engr. Journal, ASCE* **101** (1975) for a discussion of the actual process by which fares are metered.

mph above) above which mileage charges alone are accrued. (We might also note that the time period over which average speeds are calculated also influences the fare, even though this aspect of metering is usually unregulated. A taxi might average 15 mph on an arterial street, but come to rest occasionally for lights. With a short averaging period to calculate speed, these brief stops could be charged at the time-delay rate. Thus, fares *increase* with shorter averaging periods. We presume that electronic taxi meters could average speeds over a very small period indeed.)

Typical taxi mileage and time charges were 10 cents for every $\frac{1}{5}$ or $\frac{1}{6}$ of a mile (after an initial distance and flag drop charge) and $6.00 for every hour in 1973. Thus, at sustained running speeds above 10 to 13 mph, the charge per mile traveled is the dominant effect. With this low speed, time charges are only accumulated during periods in which the cab is stationary (waiting for pickups, at long red lights, etc.) or in very congested traffic. An increase in the time charge (or a decrease in the additional mileage charge) would *increase* this critical running speed, so that at speeds of, say, 15 mph patrons might be paying on the basis of required travel time rather than mileage.

Figure 13-8 shows the taxi revenue per minute as a function of speed. In order to increase revenue per unit time, it is obvious that taxi drivers

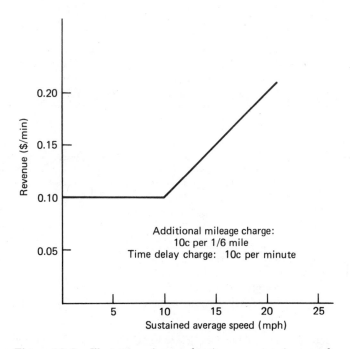

Figure 13-8.   Illustration of metered taxi revenue at various speeds.

would prefer to drive at a higher velocity: above the critical speed (shown as 10 mph in Figure 13-8), any increase in speed also increases the revenue per unit of time. Two implications of this observation are evident. First, taxis will tend to avoid congested areas or congested periods without offsetting compensations (such as higher demand densities which reduce waiting time between trips and deadheading). Second, taxis have a strong incentive to drive at unsafe speeds. An increase in the time-related charge would mitigate both these tendencies.

13-5 SOME POSSIBLE TRANSIT FARE INNOVATIONS

13-5-1 SHIFT TO PASSES

In most urban areas transit fares are collected upon entering vehicles or, in rapid rail systems, entering the system. It is not necessary to collect fares at these points, however. Conductors may collect fares while vehicles are in motion, as occurs on commuter rail systems or in two-man bus operation. More dramatically, some European systems operate on an honor system whereby passengers are expected to purchase a ticket or pass for trips. Roving inspectors check these tickets on occasion in order to enforce compliance, but drivers need not concern themselves with fare collection.

TABLE 13-2. Representative Passenger Loading and Unloading Times for Buses: Typical Weekday Rush Hour To and From Work

Condition	Item	Time per Passenger (seconds)
Unloading	Little hand baggage and parcels or few transfers	1.5–2.5
	Moderate hand baggage or many transfers	2.5–4
	Considerable baggage from racks	4–6
Loading	Single coin or token fare box	2–3
	Odd-penny cash fares	3–4
	Multizone fares:	
	Prepunched tickets and registration by driver	4–6
	Cash including registration by driver	6–8

Source: W. Rainville et al., "Preliminary Progress Report of Transit Subcommittee," *HRB Proc.* **60**, Table 6, p. 537 (1961).

Fare collection by drivers does result in a substantial amount of delay both because of collection time and inefficient use of doors for loading and unloading. For example, the time required for individual passengers to board with different fare collection schemes is shown in Table 13-3. One study of urban bus routes in St. Louis, Missouri found that 18% of the time required to traverse an average route was occupied in loading/unloading patrons.[16] If drivers were not required to collect fares, then boarding would proceed at the shortest interval shown in Table 13-3 (2 seconds per passenger) and could be accomplished at all vehicle doors. The result would be faster travel time over routes, yielding a higher quality of service and more productive use of vehicle and drive time.

How might this faster boarding/unloading be accomplished? To some extent, more reliance on monthly or weekly passes could speed up the boarding process since no fares need be collected for passholders. Or it might be advantageous to introduce a European type of system in which drivers are entirely relieved of the responsibility to collect fares. During World War II many transit agencies relied heavily upon weekly or monthly passes for use of the systems. Now, such passes are often restricted to weekend use. Moreover, the passes which are available in some transit agencies are not advertised extensively.

The use of passes has some distinct advantages and disadvantages. First, since drivers need only verify the validity of passes, their use will generally speed up the boarding and unloading process. Second, they reduce the marginal cost of transit service to pass holders, thereby increasing ridership and transit costs. Also, the introduction of passes requires a separate set of purchase transactions. To insure the easy availability of passes, numerous purchase locations should be designated. Retail stores are obvious candidates (and post offices, drug stores, or banks), but they must be induced to sell passes since sales increase the workload of clerks and management. These transaction costs are not likely to be major, however. In some cases it may be useful to have vehicle drivers equipped to sell passes.

Of more concern in the introduction of passes is the possibility of fraudulent use and loss of revenue. While measures may be taken to reduce the possibility of fraudulently exchanging passes (e.g., photographs of purchasers), such measures would be expensive.

Other than the changes in transactions costs (including fare collection time in vehicles), the most important effect of widely available passes is that heavy users of the transit would find that their average cost of using the system would *decrease* (otherwise they would not purchase the pass) and that their incremental monetary cost of additional trips would go to zero. (Individuals exchanging passes fraudulently would experience the

---

[16]W. C. Gilman, "St. Louis Metropolitan Area Transportation Study," New York, 1954.

same effect, only spread over more than one person.) Heavy users of transit service are likely to be more dependent on transit, so that the net effect is that transit-dependent individuals would tend to face lower (average) fares or, equivalently, be more heavily subsidized. A corollary of this effect is that transit agencies might face net revenue losses as heavy users switch to passes. Indeed, some empirical evidence suggests that this loss of revenue does occur.[17]

An advantage of the use of passes is that they permit the introduction of differential pricing structures. For example, elderly individuals often can register and have reduced fare on most transit services. Discounted passes might also be offered to other groups deemed to be worthy of more extensive subsidy, such as the physically handicapped and the poor. It is also possible to introduce passes which would only be accepted during off-peak travel hours. In this way differential peak and off-peak fares could be (partially) introduced.

Even more reductions in delays and costs due to boarding/unloading could be accomplished by switching to a European honor system in which drivers were not responsible for collecting fares and verifying pass validity. Of course, extra costs would be incurred in such a system due to the need for roving inspectors. A reliance on individual patron compliance would be essential to make such a system work.

13-5-2   THE CASE FOR TRANSIT FARE INCREASES

We believe that user fare payments should not necessarily be falling, as they have been for transit fares, but that fare increases (in inflation-adjusted dollars) should be considered. With the trend experienced between 1965 and 1983, it should be evident that the United States is implicitly embarking upon a policy by which the contribution of farebox revenue towards transit expenses will be falling to new historical lows: in 1980 farebox revenue contributed only 40% of operating expenses, and this ratio has continued to drop. In addition, the relative costs associated with auto and transit use are changing dramatically, with transit becoming less expensive to users while auto costs are increasing. Before accepting these changes, it would be prudent to consider the possibility of fare increases commensurate, at least, with the general increase in prices and/or transit expenditures.

First, there is considerable evidence that transit patronage is more sensitive to the quality of service provided than to the price of service. That is, fare elasticity is numerically smaller than elasticity with respect to comfort and speed. This implies that improving the quality of transit service (by increasing bus frequency, comfort, etc.) would attract patron-

---

[17]L. B. Doxsey, "Demand for Unlimited Use of Transit Passes," *J. Trans. Econ. Policy*, **18** (1984).

age more than would a policy of decreasing fares. With higher fares, of course, more revenue would be available to pay for higher-quality service (assuming that transit services do have financial constraints).

Second, many individuals argue that lower fares aid poorer individuals. In fact, many transit riders are not poor. In 1977, for example, more than 38% of all transit riders came from households with incomes of $15,000 or more, and more than 57% of all riders came from households of $10,000 or more. (For comparison purposes, the median household income for all U.S. metropolitan area residents was about $15,000 in 1977.) A number of alternatives exist which would be much more effective than lower transit fares in aiding the poor or other groups, such as special stamps for transportation similar to food stamps, more subsidized transit passes, special paratransit service, or money grants.

The case for extremely low general transit fares rests ultimately on external effects and the extent that patronage is stimulated by low fares. Proponents argue that increased transit ridership reduces roadway congestion, air pollution, energy consumption, urban sprawl, and other costs. These benefits are debatable in many instances, particularly in small urban areas. Moreover, improved quality may be more important than reduced fares in attracting people from autos (from which most external benefits are derived).

CHAPTER 14

PRACTICAL PROBLEMS IN INVESTMENT ANALYSIS

As a means of pointing out some typical pitfalls and to summarize the analysis techniques discussed in detail earlier in the book, this chapter is intended to illustrate some practical problems in investment analysis. Our intent here is not to be encyclopedic. Indeed, the variety of environments and technologies for transportation would preclude anything but gross generalities if we attempted to comprehensively discuss the problems specific to each investment decision. Instead, we will outline the various steps which have been considered in past chapters and to describe some typical problems and mistakes which arise in practice. We conclude with some suggestions for innovations.

14-1 DEFINING A POINT OF VIEW

In order to properly account for costs and benefits, it is essential to adopt a point of view for analysis. The benefits and costs of transportation investments are likely to be widespread over individuals, space, and time. In defining a point of view, an analyst makes an implicit or explicit decision about the limits for determining what is considered a benefit and what is a cost.

As an example, the viewpoint of a locality might be adopted for an investment analysis. From this perspective, subsidies received from the state or federal governments would be benefits. Any benefits received by visitors and residents of other localities might not be counted in this analysis since they would not benefit the locality directly; indirect benefits from such usage would be limited to profits and taxes from purchases made by such visitors. This local point of view clearly influences the type of projects which would be chosen. First, projects which primarily benefited local residents would be favored rather than regional facilities. Second, projects might be more capital intensive (that is, have higher initial costs) than they otherwise would so as to take advantage of capital subsidies from other levels of government.

As an illustration of a local viewpoint, consider the decision between two capital and maintenance alternatives, as shown in Table 14-1. This is an example of a cost-effectiveness analysis using equivalent uniform annual costs. With a decision to provide lower capital cost equipment, higher maintenance costs will be incurred, along with lower annual capital costs for replacement. The reverse is true for a more capital-intensive policy. The different policies are expected to have equivalent performance and usages, and therefore equal total benefits. As shown in the table, the lower capital cost policy has lower total annual costs ($1.6 million vs. $1.7 million). However, suppose that subsidy funds were available from higher levels of government such that 80% of capital investments and 50% of operating costs were subsidized. Treating these subsidies as a revenue benefit to the locality, the annual net cost for the two maintenance policies is such that the *low* maintenance cost alternative is preferred. Thus, from a *national* perspective, the high maintenance cost policy is more desirable (i.e., more cost-effective), but from the *local* viewpoint, the low maintenance cost policy is preferable. A similar analysis and results might occur if a private firm's viewpoint was adopted and differential tax rates on capital and operating expenses were applied.

Because of these sorts of differences in results, it is imperative for an objective analysis to be consistent in defining a point of view for conducting an analysis. In this text we have generally advocated using the point of view of the individuals whose resources are invested or used by a project. In this case the subsidy funds received from the federal government in Table 14-1 would suggest that a national viewpoint should be adopted. However, other viewpoints might be applicable in particular cases, such as an international point of view. What is important is that the point of view be thoughtfully and clearly established by the analyst. Analyses which are

TABLE 14-1.   An Illustration of the Effect of "Point of View" on a Cost-Effectiveness Analysis (in thousands of dollars)

	Alternative	
Item	Low Capital and High Maintenance Cost	High Capital and Low Maintenance Cost
Annual capital cost	$ 900	$1200
Annual maintenance cost	700	500
Annual total cost	1600	1700
Annual subsidy		
Capital (80%)	720	960
Operating (50%)	350	250
Total revenue	1070	1210
Annual net cost to locality	530	490

ambiguous on this point—and many are—should be carefully examined for misleading results.

Perhaps the most natural point of view to adopt in conducting an alternatives analysis is that of the provider organization or, more specifically, of the decision makers with the organization. For private providers, this practice is quite reasonable and acceptable; the public interest intrudes in such cases by tax policies, regulatory constraints, or other influences as well as by the congruence of private and public interests. Of course, there may still be a difference between the interests of company officials and that of shareholders. For public providers, the situation is different. To the extent that the organizational point of view is consistent with the public interest, then this practice is quite defendable. However, bureaucratic or political aggrandizement at the expense of a more general public interest is not desirable.

These remarks also suggest a corollary for the higher levels of government which provide subsidy funds to localities or tax deductions to private firms. Differential subsidy or deduction rates *can* influence investment choices. In the form of tax deductions, such differential rates on, say, capital investments might be justified because private firms do not consider the *external* benefits of private investment. For subsidies to local governments, however, we believe that it is desirable to insist that the national point of view be adopted and that benefits and costs "to whomsoever they may accrue" be considered.

·14-2 IDENTIFYING ALTERNATIVES FOR ANALYSIS

Perhaps the most difficult step in considering transportation investments is that of generating a set of reasonable alternatives for analysis. Clearly, the best alternative chosen for implementation will be limited to one among the set of alternatives chosen for analysis. Consequently, an analyst would like a broad range of alternative technologies and project scopes. On the other hand, the number of alternatives to consider may grow very large, thereby greatly increasing the costs of an analysis if not making detailed analysis prohibitively expensive. Indeed, the various permutations of different facility sizes, operating policies, and pricing policies can rapidly grow to a very large number.

A reasonable strategy to adopt in identifying alternatives is to use a hierarchical or iterative search procedure by which, first, the best alternative within broad technological options is found and, second, these best options for the different technologies are compared. In this process combinations of two or more investments should be considered as distinct alternatives and the interactions between such combined alternatives duly considered. In addition, the do-nothing or null alternative as well as the alternative of maintaining the status quo should be considered; the do-nothing or null alternative involves incurring no costs and no benefits through abandonment of facilities if necessary.[1]

As an example, suppose that one is considering the possible replacement of a waterway lock. In an initial analysis, the best alternative for the following set of options might be identified:

Improved operating policies to increase the lock efficiency.

Improved pricing policies for the lock.

Best alternative(s) for rehabilitation of the existing lock.

Best alternative(s) for replacement with a similar-sized lock.

Best alternative(s) for replacement with larger or smaller locks.

Best alternative(s) for relocation of the lock.

Clearly, a large number of alternatives could be analyzed within each of these options. For example, replacement locks might be constructed by different methods and with different materials.

Once a set of preliminary options has been identified, then these options, combinations of these options (such as improved operating policies and replacement with a smaller lock), as well as the null and the status quo alternatives, should be considered.

This type of iterative process is intended to develop a set of "good" alternatives for detailed analysis. The tendency in many investment analyses is to slant the analysis by introducing one reasonable and numerous "strawmen" alternatives. These "strawmen" alternatives are chosen to suggest that a comprehensive analysis has been undertaken, yet these alternatives are often inferior. By pointing to the horrors of these undesirable "strawmen" alternatives, support for a desired investment might be assured.

One particular problem in identifying alternatives deserves mention. Transportation providers are often restricted to a particular mode of travel and type of organization; in fact, it is common at the federal level to mandate an advocacy position for modal administrations. Although the provider may be restricted to particular alternatives, should a wide range of alternatives be examined? For example, an alternative to maintaining a navigable waterway might be the improvement of road and rail connections. However, the Army Corps of Engineers, which manages most U.S. water investments, cannot directly invest in general rail or roadway improvements. Should a wide range of alternative investments be considered in such cases?

Our view would be Yes, a broad range of alternatives should be analyzed, even though their implementation might fall outside of the domain

[1]See M. L. Manheim, *Hierarchical Structure: A Model of Planning and Design Processes*, MIT Press, Cambridge, 1966.

of a particular provider. Of course, in particular cases the alternative which maximizes net present value might be rejected due to constraints on agency action. But such constraints can be considered in the analysis process (as described in Chapter 10) and reporting their effect may influence the imposition of such restrictions. By analyzing a broad range of options, other private or public providers might be attracted to the alternative investments. More generally, political action might inspire such other organizations. An obvious example of the latter would occur in the case that private provision of public transit services (via taxicab or subscription bus in low-density areas, for example) might be permitted if a transit agency found that such private provision would be advantageous.

A broader role for private investment can also be considered. In some countries major transportation facilities are constructed and operated by private providers under franchise. Construction and operating costs are covered by the user fees for the facilities. After a period of some years the franchises lapse and facilities revert to public ownership.

14-3   ESTIMATING THE COST FOR EACH ALTERNATIVE

After identifying a point of view and each alternative, the next analysis step is to estimate the costs of the alternative over the relevant planning horizon. Methods for estimating such costs have been described in Chapter 12. Here we shall describe three common errors in preparing such estimates.

First, it is conceptually and computationally simpler to prepare cost estimates in constant dollar amounts. This implies that the general effects of inflation are removed from the cost estimates. Occasionally, an analysis proceeds with some estimates in constant dollars and some in nominal dollar amounts. At best, the result is confusing, and at worst would be wrong if the amounts are intermixed.

While this principle of using constant dollar estimates is straightforward, application can be exceedingly difficult since the cost of some items can increase or decrease over time at rates which differ from the general rate of inflation. Some notable examples of such differential cost changes include general construction costs (which have increased faster than the general rate of inflation) and electronic sensing and computing (for which remarkable cost reductions have occurred). Generally, corrections for such differential cost trends are to be avoided since a past trend may not hold in the future. In selected instances, however, some corrections might be desirable.

A second and more common error in preparing cost estimates is to ignore the principle of sunk costs. As described in Chapter 4, resource commitments which have occurred in the past are irrelevant in considering alternatives except insofar as they influence future costs and benefits.

In effect, past actions do not necessarily commit you to future ones. For example, suppose that a technologically superior railroad engine were developed such that its capital investment plus operating costs were less than the operating costs of the existing fleet of engines. An objective analysis would suggest replacing the existing fleet with the new engines in this instance. However, a decision maker ignoring the principle of sunk costs might argue that the old engines should be retained during their serviceable life to insure that their "cost" was covered. Unfortunately, this argument results in higher costs for service now and in the future. While this example may seem contrived, it might be reasonably accurate for the case of diesel versus steam locomotives immediately after World War II, when the performance and cost savings of diesel locomotives might have suggested a more rapid conversion than that which actually occurred.

As a third example of mistakes, it is important to insure that alternatives are considered in a consistent fashion in estimating costs. For example, maintenance costs for new equipment might be estimated by manufacturers. Since the range of maintenance problems is difficult to foresee and, perhaps, due to the optimism of the manufacturers, such cost estimates are often low. To compare these estimated maintenance costs without an adjustment to the historical average of maintenance costs for existing equipment results in an inconsistent treatment of alternatives. Alternatives should be compared on the basis of consistent and unbiased estimates to the extent possible.

As a final comment, we cannot help but record with dismay the long history of "overoptimism" that characterizes the capital and operating projections which accompany feasibility studies for public project proposals in the transportation sector. It is all too obvious that the cost estimation models and techniques systematically lead to an understatement of the real costs and that insufficient effort is made to correct this bias.

14-4 ESTIMATING THE BENEFITS OF EACH ALTERNATIVE

Benefit estimation is exceedingly difficult. For analysis of costs, accounting records are often available to check the accuracy of the past estimates. For some components of benefits, similar comparisons are possible. In particular, revenues and user payments can be obtained from accounting records and measurements. However, the amount of consumers' surplus as well as the value placed upon different components of user cost do not have such historical means of calibration. Consequently, the estimation of benefits is particularly prone to error.

One category of error in estimating benefits can be easily seen. Some analyses include the "costs avoided" from other alternatives as a benefit of the alternative chosen. For example, analysis of the expansion of an existing airport might claim as a "benefit" the costs avoided by not building a new airport or an alternative to it (e.g., a new highway or railroad). This argument is very misleading. Indeed, the "benefits" of an airport expansion as calculated in this manner could be any amount; if the new airport which was not built had been located near the central business district of the metropolitan area, then the "costs avoided" by not constructing it would have been large indeed. More properly, the airport expansion should be compared with new airport alternatives as well as the null and status quo alternatives, without including "costs avoided."

Another common error in estimating benefits occurs by assuming that there is necessarily a constant average benefit which accompanies usage of a facility. In particular, patronage attracted by reducing fares is likely to have a lower average trip benefit than existed before. After all, if the benefit of the newly attracted trips was as large, then they would already have been using the service. As a result, reports of usage figures without some consideration of the benefits actually received are difficult to interpret.

Another error in estimating benefits is to implicitly assume that benefits for all alternatives are necessarily equal. In this case analysis of alternatives is simplified since only the costs of alternatives differ, resulting in the problem of "cost-effectiveness'" analysis. However, most investment alternatives do influence usage and the total level of benefits received.

Perhaps the most common error which occurs in the estimation of benefits from transportation investment is that of overly optimistic volume forecasts. With high-volume estimates, benefit levels are correspondingly larger and more capital investment is justified than is desirable. Examining the historical record of volume forecasts, there appears to be a substantial bias towards overestimates for virtually all public projects. (A notable example of underestimates occurred for airplane and urban public highway use during the 1950s and 1960s, but more recent forecasts have been consistent with an optimistic approach.) The record of post-1950s quasi-private toll roads and public rail transit extensions or systems has been poor to dismal. Some corrections to typical forecasting methods are in order.

The reasons for overly optimistic forecasts are varied, of course. Two of the most prominent are optimistic forecasts of growth in population or employment and a misunderstanding of the basic market served by a transportation facility. For example, should one conclude that a doubling of the population in a metropolitan area will necessarily lead to a doubling of the market for transit patronage? While plausible on the surface, the historical record serves to contradict this assumption. In particular, the 1950 to 1980 growth in metropolitan areas in the United States has largely been concentrated in the suburbs or in outlying portions of large central cities. By contrast, transit patronage is more closely related to downtown employment and population in the dense urban cores. As a result, increases in the size of the transit market are not generally proportional to increases in the metropolitan level population.

A final error in benefit estimation deserves at least passing mention. This is the problem of failing to consider systematic effects which tend to dilute or reduce the benefits actually received from an investment. For example, the removal of a bottleneck along a roadway may lead to an increase in volume and to extra delays (relative to the prior situation) at some downstream point. That is, a new bottleneck may develop elsewhere along the roadway and either reduce or eliminate expected benefits. Also, in competitive situations, responses of competing service providers may result in similar benefit reductions. That is, a particular investment may induce or precipitate investments or service changes by competitors, thereby reducing the volume and benefits received from the original investment.[2] To the extent possible, such reactions or systematic effects should be considered in the evaluation process as described in earlier chapters.

14-5 ALTERNATIVE SELECTIONS

Once the alternatives are identified and their respective costs and benefits estimated over the planning horizon, the problem of project selection arises. Chapters 7 to 10 discussed relevant methods and criteria for choice. This section describes some typical mistakes which are made in the process.

Despite the great attention displayed to the mechanics of computing a project with the highest net present value, it is not unusual to find studies which misapply or misinterpret selection methods. In particular, cases in which negative benefits and negative costs appear when applying the benefit–cost ratio method have occurred. While rules exist for selecting the best project in such cases, they have often been misapplied in practice. Similarly, multiple internal rates of return may occur, and analysts often do not know how to select the best project in such cases. These difficulties are the reason that we generally recommend use of the net present value method in this text.

A second general area which deserves attention is that of dealing with uncertainty. Many alternatives analyses proceed as if all estimates of volumes, benefits, and costs are known without error. This is far from true, so some consideration of the effects of such errors is advisable. Even without conducting a formal analysis to deal with uncertainty (as described in earlier chapters), one conceptual result can often be used. All

---

[2]For example, see R. H. Haveman, *The Economic Performance of Public Investments: An Ex-Post Evaluation of Water Resources Investments*, The Johns Hopkins University Press, Baltimore, 1972, for a description of railroad reactions to waterway navigation projects.

other things being equal, it is generally preferable to select an alternative which permits a flexible response to changing conditions. For such alternatives, adjustments may be made in response to changing conditions. A good example of a flexible high-capacity alternative might be the use of express buses on exclusive rights of way for urban mass transit rather than fixed-rail systems.[3]

The influence of budget or other financial constraints on services also deserves mention. With limited financial resources, particular investments are often competing for limited capital funds. To some extent, such problems may be alleviated by the use of borrowed investment funds; however, some agencies are restricted to a pay-as-you-go financing plan. More generally, it is important in selecting a project to consider the availability of investment funds throughout the construction period. Moreover, careful staging of project elements to achieve the highest benefits at lowest costs during early stages is important. There are numerous examples of projects which were delayed or terminated when half-built after the availability of construction funds was lost.

Another common practice worthy of emphasis involves project selection on the basis of cost-effectiveness measures (e.g., lowest cost per unit of output such as dollars per passenger trip or dollars per passenger mile), of lowest long-run average total cost, or of lowest total construction and user cost.[4] For all such measures either the benefit accrued from improvement or the sensitivity of travel to improved service is improperly accounted for (or ignored altogether), thus leading to incomplete or misleading indices for making project choices or for assessing the economic feasibility of projects.

Another problem having a significant impact upon investment analysis, especially with respect to the choice of possible alternatives, involves our attitudes about "accidents" and the value of "lost lives and limbs." It is clear that the social loss associated with "lost lives and limbs" is large. Yet, it is equally obvious that neither lives nor limbs are *priceless* and that society need not do *everything* humanly possible to avoid loss of life or limb, regardless of all else. If such a view were correct, then individuals in their everyday life would not voluntarily undertake activities in which they knowingly risk their life or limbs (e.g., skiing, hang-gliding, living in houses with steep stairs, driving fast, etc.). Similarly, if lives and limbs were literally priceless, society as a whole would not permit activities

---

[3]See J. Meyer, J. Kain, and M. Wohl, *The Urban Transportation Problem*, Harvard University Press, Cambridge, MA, 1965.

[4]For examples of the first and last, see "Comparative Analysis Study of Alternative Transit Systems: South Hills Corridor," study by DeLeuw, Cather & Company for the Port Authority of Allegheny County, PA, March 1976, Chapter X; and *Transportation and Traffic Engineering Handbook*, J. E. Baerwald (ed.), Prentice-Hall, Englewood Cliffs, NJ, 1976, Figure 12.14.

(such as driving motorized vehicles) that posed any threat at all to human life or limbs. Thus, we should avoid treating the saving of lives and limbs as an end unto itself but instead must balance the net benefits of an activity or investment against the risks of loss to life or limb. Similarly, for investments intended to reduce accidents, we must assess their expected impact on the number and severity of accidents as well as the consequent value of lives or limbs saved. (Chapter 10 dealt with relevant techniques in this regard.)

As a final note, it is important to recognize that when conducting investment analysis *some* decision must be or is reached during the process. That is, to delay carrying out some project or improvement while we continue to study the matter is, thereby, to decide that for the time being the best decision is the status quo. Such a decision, however, should be made explicit rather than by default. As a related matter, we would also point out that once a decision to undertake some long-term project has been made, and once initial commitments have begun, there is no absolute or binding reason (aside from legal mandates which may or may not be insurmountable) which necessitates the completion of the entire program as initially envisioned. The completion of the 41,000-mile Interstate Highway System or the U.S. supersonic transport in the 1960s are two cases in point. Simply stated, the prior and heavy resource commitments in no way *require* that henceforth we must complete the full system; rather, in each future year following the initial decision, the decision to complete the system is an open one which is dependent on the more up-to-date forecasts of expected costs and benefits. If you will, this is to restate the relevance of the ages-old adage: Do not throw good money after bad.

14-6 SOME POSSIBLE INVESTMENT INNOVATIONS

Before ending this chapter, we might note a few innovations which could be introduced into the transportation investment process. Again, these suggestions are intended as illustrations of the types of questions and analysis options which could be implemented in practice.

14-6-1 USER FEE FINANCING

Financing transportation investment by means of user fees has a number of desirable features.[5] It is a practice which should always be considered and, more often than not, adopted. By user fee financing, we include

---

[5]For a lengthier discussion, see C. Hendrickson, "Financing Civil Works with User Fees," *Civil Engineering* **53**(2), Feb., 1983.

excise taxes which go to support investment in facilities such as gasoline taxes or airline ticket surcharges. These taxes have the property that the users of the facilities directly pay for the construction and, usually, operating expenses.

The justification for user fee financing is that the benefits for most transportation facilities are primarily (if not almost exclusively) received by the users. Thus, there is a certain fairness in having the users actually pay for the services. (If you will, the situation is no different than those in which home owners or renters, car owners or renters, and so forth, make user payments to cover the associated costs of such services.) Moreover, most user fees will increase the efficiency of use of the services by insuring that only those trips yielding benefits at least as high as the fees use the facility (for a detailed analysis of this point, see Chapter 3). With user fee financing, there is also the possibility of permitting private provision of services, which may often be more efficient and less expensive than requiring public provision of services.

Of course, a disadvantage of user fee financing is that some desirable projects cannot be supported from such fees. That is, there might be no monetary charge which could pay for the services even though the total benefits exceed total costs; Chapter 7 describes several such cases. Even with price discrimination among different user groups, completely funding a facility or service from revenues may be impossible.

However, the advantage of user fee financing is that a discipline is enforced upon transportation providers. Too often, projects have been built for which benefit estimates were exceedingly optimistic. With the imposition of the user fee financing requirement, such benefit estimates might be examined more closely.

For cases in which it is socially desirable to encourage or allow certain needy or worthy groups to use services they otherwise could or would not afford, it is always possible to provide subsidies directly to those individuals for use on either public or private services. A major advantage of these "user side" subsidies is that in the process of helping certain needy or worthy people we do not also help the less needy or worthy at the same time, the latter being the case with systemwide fare subsidies.

14-6-2   REHABILITATION INVESTMENT

For the next few decades investment in restoration and rehabilitation of existing facilities is likely to be the largest component of U.S. transportation investment. In making such rehabilitation decisions, it would be desirable to conduct full-scale investment analyses. Too often, the tendency exists to simply replace a facility by one of the same size and capability, albeit with new design standards and construction techniques.

In deciding on rehabilitation, some additional options should always be considered, including:

Abandonment. With substantial population declines occurring in some areas (e.g., central cities in the Northeast), many existing facilities might not now be necessary or might be combined with others.

Improved Operation. Some older facilities might be altered during reconstruction to incorporate new functions. For example, roadways and bridges might include provisions for reversible lanes or one-way toll collections (see Chapter 13). Automated controls for entering a facility or improving the facility service are also obvious candidates for new improvements.

Construction. With improved operation, congestion tolls, or reduced population sizes, smaller facilities might be more desirable.

Expansion. Finally, expansion of a facility during rehabilitation is often a desirable alternative to examine.

In effect, we suggest that rehabilitation investments be given the same level of analysis and attention as new expenditures. After all, there may be even a wider range of opportunities for improvement in such cases than for *de novo* investments.

APPENDIX I

MATHEMATICAL NOTATION AND OPERATIONS

Throughout this book concepts are explained verbally, illustrated graphically and by example, and formalized mathematically. These mathematical representations are intended as a form of shorthand to formalize the presentation and to summarize concepts. To the extent possible, the mathematical representations are restricted to simple algebraic expressions, although at times a calculus derivative is used in addition to simple difference operators. This appendix is intended to summarize the mathematical notation used and to define various mathematical operations.

I-1 PARAMETER AND VARIABLE NOTATION

Variables are introduced throughout the book to represent different quantities for the variety of situations which may arise in practice or in planning. Generally, lowercase letters are used to represent unit quantities, such as price per trip (p), fare per person (f), or short-run average total cost in dollars per trip ($sratc$). Capital letters are used in two ways. First, variables referring to totals appear as capital letters. Examples include short-run total cost in dollars ($SRTC$) or net present value in dollars (NPV). As a second use, capital letters are used in figures to represent particular points.

Parameters or coefficients represent numerical values in mathematical expressions, such as expressions representing demand, price, or costs. For application, these parameter values must be estimated (using the statistical techniques described in Chapters 11 and 12 and in Appendix III) or assumed to have some particular value. In this book greek letters such as α, β, γ, θ, λ, τ, and ϕ are used to represent the true parameter values which must be estimated; Table I-1 lists all such parameters used in the book. With this notation, a simple linear demand function (defined below) relating the volume to trip price might be represented as

$$q = \alpha - \beta p \tag{I-1}$$

TABLE I-1. Parameter Values and Uses

Parameter Symbol	Name	Parameter Use[a]
α	Alpha	Demand or statistical function (Eq. 2-1 or III-1)
β	Beta	Demand or statistical function (Eq. 2-1 or III-1)
γ	Gamma	Demand function (Eq. 3-1)
δ	Delta	Price/volume or user cost function (Eq. 2-13)
ϵ	Epsilon	Elasticity (Eq. 2-8)
ζ	Zeta	User cost function (Eq. 2-15)
η	Eta	Demand function with respect to fares (Eq. 3-9)
θ	Theta	Demand function (Eq. 11-2)
κ	Kappa	Demand function (Eq. 3-9)
λ	Lambda	Demand function with respect to travel time (Eq. 3-19)
μ	Mu	True variable mean value (Eq. III-16)
ν	Nu	Unit value of time (Eq. 2-12)
ξ	Xi	Demand function (Eq. 11-7)
ρ	Rho	User cost function (Eq. 6-13)
σ	Sigma	Standard error
τ	Tau	User cost function (Eq. 2-15)
ϕ	Phi	Demand function (Eq. 11-2)
ψ	Psi	Demand function (Eq. 11-2)
ω	Omega	Demand function with respect to travel time (Eq. 3-19)

[a]Equation numbers indicate first uses of each parameter.

where q is volume (trips per hour), p is price (in dollars per trips), and α and β are the coefficients to be estimated. Also, when a hat (or ˆ) is shown over the parameter (such as $\hat{\alpha}$), it simply means that the value of $\hat{\alpha}$ is an estimated value of the true parameter value α.

I-2 MATHEMATICAL FUNCTIONS

One of the central purposes of this book is to describe the relationships between quantities such as volumes, prices, travel times, and others. To some extent, these interrelationships can be represented by mathematical functions which relate the value of some variable to other quantities. Simple examples include demand relationships in which volumes depend upon price (and other variables) or cost functions in which total cost depends upon volume (and other variables). Equation (I-1) above illustrates one such function relating volume and price. These mathematical functions can be illustrated graphically so they are also called *curves*, as in a "demand curve."

The mathematical functions of the natural logarithm, $\ln(y)$, and exponential, $\exp(x)$, are also examples of such functions. These two functions are standard in virtually all mathematical texts. The exponential function of x, $\exp(x)$, is the value of e (equal to $2.71828\ldots$) raised to the power of x: $\exp(x) = e^x = (2.71828\ldots)^x$. The natural logarithm function is to find the value of the power on e which will equal a particular number y. Clearly these two functions are related: indeed, the exponential of the natural logarithm of y or $\exp\{\ln[y]\}$ is y. In this book the logarithm and exponential functions are introduced since they are used in certain popular demand functions.

To simplify mathematical expressions, it is often useful to introduce a shorthand or abbreviated notation for functions. We use two such conventions. First, we define functions of particular variables. For example, $g(p)$ or $g\{p\}$ might represent some function of price, such as $g(p) = \alpha - \beta p$. In this notation the value of $g(p)$ for some particular level of price is found by inserting the value of p into the expression $\alpha - \beta p$ with the use of appropriate values for the parameters α and β. In this functional notation we generally assume that the values of parameters (such as α and β) are constant in any particular application.

As a second use of mathematical functions, we may use a particular variable to indicate a function, rather than an expression such as $g(p)$. For example, $sratc(q)$ represents the level of short-run average total cost at the volume level q. More formally, we know that short-run average total cost is some function of q. Our notation $sratc(q)$ simply summarizes and emphasizes this dependent relationship between $sratc$ and q. More succinctly, we may write an expression such as $q|p_0$, which is the value of the variable q evaluated at price $p = p_0$ (i.e., the value of q *given* $p = p_0$).

Some terminology for mathematical functions is worth noting. A function relates the value of one variable, say y, to one or more other variables. For example, $y = g(x, z)$ implies that y is a function of the variables x and z. In this case y is referred to as the dependent variable, whereas x and z are termed the explanatory or independent variables.

I-3 SUMMATION AND SUBSCRIPTS

In adding up benefits, costs, revenues, and other quantities, it is often the case that we wish to add or sum values over all users of a facility or service. Alternatively, we often wish to indicate the values of variables—such as cost or benefit—for different service or facility alternatives. To simplify mathematical expressions in such cases, we introduce subscripts. A subscript is used to indicate a particular trip, person, or alternative. For example, mb_i might represent the marginal benefit derived from the ith trip on a facility or service. As an alternative use of subscripts, $SRTC_x(q)$ would represent the short-run total cost of the xth service alternative at a volume of q. Generally, the interpretation attached to a particular subscript is defined at the time it is used.

To indicate summation over quantities, we use the symbol Σ. For example, total benefits obtained from q trips might be represented as

$$TB(q) = \sum_{i=1}^{q} mb_i = mb_1 + mb_2 + mb_3 + \cdots + mb_q \qquad \text{(I-2)}$$

where mb_i is the marginal benefit obtained from the ith trip. The symbol Σ indicates that the values of mb_i are to be summed for $i = 1$ to $i = q$.

On occasion, subscripts may become somewhat complex. For example, $\epsilon_{p_2}^1$ indicates the elasticity of demand on mode 1 with respect to the price on mode 2. When such complicated subscripts are used, they are introduced or reintroduced in each instance.

I-4 DIFFERENCES, RATES OF CHANGE, AND DERIVATIVES

In several places in this book it is useful to compare or to consider the *marginal* changes in different variables. For example, one might wish to compare the change in benefits with the change in costs due to the attraction of additional travel volume onto a facility or service. Indeed, such marginal changes are of such interest that several marginal functions are explicitly defined and discussed, including the short-run marginal cost function [*srmc(q)*] or the marginal benefit curve [*mb(q)*]. These functions are defined as the rate of change of a particular variable with respect to an explanatory variable such as volume (q).

The difference between *marginal* and *incremental* changes also deserves mention. Technically, a *marginal* change occurs with a very small change in an explanatory variable. This small change is often referred to as "due to an *infinitesimal* change in the explanatory variable". An *incremental* change occurs with larger changes in the explanatory variable of more than one unit of volume.

One notation to formalize these rates of change is that of the difference operator. For example, suppose that the variable y is a function (as defined above) of a variable x. Then the rate of change of y with respect to x is the change which occurs in y (say, the value y_2 vs. y_1) as x changes (from, correspondingly, x_1 to x_2). In mathematical notation this difference is

$$\frac{\Delta y}{\Delta x} = \frac{y_2 - y_1}{x_2 - x_1} \qquad \text{(I-3)}$$

Clearly this rate of change may be different at different values of x.

In many cases it is desirable to examine the rate of change in the dependent variable [which is y in Eq. (I-3)] for very small changes in the explanatory variable [x in Eq. (I-3)]. This situation would occur when *marginal* changes were being considered. In this case the calculus derivative is useful. It can be (loosely) interpreted as the change in the dependent variable as the change in x becomes very small:

$$\frac{\partial y}{\partial x} = \lim_{\Delta x \to 0} \frac{\Delta y}{\Delta x} \qquad (I\text{-}4)$$

The notation $\partial y/\partial x$ indicates that the change in y is evaluated with all other variables held constant. In contrast, the notation dy/dx is used for calculus derivatives in which the effects of the changes in all other variables affected by the change in x are considered.

The calculus derivative has three advantages for analysis purposes. First, it is very often easier to calculate and manipulate than the difference value [Eq. (I-3)]. Second, it can be illustrated graphically as the *slope* of a function at any particular point; this interpretation is illustrated in Chapter 4 in the definition of the short-run marginal cost function as the *slope* of the total cost function. Finally, it insures that comparisons between, say, benefits and costs, are conducted at the best or "optimal" point because all potential values of the dependent variable are considered.

As an example, suppose we wish to find the marginal revenue function, or $\partial TR/\partial q$, and we know that revenue is the monetary charge times volume: $TR = fq$. In this case

$$\frac{\partial TR}{\partial q} = \frac{\partial(fq)}{\partial q}$$

$$= f\frac{\partial q}{\partial q} + q\frac{\partial f}{\partial q}$$

$$= f + q\frac{\partial f}{\partial q} \qquad (I\text{-}5)$$

which uses the chain rule of calculus derivatives.

General rules and procedures for obtaining the calculus derivative are beyond the scope of this work. Interested readers are urged to consult any introductory calculus text.[1]

[1]Appropriate texts include G. B. Thomas, *Calculus and Analytic Geometry*, Addison-Wesley, Reading, 1962, or A. Schwarz, *Calculus and Analytic Geometry*, Holt, Rinehart and Winston, New York, 1967.

CRITIQUE OF THE INTERNAL RATE-OF-RETURN METHOD AS USUALLY APPLIED WITH DISCUSSION OF REINVESTMENT IMPLICATIONS AND THE EFFECTIVE RATE OF RETURN

Engineering economists, especially, and the engineers and planners who adopt their views about the appropriate engineering economy (or benefit–cost analysis) methods invariably are misleading in three important respects. First, engineering economists usually contend that, properly applied, all methods of analysis will invariably lead to the same conclusions. Second, they generally contend that multiple solutions for the internal rate-of-return method are rarely encountered, thus offering no reason for rejecting the method as invalid. Third, engineering economists invariably misunderstand (and sometimes distort) consideration of reinvestment circumstances for projects (whether they be publicly or privately financed), and thus misstate the overall yield stemming from some particular course of action.

These problems were improperly treated not only in many early articles or engineering economy textbooks, but also in some more recent ones. Thus, a clarification of these aspects may be useful.

II-1 MULTIPLE RATE PROBLEM FOR THE USUAL DEFINITION OF THE INTERNAL RATE-OF-RETURN METHOD

Multiple solutions for the internal rate-of-return method can arise when there are two or more sign changes in the net benefits in various years. For example, when heavy future costs are expected to arise (for, say, rolling stock replacement or highway resurfacing, rehabilitation, and restoration) and when the costs are expected to exceed the benefits during those same years, such sign changes might be expected. Highway resurfacing, rehabilitation, and restoration both with respect to roadways and bridges provides a typical example in which multiple rates *probably* would occur; this would be particularly true if the roadway or bridge repairs caused some or all of the lanes to be closed during resurfacing, rehabilitation, or restoration. That is, in the latter case tripmaking and travel benefits would be substantially reduced while heavy costs would be incurred. The example in Table II-1 illustrates this first case.

The maximum number of multiple rates can be determined from an inspection of the variation in the cash flow stream. Referring to the example in Table II-1, the right-hand column shows the estimated year-by-year net benefits or $B_t - C_t$. In turn, the number of sign changes which occurs over the 30-year horizon indicates the maximum possible number of nonnegative rates of return which can result. In this case the net benefits changed signs three times, thus indicating that as many as three nonnegative (i.e., $\geq 0\%$) solutions or rates of return could occur.

In short, whenever costs in some future year will exceed the benefits in that year, one may expect two or more sign changes to occur and thus to lead to the possibility of multiple rates of return. Such a possibility hardly seems rare; in fact, it might be rather common when rolling stock is

TABLE II-1. Costs and Benefits for Two-Stage Improvement of an Existing Bridge (in $1000s)

End of Year t	$B_{1,t}{}^{a}$	$C_{1,t}{}^{b}$	$B_{1,t} - C_{1,t}{}^{c}$
0	—	50	−50
1	61	55	6
2	63	0	63
3	65	0	65
⋮	⋮	⋮	⋮
9	77	0	77
10	79	705	−626
11	81	610	−529
12	83	495	−412
13	85	0	85
⋮	⋮	⋮	⋮
29	117	0	117
30	119	0	119

Internal rates-of-return = r_1 = 8.52%, 18.66%, *and* 73.57%, *where* r_1 is the interest rate (or rates) which satisfies the following identify:

$$\sum_{t=0}^{30} \frac{B_{1,t}}{(1+r_1)^t} = \sum_{t=0}^{30} \frac{C_{1,t}}{(1+r_1)^t} \quad \text{or} \quad \sum_{t=0}^{30} \frac{B_{1,t} - C_{1,t}}{(1+r_1)^t} = 0$$

[a]Benefits in year t, *net* of annual operating and maintenance costs.

[b]Nonrecurring capital outlays in year t.

[c]The number of sign changes in this column indicates the maximum number of nonnegative rates of return which can (and in this case do) occur.

TABLE II-2.   Rate-of-Return Analysis for Two Oil Pump Alternatives

Year	Alternative 1		Alternative 2	
t	$B_{1,t}$	$C_{1,t}$	$B_{2,t}$	$C_{2,t}$
0	0	$100,000	0	$110,000
1	$70,000	0	$115,000	0
2	$70,000	0	$30,000	0
r_x	25.69%		26.16%	
$r_{1/2}$	21.92% *and* 228.08%			

Note: The internal rate of return for alternative x, or r_x, would be the interest rate at which the discounted benefits just equal the discounted costs; the formulation would be roughly the same as that shown in Table II-1. The internal rate of return for the incremental benefits and costs between alternatives 1 and 2, or $r_{1/2}$, would be the interest rate at which the net present value of alternative 1 is just equal to the net present value of alternative 2. That is, $r_{1/2}$ is the discount rate which satisfies the following identity:

$$\sum_{t=0}^{2} \frac{B_{2,t} - B_{1,t}}{(1 + r_{1/2})^t} = \sum_{t=0}^{2} \frac{C_{2,t} - C_{1,t}}{(1 + r_{1/2})^t} \quad \text{or} \quad \sum_{t=0}^{2} \frac{B_{1,t} - C_{1,t}}{(1 + r_{1/2})^t} = \sum_{t=0}^{2} \frac{B_{2,t} - C_{2,t}}{(1 + r_{1/2})^t}$$

replaced, when reconstruction and improvement leads to especially heavy outlays (and perhaps even to a reduction in benefits as well because of disruptions to traffic), or when large periodic payments are received during a construction project.

A *second* case in which multiple rate-of-return solutions can arise is when carrying out the incremental analysis for pairs of alternatives, that is, when determining the value or values of $r_{x/x+1}$ as defined previously in Equation (8-23). It appears that this possibility is more common than one might be led to believe. It could apply, for instance, when higher initial outlays lead to different benefit accrual patterns. The example shown in Table II-2 illustrates this situation and might be applicable if, say, some firm was deciding between two different oil pumps for extracting oil from a well. The more expensive pump would permit the oil to be extracted quicker, as well as slightly increase the total amount of oil extracted. In this instance there is a single rate of return for each alternative (analyzed separately), but there are two solutions or internal rates of return associated with the incremental costs and benefits between alternatives 1 and 2.

As a general proposition, both of these cases *can* and *do* arise. Yet, Grant et al., in the seventh edition of *Principles of Engineering Economy*, argued:[1]

---

[1] E. Grant, W. Ireson, and R. Leavenworth, *Principles of Engineering Economy*, 7th ed., Wiley, New York, 1982, p. 606.

It cannot be emphasized too strongly that [multiple solution] cases...are the exception rather than the rule. They occur chiefly in the mineral industries and the petroleum industry; even there they arise only in rather specialized circumstances.

Similarly, Winfrey in *Economic Analysis for Highways* assumes away the multiple solution problem for the internal rate-of-return method by saying,[2]

Since the situation of two or more rates of return is so infrequent, there is no need to outlaw the rate of return method, a highly useful and understandable method of analysis.

For one, it is far from clear that such instances are indeed exceptional or infrequent. Rather, for highways and bridges, as well as transit systems, the former of which may require heavy outlays for reconstruction or replacement in future years, and the latter of which may require costly rolling stock replacement every 10 to 30 years, the possibility of multiple rates of return is high, if not the typical expectation. This would be particularly true for rapid transit systems (such as the ones in Montreal and Toronto) or turnpikes (such as the New Jersey Turnpike) which undertake very heavy capital improvements after the initial system has been opened and is in full swing. Moreover, for nontransportation projects—especially, as Grant notes, in the mineral and petroleum industries— the occurrence of multiple rates of return is probably commonplace.

Since analysts often (or at least may) overlook the existence of multiple solutions when using the internal rate-of-return method, it is difficult for one not to conclude that a less ambiguous and more clear-cut method of analysis should be adopted. In fact, it is difficult to understand why engineering economists argue so vociferously for the internal rate-of-return method and for the rareness of multiple solution cases when the evidence is to the contrary or at least lacking.

Nor should we fail to point out the tendency of analysts to disregard especially high or low rate-of-return values as being unrealistic or inappropriate. To the contrary, all multiple rates are valid, and all must be considered.

II-2   THE FALLACY IN THINKING THAT ALL ANALYSIS METHODS (WHEN PROPERLY APPLIED) YIELD THE SAME CONCLUSION

Many engineering economy textbooks incorrectly claim that all analysis methods as *defined in Section 8-3* when properly applied lead to an identi-

---

[2]R. Winfrey, *Economic Analysis for Highways*, Int. Textbook Co., Scranton, PA, 1969, p. 161.

cal ranking of alternatives. For instance, Grant et al. in their latest edition say,[3]

> *Once a particular [minimum attractive rate of return] is selected for the comparison of alternatives, a correct analysis of relevant rates of return will invariably lead to the same conclusion that will be obtained from a correct annual cost comparison or a correct present worth comparison.*

In a later section entitled "The Cult of 'Net Present Value,'" these same authors add:[4]

> *Some writers on economics, finance, and operations research have taken the position that present worth (or* net present value, *as they usually call it) is the only valid method for evaluation of investment proposals. One of several arguments advanced against evaluation by prospective rate of return is that under certain circumstances two or more answers can be obtained for a "solving rate of return."*
>
> *Our position in this book has been that when the methods are properly applied, sound conclusions can be obtained with a variety of methods, including equivalent uniform annual cash flow, present worth, rate of return, and analyses comparing benefits with costs either with or without the calculation of B/C ratios....*

Contrarily, the economist has repeatedly demonstrated (for more than two decades) the problems and inadequacies of the internal rate-of-return method. Moreover, and even in those instances when the internal rate-of-return method does lead to the correct decision, the yield indicated by the internal rate-of-return figure will often be misleading. Thus, to fully illustrate the vagaries of the internal rate-of-return method, a number of examples will be explored.

To begin, it seems necessary to emphasize the objective of the analyst or decision maker—whether the project (or set of projects) being analyzed is a public or private one. Simply, it is to maximize the net gains (whether measured in terms of total net revenues or total net benefits for the private or public sectors, respectively) over the appropriate planning horizon or analysis period. Also, in insuring that the net gains or "profits" are maximized over the planning horizon, it is important to place all present and future costs and gains on a commensurate value scale. (The latter, of course, can be accomplished either by using discounted costs and gains or by using equivalent uniform annual costs and gains.)

Put differently, we wish to know which course of action—to be taken over the planning horizon—will produce the highest net gains or profits during the planning horizon, in light of the expected initial capital

---

[3]Grant et al., op. cit., p. 127.
[4]Ibid., p. 604.

outlays, as well as all future expected outlays, maintenance and operating expenses, and gains (the last whether measured in revenues or benefits).

To explore the claim of engineering economists (cited earlier) that all methods of analysis will invariably provide the same sound conclusion, let us make use of two examples—the first shown in Table II-1 and the second shown in Table II-2.

The data shown in Table II-1 represent the expected year-by-year costs and benefits associated with undertaking a specified course of action over a 30-year analysis period or planning horizon. The numbers appear somewhat typical for previously built highways or bridges which now are in need of repair, restoration, or replacement. (Or they could apply to a transit system which plans to extend its lines in the future.) In this case, however, assume that some community has an old bridge which is in imminent danger of collapse. In turn, the public works department was ordered by the city council to analyze the various repair strategies which would insure safe operation of the bridge for at least the next 30 years. Among the possibilities are (1) minor repairs to the bridge now, thus deferring a major overhaul until some future date, or (2) complete overhaul of the bridge now. The appropriate benefit and cost data for the first of these two alternatives are shown in Table II-1. Presumably, the second alternative would have higher initial outlays and thus would be analyzed in terms of the incremental benefits and costs after the first alternative has been analyzed in terms of its acceptability.

Accordingly, the data in Table II-1 represent the incremental costs and benefits for the first alternative relative to bridge abandonment. In turn, then, we can calculate the internal rate of return for this lowest-cost alternative. The discounted internal rate-of-return method, strictly applied, would yield three rates of return in this instance: 8.52% 18.66%, and 73.57%. First, all of these solutions are correct, mathematically and otherwise. (That is, they do represent the interest rates for which the discounted benefits just equal the discounted costs.) Second, in the absence of any other information (which is not part of the internal rate-of-return method), how do we interpret these rates? And, how do we decide which rate to use in making a decision? Suppose, for instance, the appropriate minimum attractive rate of return (MARR) is judged to be approximately 10%. Then, using just the internal rate-of-return figures, we will obtain *either* an ambiguous answer *or* an incorrect one. That is, which of the three internal rate-of-return results do we compare with the MARR value of 10%? And do we reject this alternative (and then consider the next higher-cost alternative) or not? The internal rate-of-return method as usually applied does not tell us!

By contrast, if we had simply computed the net present value (or discounted benefits minus discounted costs) for the stated MARR of 10%, we would have learned that the net present value was negative and thus that the bridge repair and later overhaul alternative was economically *infeasible* and should be rejected. Specifically, for a MARR of 10%, the net present value would be equal to −$14.14 (in thousands). In addition, the benefit–cost ratio for this alternative would be 0.981 (or less than 1.0, indicating rejection) for an interest rate of 10%. In sum, we see that the methods of analysis *do not invariably* provide sound conclusions or the same conclusions. Moreover, whereas the net present value and benefit–cost ratio methods are conclusive and unambiguous, the internal rate-of-return method is ambiguous and inconclusive.

Moreover, it is worth noting that the internal rate-of-return method could have led us astray for a wide range of circumstances in this situation. In Figure II-1 a plot of the appropriate net present values *versus* the interest rate is shown for the full range of interest possibilities. Clearly, if the appropriate MARR was deemed to be between 8.52 and 18.55%, then the analyst would be incorrect if he did not reject this alternative—a result which would not necessarily result from strict application of the internal rate-of-return method.

It is also important to emphasize the difficulties which arise from calculating internal rates of return, as compared to those for net present value. Using the formulation shown in Equation (8-18), the internal rate(s) of return, or r_1, for the alternative shown in Table II-1 will be those which satisfy the following 30th-order polynomial:

$$\frac{61}{(1+r_1)^1} + \frac{63}{(1+r_1)^2} + \cdots + \frac{117}{(1+r_1)^{29}} + \frac{119}{(1+r_1)^{30}}$$
$$- 50 - \frac{55}{(1+r_1)^1} - \frac{705}{(1+r_1)^{10}} - \frac{610}{(1+r_1)^{11}} - \frac{495}{(1+r_1)^{12}} = 0$$

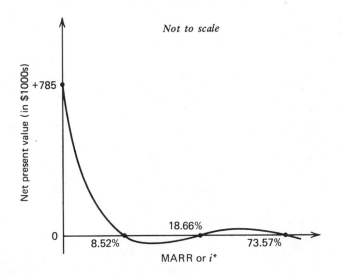

Figure II-1. Net Present Value (*NPV*) at different minimum attractive rates of return (MARR) for a bridge alternative (described in Table II-1).

Without access to an electronic computer, or an advanced programmable professional calculator, a lengthy computation process would be required to estimate all the positive roots for this equation, at least if reasonable accuracy is desired. By contrast, to determine the net present value for any MARR value would require one to merely discount and sum up the 30 cash flow figures shown in the right-hand column of Table II-1, a calculation which would take less than 5 minutes with a simple pocket calculator.

A word of caution to those using professional calculators. A number of advanced professional or electronic pocket calculators now have the capability to compute the internal rate of return for a cash flow stream. Most of them, however, are programmed *only* to determine the *lowest* positive rate of return. Thus, in multiple-root circumstances, the results will not be complete and may be misleading.

Now let us review the circumstances for another example situation, one involving overall analysis as well as incremental analysis between pairs of alternatives. The particular example was chosen for clarity and to minimize calculations.

The example shown in Table II-2 deals, as noted previously, with two investment alternatives, each having 2-year cost and benefit streams as shown. Effectively, the additional initial investment (of alternative 2 over alternative 1) will permit earlier recovery of the overall gains (whether regarded as revenues or benefits), though the additional initial outlay will also lead to slightly higher 2-year gains (measured in current or undiscounted dollars).

To apply the internal rate-of-return method, we first need to specify the minimum attractive rate of return or MARR. Let us assume it is 15%. Second, we calculate the internal rate of return for the lowest-cost alternative and then ask whether the rate is at least as high as the MARR. (This is the first step in answering the question, "Is *any* alternative worth undertaking?") Since the internal rate of return for alternative 1 (25.69%) is higher than the MARR, alternative 1 is judged to be economically acceptable. In turn, we must calculate the incremental internal rate of return (or $r_{1/2}$) associated with the incremental costs and benefits between alternatives 1 and 2, the latter being the higher initial-cost alternative. The internal rate of return for the incremental costs and benefits is not a single rate, but two of them, 21.92 and 228.08%. Since both of these rates—examined without any other information—are greater than the MARR, the analyst presumably would conclude that alternative 2 is more attractive than alternative 1, economically speaking, or he would regard the decision as ambiguous.

Contrarily, neither conclusion would be correct. For instance, simple application of the net present value method will show that for a MARR of 15%, the net present value of alternative 1 is $13,800 as compared to only $12,684 for alternative 2, thus unambiguously indicating the preferability of alternative 1. Similarly, if the benefit–cost ratio method had been used, the ratio for alternative 1 would have been 1.138 for an interest rate of 15%; thus, alternative 1 is acceptable. In turn, the incremental benefit–cost ratio for the increments in benefits and costs between alternatives 1 and 2 can be shown to be 0.884, or less than 1.0, thus indicating that alternative 2 should be rejected. Moreover, misleading or ambiguous answers could result from use of the internal rate-of-return method for any MARR value below 21.92%. This can be seen from Figure II-2.

Thus, once again we see that the various analysis methods do not invariably lead to the same sound conclusions about which alternative is best.

II-3   UNDERLYING REASONS FOR DIFFERENT CONCLUSIONS FROM USE OF DIFFERENT METHODS: REINVESTMENT CONSIDERATIONS AND EFFECTIVE RATES OF RETURN

In the previous section we saw that the internal rate-of-return and net present value methods can provide conflicting results. In turn, we should ask: Why can and do the results differ? Which method gives correct results? Let us consider the latter question first.

To begin, recall what was earlier stated to be the objective of the analyst: Maximize the net gains (or profits) to be accrued over the planning horizon or analysis period. In other words we wish to identify the project which will maximize the surplus (net of costs) which a firm or community will accrue over the analysis period. For these purposes consider alternatives 1 and 2 shown in Table II-2. For the first of these we

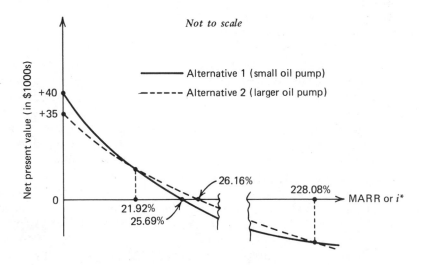

Figure II-2.   Net present value (*NPV*) at different minimum attractive rates of return (MARR) for the two (oil pump) investment alternatives (described in Table II-2).

must commit resources of $100,000 now, and in turn will accrue $70,000 in revenues or benefits (net of annual operating costs) at the end of 1 year and another $70,000 at the end of the second year. For the second alternative we must invest $110,000 now but will accrue $115,000 at the end of the first year and another $30,000 at the end of the second year. In turn, which of these two investment options—*relative to investing in neither*—will permit us to have accumulated the largest profit or net gain over the 2-year period?

The key to the answer involves two aspects: (1) the minimum attractive rate of return (MARR) or opportunity cost of capital, which informs us about the yield possibilities we must forego if we invest in alternative 1 or 2 rather than in other possibilities which we thereby would forego and (2) the possible uses of any net revenues or benefits accrued prior to the end of the planning period. For the first aspect, and again assuming that the MARR was 15%, to invest $100,000 in alternative 1 would mean that we would forego the opportunity to earn 15% per year (compounded annually) for 2 years and thus would forego the opportunity to accumulate $132,250 by the end of year 2. But by foregoing this opportunity and investing in alternative 1, we would accrue annual net earnings of $70,000 at the end of years 1 and 2. Obviously, though, if one had invested in alternative 1 and had accrued earnings of $70,000 at the end of the first year, these first-year earnings would be reinvested during the second year—rather than "sit idle." It seems reasonable to assume (as is implicit with the net present value method) that these early-year earnings are reinvested at the minimum attractive rate of return (which, after all, represents a firm or agency's best estimate of the potential yield of other opportunities it is foregoing). If, then, the first-year earnings of $70,000 were reinvested at 15%, 1 year later the firm or agency would have accumulated $80,500 (or $70,000 plus $10,500 in yield), plus of course the $70,000 in the second year which was generated by the initial investment. All together, then, an investment in alternative 1 would require a firm or agency to forego $132,250 and instead to accumulate $150,500 over the same 2-year period. The extra profit or net gains to be accumulated by the end of 2 years would be $18,250 (or $150,500 less $132,250). Also, and of some importance, if this 2-year extra profit is discounted at a rate of 15%, its present value is $13,800—a figure identical to the net present value obtained by discounting at 15% the benefits and costs shown in Table II-2 for alternative 1. Or, $18,250 is simply equal to $13,800 times the compound interest factor for 2 years or $(F/P,0.15,2) = (1.015)^2$.

A similar kind of analysis can be carried out for alternative 2, again assuming that the MARR is 15%. In that case, by investing in alternative 2, we would forego the opportunity to accumulate $145,475 by the end of the second year, but instead would accrue total gains of $162,250 if we invested in alternative 2, thus profiting by $16,775 by the end of the 2-year period.

Note that alternative 1 will have accumulated larger profits or net gains by the end of year 2, $18,250 for alternative 1 *versus* $16,775 for alternative 2. This result is identical, relatively, to the net present value figures provided earlier for the same interest rate (15%). Importantly, either the net present value or accumulated profits figure will properly indicate which alternative is "best" at the appropriate MARR while, by contrast, the internal rate-of-return figures would unambiguously and properly identify the "best" alternative *only* if the MARR is above 25.69% and below 26.16%.

Why then does the internal rate-of-return method give misleading results, and ones which differ from those obtained by using either net present value or benefit–cost ratio calculations? *Simply stated, they differ because of different assumptions with respect to reinvestment or valuation of early-year benefits or revenues.* To use the internal rate-of-return method (without any additional data or calculations) is to assume *implicitly* that earnings accrued prior to the end of the analysis period are reinvested at the *internal* rate of return for the remaining years. To use the net present value (or benefit–cost ratio) method is to assume *implicitly* that prior-year earnings are reinvested at the MARR (or opportunity cost of capital) for the remaining years. In the Table II-2 example, for instance, the *internal* rate-of-return calculations imply that the $115,000 first-year earnings for alternative 2 are reinvested during the second year at 26.16% while the net present value method assumes that the earnings were reinvested at the MARR (of 15%) during the second year. Also, for this example, the internal rate-of-return method would imply that the first-year earnings for alternative 1 would be reinvested at 25.69% while those for alternative 2 would be reinvested at 26.16%. Alternatively, we could say that the internal rate of return makes the implicit *valuation* that $115,000 of first-year earnings in alternative 2 is worth $115,000 · $(P|F, 26.16, 1) = 115{,}000/1.2616 = \$91{,}154.09$ in the present. But we have already assumed that the proper intertemporal relative *valuation* of earnings, costs, or other benefits is performed by discounting at the MARR.

Some engineering economists argue the inappropriateness of considering reinvestment possibilities for any revenues or benefits accrued prior to the end of the planning horizon (such as those accrued at the end of year 1 for alternatives 1 and 2, shown in Table II-2). Winfrey, for example, says,[5]

> It is most difficult to convince the layman that his rate of return on a given investment is dependent upon how he reinvests his return from that investment; neither does it seem logical when comparing possible investment alternatives that the choice of investment could depend upon how the return from each alternative would be reinvested.

Personally, we find it difficult to believe that either laymen or analysts would be unconcerned about how much profit or net gain they could

[5]Winfrey, op. cit., pp. 162–163.

TABLE II-3.   Two Loan and Payback Possibilities From the ABC
Company's Viewpoint

(a)		Loan Plan 1		Loan Plan 2	
	Year t	Loan Amount	Payback Amount	Loan Amount	Payback Amount
	0	−$70		−$90	
	1	0	+$75	0	+$115
	2	0	0	0	0
	3	0	0	0	0
	4	0	0	0	0
	5	0	0	0	0
	6	0	0	0	0
	7	0	0	0	0
	8	0	0	0	0
	9	0	0	0	0
	10	0	+$70	0	+$5
	r_x	22.84%		28.37%	
	$r_{1/2}$		16.26% and 99.35%		
(b)		$[NPV_{1,10}]_{8\%} = \$31.87$		$[NPV_{2,10}]_{8\%} = \$18.80$	
(c)		$[BCR_{1,10}]_{8\%} = 1.455$		$[BCR_{2,10}]_{8\%} = 1.209$	
			$[IBCR_{1/2,10}]_{8\%} = 0.347$		

Note: The net present values and benefit-cost ratios were computed for a MARR of 8%.

accrue during the analysis period for whatever project they were investigating. That is, accumulated profit or net gain over the entire investment period *is* clearly related to and thus dependent upon reinvestment of revenues or benefits gained along the way; thus, no wise investor will choose to ignore them. Let us demonstrate the point by an example.[6] Suppose, for instance, that we want to borrow an amount on the order of $70 to $90 now and that, in turn, we go to ABC Loan Company to request a loan. After due consideration, let us say that the loan officer gives us a choice between one of the following two loan plans (shown in Table II-3):

1. A $70 loan *now* to be paid back in two installments, the first one of $75 one year from now and the second of $70 ten years from now; or

2. A $90 loan *now* to be paid back in two installments, the first one of $115 one year from now and the second of $5 ten years from now.

Also, assume that the ABC Loan Company estimated its MARR to be 8%

---

[6]Another interesting example and discussion of this same aspect appears in E. J. Mishan, *Cost-Benefit Analysis*, Praeger Publishers, New York, 1976, pp. 225 ff.

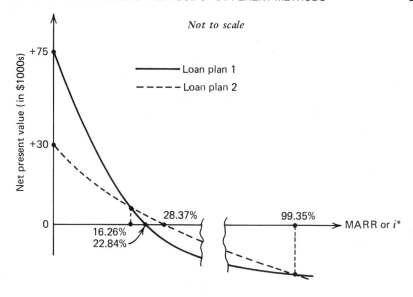

Figure II-3. Net present value (*NPV*) at different minimum attractive rates of return (MARR) for the two ABC loan company plans (described in Table II-3).

and that the company wants to know which loan plan (if any) would be most profitable to them.

In turn, let us assume the ABC Loan Company uses the internal rate-of-return method and calculates the various rates of return, as shown in Table II-3(a). Accordingly, the company notes (from Table II-3) that plan 1 has a rate of return (22.84%) higher than its MARR (of 8%) and thus is acceptable. Next, the company notes that the incremental rates of return ($r_{1/2}$) of 16.26 and 99.35% are both higher than its MARR, thus suggesting that plan 2 is better than plan 1 or that it is not clear which plan is best. However, if the company had used either the net present value or the benefit–cost ratio method instead, then it would have discovered that loan plan 1 is unambiguously the best one for its MARR value, as shown in Table II-3(b) and II-3(c). Also, the data in Figure II-3 will show that loan plan 1 is better for the ABC Company so long as its MARR is below 16.26%.

Again, the differences between the net present value and internal rate-of-return methods (in indicating the best alternative for a MARR of 8%) stem from the different assumptions with respect to reinvestment of its earnings. That is, it should be obvious that the ABC Loan Company would not ignore the reinvestment possibilities for the payback amounts received in year 1. Neither the $75 received in year 1 for plan 1 nor the $115 received in year 1 for plan 2 would simply be ignored or placed in a drawer for the remaining 9 years. Rather, they would be reinvested in other investment opportunities or in early (rather than later) year enjoyment. The most reasonable assumption is that early-year earnings will be invested at the MARR, an interest rate which reflects the potential yield from other foregone opportunities.

By a similar process, it can be shown that for the internal rate-of-return method, early-year earnings are assumed to be reinvested at the internal rate of return. If this is true, then for plan 1 the first-year payment of $75 is reinvested for the remaining 9 years at 22.84%, thus accumulating $477.66 by the end of 10 years, since $477.66 = $75(1.2284)^9$, to be added to the 10th-year payment of $70. The accumulated 10-year earnings will be 477.66 + $70 = $547.66. These accumulated earnings, when discounted to their present value, will be identical with the initial investment of $70 only for an interest rate of 22.84%, the internal rate of return. (Recall that the internal rate of return is defined as the interest rate at which the discounted benefits are just equal to the discounted costs.) That is,

$$\frac{\$547.66}{(1.2284)^{10}} = \$70$$

In short, this proves that the early-year earnings *were* assumed (albeit implicitly) to be reinvested at the internal rate of return, an assumption which is clearly different from that used for the net present value method. Moreover, if the early-year earnings were reinvested at any reinvestment rate other than the internal rate of return, the 10-year accumulated earnings, when discounted at the internal rate of return, would not be equal to the discounted costs (which in this case were equal to the initial loan amount).

Given that the internal rate-of-return method uses the internal rate of return as the reinvestment rate, while the net present value method uses the MARR as the reinvestment rate, we can be more explicit about the confusion in applying the internal rate-of-return method to the selection of the best loan plan in Table II-3. Note first that plan 1 has an internal rate of return of 22.84%, while plan 2 has a rate of 28.37%. As a consequence, the method assumes that the year 1 payment for plan 2 can be reinvested at a higher rate than the payment for plan 1. What rationale is there for assuming different reinvestment rates for earnings accrued at the same point in time? None that we can think of. By the same token, in computing the incremental rates of return, it was assumed that the difference in first-year payments (or $115 – $75) was reinvested at either 16.26 or 99.35%, again, an assumption without rationale and one which is very different from that used to analyze separate projects.

Of no small importance, *if identical assumptions are made about reinvestment for all methods*, then invariably the same conclusions will result. As noted before, for both the net present value and benefit–cost ratio methods, it was assumed that MARR would be the proper reinvestment rate. Thus, let us use the same reinvestment assumption for the rate-of-return method. That is, we will assume that early-year earnings are reinvested at the MARR and then determine the interest rate at which the discounted accumulated earnings just equal the discounted costs. This interest rate, strictly speaking, reflects more than internal earnings and thus will be designated by a capital R_x instead of a lowercase r_x. This R_x value will represent the *effective* yield to be obtained over the analysis period and will be equivalent to the internal rate of return only in exceptional cases. (This adjusted rate-of-return value has been termed *equivalent rate of return* by Solomon and *reinvestment-corrected internal rate of return* by Mishan and the *overall rate of return* by Au.[7]) Accordingly, the calculations for a MARR (and reinvestment rate) of 8% would be as follows:

1. Effective Rate of Return (R_1) for Loan Plan 1. Accumulated 10-year earnings = $75(1.08)^9 + $70 = $219.93. In turn, find R_1, such that the discounted earnings are just equal to the discounted costs, or

$$\$70 = \frac{\$219.93}{(1 + R_1)^{10}}$$

Thus,

$$R_1 = 0.1213 \text{ or } 12.13\%$$

2. Effective Rate of Return (R_2) for Loan Plan 2. Accumulated 10-year earnings = $115(1.08)^9 + $5 = $234.89. Find R_2, such that

$$\$90 = \frac{\$234.89}{(1 + R_2)^{10}}$$

Thus,

$$R_2 = 0.1007 \text{ or } 10.07\%$$

3. Effective Rate of Return ($R_{1/2}$) on Increments Between Loan Plans. Accumulated 10-year extra earnings = ($115 − $75)(1.08)^9 + ($5 − $70) = $14.96. Find $R_{1/2}$, such that

$$\$90 - \$70 = \frac{\$14.96}{(1 + R_{1/2})^{10}}$$

Thus,

$$R_{1/2} = -0.0286$$

and, by inspection, there is no positive root.

[7]E. Solomon, *The Management of Corporate Capital*, The Free Press of Glencoe, London, 1959, p. 74; Mishan, op. cit., p. 228; T. Au and T.P. Au, *Engineering Economics for Capital Investment Analysis*, Allyn and Bacon, Boston, 1983.

When the modified or effective rate-of-return method uses a reinvestment rate assumption identical to that used in the net present value and benefit–cost ratio methods, the outcome and conclusions will be identical for all methods. That is, loan plan 1 provides an acceptable rate of return (i.e., one which is higher than 8%) and has a yield which is higher than that for plan 2. (One could have eliminated either step 2 or step 3; the reason that R_2 was lower than R_1 is that the yield on the increment, or $R_{1/2}$, was lower than 8%.)

Restating and summarizing:

For the net present value method, if the early-year earnings are reinvested at any rate other than the MARR, then the accumulated earnings over the entire analysis period when discounted at the MARR will not equal the earnings when discounted at the MARR. Thus, the implicit reinvestment rate must be the MARR (i.e., the same discount rate which was used to compute the net present value).

For the internal rate-of-return method, if the early-year earnings are reinvested at any rate other than the internal rate of return, then the accumulated earnings over the entire analysis period when discounted at the internal rate of return will not be equal to the costs when discounted at the internal rate of return. Thus, the implicit reinvestment rate must be the internal rate of return.

Also, with both public and private investment projects, multiple solutions can occur and thus can lead to ambiguous or incorrect investment decisions if one uses the internal rate-of-return method. Even if this occurrence is rare (a fact which has yet to be established), its possibility alone should discourage even the most serious advocate of the internal rate-of-return method. Succinctly, this method as usually defined lacks generality. The reason the internal rate of return will sometimes lead to improper investment decisions in multiple-rate situations is that inconsistent (albeit implicit) assumptions are embodied with respect to the reinvestment or relative valuation of early-year earnings.

Moreover, the internal rate of return will be a misleading measure of the overall yield to be anticipated from investment, other than in two very special cases:

1. When the project earnings are all accrued during the last year of the planning horizon or
2. When the reinvestment rate is identical to the internal rate of return.

Consider the circumstances for the pair of investment situations shown in Table II-4. Both alternatives have an equal internal rate of return of 8% and thus would appear to be equally attractive when an investor's MARR is less than 8%; that is, the (so-called) yield for both is said to be 8%. Yet, we know that investment 2 is better for a MARR of less than 8% since the internal rate of return on the increment or $r_{1/2}$ is 8%. Of more than

TABLE II-4.   Earnings to be Accrued from Two Investment Situations

	Investment 1		Investment 2	
Year t	Earnings in Year t	Investment in Year t	Earnings in Year t	Investment in Year t
0	0	$1000	0	$1000
1	$250.46	0	0	0
2	$250.46	0	0	0
3	$250.46	0	0	0
4	$250.46	0	0	0
5	$250.46	0	$1469.33	0
Rate of return, r_x	8%		8%	
Incremental rate of return		$r_{1/2} = 8\%$		

passing interest, *if* the analyst (by accident) had ranked the two invest-ment alternatives in Table II-4 *in reverse order*, then an incorrect invest-ment choice would have resulted from use of the internal rate-of-return method whenever the MARR was less than 8%. The reason that alterna-tive 2 is better for a MARR of less than 8% is simply that the *effective* yield for the 5-year period would be higher for project 2 than for project 1. In short, the internal rate of return does not reflect the true yield for both of the alternatives (otherwise an investor would be indifferent between the two). That is, if the investor has a MARR of (say) 6%, then invest-ment 1 will not accumulate as much as $1469.33 by the end of year 5. This is the amount accumulated by investment 2 for 5 years and is equal to $1000(1.08)^5$, thus indicating that the effective (true) yield of this project is exactly 8%. Specifically, he can reinvest the first-, second-, third-, and fourth-year earnings at 6% per annum for the remainder of the 5-year period and can accumulate the following by the end of year 5:

$$(\$250.46)(1.06)^4 + (\$250.46)(1.06)^3 + (\$250.46)(1.06)^2 +$$
$$(\$250.46)(1.06) + \$250.46 = \$1411.87.$$

In turn, the interest rate at which this amount, when discounted to its present value, will just equal the initial investment of $1000 will be 7.142%, a true indicator of the effective yield to be anticipated from investment 1.[8] Again, and quite simply, if the effective yield from invest-ment 2 was not larger than that from investment 1, *then investment 2* would not be preferable to investment 1.

---

[8]This procedure for computing the effective yield to be anticipated over some given planning horizon dates back over many years. For discussion of the determination of the overall or effective yield or what is also termed the normalized or *"reinvestment-corrected"* internal rate-of-return," see T. Au and T. P. Au, *Engineering Economics for Capital Investment Planning*, Allyn and Bacon, Boston, 1983.

II-4   OTHER CONFUSING ASPECTS ABOUT REINVESTMENT OF EARLY-YEAR BENEFITS AND EFFECTIVE RATES OF RETURN

Another aspect regarding reinvestment of early-year gains which has troubled analysts involves benefits or gains which are accrued in nonmoney rather than money terms. How does the concept of reinvestment apply, for example, to time savings accrued in some year prior to the end of the analysis period? The answer is simple and straightforward. Reinvestment principles (broadly construed) apply with equal validity to any benefits—whether measured in money or nonmoney terms—which are accrued prior to the end of the analysis period. Why? Because time savings accrued in earlier years are more valuable to people than the same amount of time savings accrued in a later year. Or, put somewhat differently, enjoyment or consumption now is more highly valued (ceteris paribus) than later. Also, the minimum attractive rate of return, rather than the *internal* rate of return, reflects the strengths of peoples' tastes and preferences with respect to the importance of enjoyment now versus enjoyment later. Specifically, the minimum attractive rate of return reflects the tradeoff between peoples' time preferences and the rate of productivity of investments, and thus the marginal rate of time preference is (roughly) equal to the marginal rate of productivity, both being equal to the minimum attractive rate of return. Thus, reinvestment is only one aspect of the intertemporal valuation of benefits and costs.

Note that benefit–cost analysis generally uses the same discount rate for all cost and benefit components. Recall that the opportunity cost of capital reflects both the marginal rate of productivity and marginal rate of time preference for earlier rather than later enjoyment or consumption. Implicitly, then, benefit–cost analysis treats nonmoney benefits (such as travel time savings) which are accrued prior to the end of the planning horizon as having the same "time value of money" as other resources. Put differently, travel time savings of T at the end of year 1 would be equivalent to $T/(1 + i)$ at the end of year 0; moreover, travel time savings of T accrued at the end of year 1 would be considered to be worth $T + iT$ by the end of year 2 by virtue of the fact that people would have been able to enjoy these benefits 1 year earlier than would otherwise have been possible. It might be possible to weight benefits accruing to different individuals by their individual MARRs, but as described in Section 8-2-3 this greatly complicates the analysis.

Grant et al. dealt extensively—but improperly—with the matter of reinvestment in the 7th edition of *Principles of Engineering Economy*. (The discussion appears in an appendix, entitled "The Reinvestment Fallacy in Project Evaluation."[9]) In essence, they deal with the calculation and inter-

---

[9]Grant et al., op. cit., pp. 610 ff.

TABLE II-5. Benefits and Costs for
Project X Over a 2-Year Period
(in $1000s)

Year t	Cost $C_{x,t}$	Benefit[a] $B_{x,t}$
0	100	0
1	0	20
2	0	120
Rate of return	$r_x = 20\%$	

[a]Gains (or benefits, however measured) in year
t, *net* of any annual operating expenses.

pretation of an adjusted rate-of-return figure, one which Solomon labeled
equivalent rate of return and Mishan labeled *reinvestment-corrected internal rate of return*.[10] Wohl and Martin presented a similar example problem
in *Traffic System Analysis* and termed the figure *corrected rate of return*.[11]
Here, we use the term *effective rate of return* to denote this figure.

The essentials of the issue being discussed by these authors can be
explained by the following simple example and is illustrated in Table II-5.
First, for this stream of costs and benefits, we can compute the internal
rate of return. Simply, r_x, the internal rate of return for project x, can be
solved as follows:

$$\frac{100}{(1 + r_x)^0} = \frac{20}{(1 + r_x)^1} + \frac{120}{(1 + r_x)^2}$$

and

$$r_x = 0.20 \quad \text{or} \quad 20\%$$

This figure of 20% reflects the yield from the *internal* costs and gains
stemming from this project; but it also implicitly assumes that the *external* gains accrued from reinvestment of the first-year gains (or $20K) will
yield 20% in the second year. That is, implicit in the internal rate-of-
return method is that we will accumulate total 2-year gains as follows:

$$\$120K + \$20K(1 + 0.2) = \$144K$$

In turn, these accumulated gains when discounted to the present (or year

[10]Solomon, op. cit., pp. 74 ff.; Mishan, op. cit., p. 228.
[11]M. Wohl and B. V. Martin, *Traffic System Analysis*, McGraw-Hill, New York, 1967, p. 243.

0) at the internal rate of return of 20% will be equal to $100K—a figure just equal, of course, to the initial outlay. Put differently, if the first-year gains of $20K are reinvested during the second year *at any interest rate other than 20%*, then the full 2-year accumulated gains when discounted to the present (or year 0) at the internal rate of return will *not* be equal to $100K.

Suppose, for instance, that our investigation of foregone investment opportunities leads us to believe that the appropriate minimum attractive rate of return is 10%. Obviously, in this case, what is suggested is that the $20K in gains received at the end of year 1 will be reinvested in external or outside opportunities and will accrue a yield of only 10% during the second year. Accordingly, by the end of year 2 we will accumulate total gains as follows:

$$\$120K + \$20K(1 + 0.10) = \$142K$$

In turn, if we then calculate the interest rate at which these accumulated gains, when discounted to the present, just equal the initial capital outlay of $100K, we obtain a figure as follows:

$$\$100K = \frac{\$142K}{(1 + R_x)^2}$$

and

$$R_x = 0.1916 \quad \text{or} \quad 19.16\%$$

This discount rate or R_x is, of course, the *effective* rate of return which reflects *both* the internal gains anticipated from an investment *and* the external gains which accrue from reinvestment of early-year gains. Importantly, this adjusted rate of return represents the true overall yield which will result from following some course of action over the entire analysis period. By contrast, if the *internal* rate of return is higher than the minimum attractive rate of return, then it will overstate the true yield to be expected from some project; if it is lower than the MARR, then it will understate the true yield.

Grant et al. argue that such a method of computing an adjusted rate of return (or R_x) is fallacious, saying in part,[12]

Sometimes an analyst uses two or more interest rates because this method of analysis is required by company policy. Or an analyst may mistakenly believe that this technique will give useful conclusions. In either case, one aspect of the computational procedure will be the assumption of reinvestment at some

[12]Grant et al., op. cit., pp. 611–612.

stipulated interest rate. Various weaknesses in the reinvestment assumption are brought out in [the Table II-6 example, to be discussed] and in several of the problems at the end of this appendix....

The authors have also observed cases where it seemed to them that sophisticated analysts were intentionally distorting the conclusions of an evaluation by making compound interest conversions that used two or more interest rates during the same time period. For some reason, it was desired to make a particular investment proposal appear to be better or worse than it would have seemed to be if it had been evaluated on its own merits. The analysis seemed to have been manipulated to support predetermined conclusions.

Later, these authors say, "The fallacy in this type of analysis [i.e., that in which an effective rate of return is calculated] may be even more evident if we apply the [effective rate-of-return] method to the following estimates for another investment proposal [shown in Table II-6]."[13]

For the cash flows shown in Table II-6, one can show that the internal rate of return is 0%, thus indicating that the net present value is zero at 0%. Moreover, for *any* larger (positive) discount rate, the net present value is negative, thus indicating that the investment proposal is financially unattractive. In turn, Grant et al. state that 10% is the "...rate that the company is expected to make on other investments," thus indicating that 10% is the minimum attractive rate of return as well as the appropriate reinvestment rate for early-year gains.[14] Accordingly, Grant et al. calculated the effective rate of return, or R, as follows:

1. Discount the year 0 and year 1 negative cash flows to the present (i.e., year 0) at a discount rate of 10%; the total is $427,300 when rounded off to the nearest $100. In analytical form,

$$\text{Present worth of costs} = \$200,000 + \frac{\$250,000}{(1.1)} = \$427,300$$

2. Determine the gains accumulated by the end of year 5, assuming that the year 1 through year 4 positive cash flows are reinvested at 10% per annum; the accumulated gains are $572,600 when rounded off to the nearest $100. In analytical form

$$\text{Accumulated gains at end of year 5} = \$130,000(1.1)^4 + 110,000(1.1)^3$$
$$+ 90,000(1.1)^2 + 70,000(1.1) + 50,000 = \$572,600$$

3. Determine the interest rate at which the accumulated gains in part

---

[13]Grant et al., op. cit., pp. 614–615.

[14]Grant et al., op. cit., p. 615.

TABLE II-6.   Example Cash Flows for a Project[a]

Year	Cash Flow for Investment	Cash Flow from Excess of Operating Receipts over Disbursements
0	−$200,000	0
1	− 250,000	+$130,000
2	0	+ 110,000
3	0	+ 90,000
4	0	+ 70,000
5	0	+ 50,000
Totals (PV at 0%)	−$450,000	+$450,000

[a]Reproduced from Grant et al., op. cit., pp. 614–615.

2 when discounted to the present (or year 0) just equal the discounted costs in part 1. Or, find R such that

$$\frac{\$572,600}{(1 + R)^5} = \$427,300$$

and

$$R = 0.06 \quad \text{or approximately 6\%}$$

(While we have some problems with the fashion in which Grant et al. calculated the effective rate of return or R, let us withhold discussion of that point until later.) In short, the true yield which a firm could expect over a 5-year period—given the cash flows shown in Table II-6 and a MARR of 10%—would be about 6%. Obviously, this would be an unattractive project for the firm to undertake since it can earn more than that—or 10%—simply by investing its funds in other foregone alternatives. Or, put differently, the firm would lose—relative to other foregone opportunities— if it chose to undertake this proposal, regardless. Yet, Grant et al. thoroughly distort the meaning of this 6% effective rate-of-return figure by stating,[15]

> In effect, the investment proposal yielding 0% has been combined with the 10% assumed to be earned elsewhere in the enterprise to give the misleading conclusion that the proposal will yield 6%.

Why is the last statement a distortion? For one, it fails utterly to recognize the fact that the year 1 through year 4 gains from the invest-

[15]Grant et al., op. cit., p. 565.

ment proposal will produce outside earnings during the remaining time until year 5. (Those funds will not sit idle in the company coffer!) For another, it implies that the prospective worth of the proposal to the firm is in no way affected by these outside reinvestment earnings and that, furthermore, the 5-year profitability of the firm (since the *internal* rate of return is 0%) would in no way be affected by the time pattern of the gain shown in the right-hand column of Table II-6. To show the fallacy of this last line of reasoning, let us alter the Table II-6 cash flows to be as shown in Table II-7. Then, we again will find that the internal rate of return is 0%, thus indicating that the proposal is unattractive (since the MARR is 10%). But if we are to follow the line of reasoning espoused by Grant et al., then presumably this new proposal (i.e., that in Table II-7) is *no more and no less attractive* than that in Table II-6. In fact, the proposal in Table II-6 is *much more* attractive financially than that in Table 11-7—for the simple reason that the reinvestment gains to be accrued from the Table II-6 proposal are much larger than those of the other proposal. How much better is the proposal in Table II-6 than that in Table II-7? Simply, the effective rate of return for the former was shown to be about 6% (using the same procedure that was followed by Grant et al.), while the effective rate of return for the latter is only about 2%. All in all, we do not find the arguments or examples used by Grant et al. to be compelling.

II-5 CONCLUDING REMARKS

In all but rare cases benefit–cost analysis is a straightforward process, one which can be carried out most simply and unambiguously using the net present value (or if one prefers, the net future value or the equivalent uniform value) method. By contrast, many seem enamored with the more

TABLE II-7.   Cash Flows for a Project with Returns Different than Table II-6

Year	Cash Flow for Investment	Cash Flow from Excess of Operating Receipts over Disbursements
0	−$200,000	0
1	− 250,000	+ $10,000
2	0	+ 20,000
3	0	+ 30,000
4	0	+ 40,000
5	0	+ 350,000
Totals (PV at 0%)	−$450,000	+$450,000

complicated and tedious internal rate-of-return method despite its many pitfalls. Accordingly, we have devoted considerable attention to the differences between the methods, especially that having to do with assumptions about reinvestment of earnings or benefits accrued prior to the end of the planning horizon. More than anything else, lack of understanding about reinvestment assumptions had plagued advocates of the internal rate-of-return method and has prolonged its usage. In effect, the internal rate-of-return method—as typically defined—implicitly assumes that reinvestment or intertemporal valuation occurs at the internal rate of return rather than the MARR. But the MARR is defined to be the preferred or chosen way to make such intertemporal valuations!

In any event, the revised rules for the internal rate-of-return method in Chapter 8 will lead to the same choices which would be obtained from either the net present value or benefit–cost ratio methods. They will properly treat multiple rates of return and other problems of the internal rate-of-return method as normally defined. Unfortunately, they are somewhat cumbersome to apply. Consequently, we generally recommend use of the net present value for project selection. Once project selection occurs, then the IRR or the effective rate of return can be calculated as indicators of the project's desirability.

SOME SIMPLE STATISTICAL TESTS FOR EMPIRICAL FUNCTIONS

For readers unfamiliar with statistical estimation, we provide in this appendix an introduction to simple tests and procedures to evaluate the validity and accuracy of particular empirical models. More detailed discussion and guidance may be found in standard texts on statistics or econometrics.[1]

III-1 ORDINARY LEAST-SQUARES REGRESSION

For ordinary least-squares regression, we assume that the *true* relationship between the expected or average value of some dependent variable y or $E(y|x)$ and the value of an explanatory variable x *is* linear, albeit with some random error and unknown parameters. For estimation, we obtain a sample of paired observations of the two variables; that is, given the value of the ith observation of the independent variable (x_i), observe the value of the dependent variable (y_i) which accompanies it for the n observations $i = 1, 2, \ldots, n$. This sample of observations is used to estimate the function

$$Y_i = \hat{\alpha} + \hat{\beta} x_i \qquad \text{(III-1a)}$$

where Y_i is an *estimate* of the true mean value of the dependent variable when the value of the independent variable is x_i and $\hat{\alpha}$ and $\hat{\beta}$ are the estimated parameter values.

---

[1] In increasing order of complexity, readers might consult Taro Yamane, *Statistics: An Introductory Analysis*, Harper & Row, New York, 1964; A. Koutsoyiannis, *Theory of Econometrics*, Macmillan, New York, 1972; J. Kmenta, *Elements of Econometrics*, Macmillan, 1971; or H. Theil, *Principles of Econometrics*, Wiley, New York, 1971.

In essence, ordinary least-squares regression assumes that Equation (III-1a) is an accurate model of the average values of y_i. However, a variety of random errors or residual factors affect the observed values of y_i so that the model is inexact in estimating observed values. This is expressed as a linear error or residual e_i; thus

$$y_i = \hat{\alpha} + \hat{\beta} x_i + e_i \qquad \text{(III-1b)}$$

where y_i is an observed value, e_i is the residual error (which is unobservable), and $\hat{\alpha}$, $\hat{\beta}$, and x_i are as defined above. The residual term e_i is assumed to be the result of numerous small events which affect y_i. Technically, the residual term is assumed to be normally distributed with zero average and a constant variance or variability for each value of x_i.[2]

Unbiased estimates of the parameters α and β, or $\hat{\alpha}$ and $\hat{\beta}$, in Equation (III-1) are easily and efficiently determined by the method of ordinary least squares. For this method coefficients are chosen to minimize the sum of the squared differences between the estimated (or Y_i) and observed (or y_i) values of the dependent variable, which are the residual terms e_i in Equation (III-1b) for each observation. The resulting estimated parameter values are:

$$\hat{\alpha} = \bar{y} - \hat{\beta}\bar{x} \qquad \text{(III-2)}$$

and

$$\hat{\beta} = \frac{\sum\limits_{i=1}^{n} x_i y_i - n \bar{x} \bar{y}}{\sum\limits_{i=1}^{n} x_i^2 - n \bar{x}^2} \qquad \text{(III-3)}$$

where

$$\bar{x} = \sum_{i=1}^{n} \frac{x_i}{n} \qquad \text{(III-4)}$$

and

$$\bar{y} = \sum_{i=1}^{n} \frac{y_i}{n} \qquad \text{(III-5)}$$

[2]Formally, three assumptions are typically made. (1) The observed values of y_i for all i are independent and normally distributed about the true mean value of y_i and have an equal variance; that is, σ^2 or Var$[y_i]$ is constant for all i and equal to σ^2; (2) the true relation between the mean of y and value of x is linear; and (3) the error in measuring x is negligible. All of the following statistical measures and tests are based on these assumptions.

Similar estimation equations also exist for models with more than one explanatory variable, such as

$$Y_i = \hat{a} + \hat{\beta}_1 x_i + \hat{\beta}_2 z_i \tag{III-6}$$

where x_i and z_i are explanatory variables and $\hat{\alpha}$, $\hat{\beta}_1$, and $\hat{\beta}_2$ are estimated parameters.

As examples of regression models, the following two models were fit to the transit cost data shown in Table III-1:

$$C = \underset{(0.13)}{3.05} V + \underset{(2.79)}{22.98} E + \underset{(1.02)}{96.77} A \quad r^2 = 0.82 \tag{III-7a}$$

or

$$C = \underset{(-0.01)}{-7.83} + \underset{(7.57)}{26.44} E \quad r^2 = 0.80 \tag{III-7b}$$

where C = total annual operating costs of a transit system
 V = number of vehicles in typical weekday operation

TABLE III-1.   Data Used to Estimate the Transit Cost Function Example

System ID Code	(A) Average Fleet Age (yrs.)	(V) Vehicles in Operation Weekday	(C) Total Operating Costs (1000's)	(E) Equivalent Full-time Employee Count
2002	8.7	184	$ 9922.7	437
2013	9.6	189	13990.5	520
1001	7.8	165	11264.0	499
2059	14.9	190	13510.2	501
2038	9.9	167	16888.2	524
3006	6.1	167	10109.7	422
1055	6.8	105	6751.2	257
4042	15.7	98	7073.5	291
2046	11.0	157	11376.5	369
4029	4.3	93	7421.6	331
4004	6.1	124	6857.1	295
9023	10.2	121	9544.8	323
2039	11.7	80	7838.2	239
9033	4.1	89	6274.6	264
2045	10.7	105	7235.1	199
4008	11.3	78	4574.9	230

Source: *National Urban Mass Transportation Statistics*, UMTA, May 1981.

E = equivalent full-time employee count
A = average fleet age

In Equation (III-7a) C is the dependent variable and V, E, and A are independent or explanatory variables. In the alternative model Equation (III-7b) C is the dependent variable and E is the explanatory variable. The parameter estimates are as shown (3.05, 22.98, and 96.77) for Equation (III-7a) and −7.83 and 26.44 for Equation (III-7b). Below each parameter estimate is a t statistic in parentheses; this statistic indicates the reliability of the parameter estimate and is discussed below.

Two tests on equations such as (III-7a) or (III-7b) can be performed immediately. First, are the magnitudes and signs of the parameters as we would expect? In the case of Equation (III-7a) operating costs would indeed be expected to increase with increases in fleet size, employees, and vehicle age. For Equation (III-7b), however, we would not expect negative costs for employment levels (i.e., values of E) less than 0.296, as the equation indicates. It is often the case that estimated equations are inappropriate over some range of the explanatory variables, as discussed further below. Second, the r^2 value indicates the proportion of the variation in the observed values of the dependent variable (C) which is explained by the regression equation. In this case a relatively large proportion (80% or more) is explained by both equations. This degree of explanation is not surprising, however, given the limited number of observations (16) used for estimation.

How reliable are the parameter estimates in Equations (III-7a) and (III-7b)? Is it reasonable to regard them as highly significant? Or should they be viewed as insignificant? Answers to such questions are invariably judgmental and hinge importantly on the available statistical information together with associated hypotheses. On the statistical side, determination of the t statistic which accompanies a parameter estimate is a first step for an answer. A t statistic is one indication of the relative uncertainty associated with a parameter estimate. This uncertainty arises because different sets of observations of the dependent and explanatory variables will have different residual, random errors, and consequently result in a slightly different parameter estimates. A t statistic indicates the likelihood of significant variation in the estimates from sample to sample. As such, a t statistic value presumes that the least-squares estimation model is correct. Formally, a t statistic for a parameter β is

$$t \text{ statistic} = \frac{\hat{\beta} - \beta}{SE\{\hat{\beta}\}} \quad \text{with DF} = n - k - 1 \qquad \text{(III-8)}$$

where $\hat{\beta}$ is the parameter estimate, β is the true value of the parameter, $SE\{\hat{\beta}\}$ is the estimated standard error of the parameter, DF is called the degrees of freedom, n is the number of observations, and k is the number of β parameters estimated in the regression equation. (In passing, we can note that the square root of the estimated *variance* of an estimate is the standard error. Thus, $\{\text{V}\hat{\text{a}}\text{r }[\hat{\beta}]\}^{1/2} = SE(\hat{\beta})$.) Though seldom stated as such, the t statistics shown along with parameter estimates—as in Equation (III-7)—are those which result from hypothesizing that the true value of the parameter was equal to zero. For *this* hypothesis the analyst is simply trying to establish the probability that the parameter estimate is different from zero or "significant," and thus $\beta = 0$ is hypothesized.

The t statistic shown in Equation (III-8) will be distributed as the Student's t distribution with $n - k - 1$ degrees of freedom, where n is the number of observations used for estimation and k is the number of estimated β parameters. As shown in Figure III-1, this distribution can be closely approximated by the normal distribution when the sample size is large, but will differ substantially at the two tails or extremes when the sample is small. In turn, the probabilities that a t statistic will be above and/or below some critical t value or t_c are given in Tables III-2 and III-3 at the end of this appendix. Table III-2 shows the values of t_c for different probability levels and degrees of freedom. When one is interested in the probability of being *either* above $+t_c$ *or* below $-t_c$, then a one-sided test applies and α_1 is the appropriate probability value. When one is concerned with the probability of being above $+t_c$ *and* below $-t_c$, then a two-sided test applies and α_2 is the appropriate probability. Table III-3 shows the probability of having a t-distributed variable *exceed* a specified t value for different degrees of freedom. To find the probability that the *absolute* value of a t variable exceeds a particular value, the probabilities in

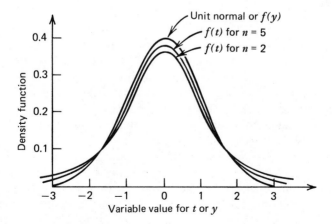

Figure III-1. Density functions for unit-normal and for student's t distributions with various sample sizes.

Table III-3 should be multiplied by 2 to reflect the possibility of variable values being above t or below $-t$. These two tables provide identical information; one or the other may be preferred depending on whether a probability or a value of t_c is desired.

Two important uses can be made of estimated t statistics: (1) tests of the statistical significance of various hypotheses about the true parameter value can be conducted and (2) confidence intervals for the true parameter value can be determined. Each of these will be discussed in turn.

III-2   SIGNIFICANCE TESTS FOR A PARAMETER ESTIMATE

Given a parameter estimate (such as $\hat{\beta}$) and hypothesis about the true parameter value (denoted β), as well as its estimated standard error ($SE\{\hat{\beta}\}$) and degrees of freedom (DF), the t statistic can be determined using Equation (III-8). In turn, we can ask: What is the probability that a t statistic of that magnitude or greater could have occurred by pure chance? Simply, for a one-sided test,

$$\Pr\{\, t \geq t \text{ statistic} \,\} = 1 - F(t \text{ statistic}) \qquad \text{(III-9)}$$

For a two-sided test,

$$\Pr\{\, -t \text{ statistic} \geq t \geq t \text{ statistic} \,\} = \\ 1 - F(t \text{ statistic}) + F(-t \text{ statistic}) \qquad \text{(III-10)}$$

where $F(x)$ is the probability that the t variable has a value of x or less.

Suppose we want to test the null hypothesis that β is zero, the alternative hypothesis being that it is not equal to zero. For a t statistic of about 2.02, with DF = 40, and using Table III-2, we see there is a probability of about 0.025 that a t value so large would result from pure chance and a probability of about 0.05 that an *absolute* t value (i.e., greater than 2.02 or less than -2.02) this large would result from chance. Accordingly, we would *tend* to reject the null hypothesis and to regard the parameter estimate as statistically significant (that is, significantly different from zero).

As a more specific illustration, consider the parameter estimate for the number of employees (E) in Equation (III-7a). In that instance, the parameter estimate was 22.98 and the t statistic (for the null hypothesis that the true parameter value was zero) was 2.79. (Since $\hat{\beta}/SE\{\hat{\beta}\}$ is 2.79, $SE\{\hat{\beta}\}$ is about 8.24.) Also the sample size was 16 and there were 12 degrees of freedom. The probability of a t statistic of that magnitude or greater occurring due to random chance is about 0.008 (as shown in Table III-3), while the probability of an absolute t value so large would be 0.016. These results almost certainly would lead one to conclude that the parameter estimate was quite significant; put differently, there is good reason to reject the null hypothesis and therefore to infer that the true parameter is significantly different from zero.

Of no little importance is the matter of deciding what probability or significance level (i.e., α level) is low enough to permit one to reject the null hypothesis. While it is *common* to use the 5% (0.05) acceptance or significance level as the cutoff point, it must be recognized that, for the most part, convention underlies this practice, While one certainly can be more comfortable when rejecting the null hypothesis at the 0.025 level rather than the 0.05 level, the fact remains that there is no rigorous basis for selecting one significance level over another, whether higher or lower than 0.05.

III-3 CONFIDENCE INTERVALS FOR THE TRUE PARAMETER VALUES

As noted earlier, the t statistic as calculated from Equation (III-8) will be distributed as the Student's t distribution with $n - k - 1$ degrees of freedom. Thus, using the notation given in Table III-2, there is a probability of $1 - \alpha_2$ that

$$-t_c < \frac{\hat{\beta} - \beta}{SE\{\hat{\beta}\}} < t_c \qquad \text{(III-11)}$$

where t_c is the critical value of t for a significance (or probability) level of α_2 with $n - k - 1$ degrees of freedom, as shown in Table III-2. Rearranging the above expression, we can then say that there is a probability of $1 - \alpha_2$ that the true parameter value β lies in the range of

$$\hat{\beta} - t_c SE\{\hat{\beta}\} < \beta < \hat{\beta} + t_c SE\{\hat{\beta}\} \qquad \text{(III-12)}$$

Equation (III-12) defines the $1 - \alpha_2$ confidence interval for the true parameter value β. That is, there is a probability of $1 - \alpha_2$ that the true value of β is larger than $\hat{\beta} - t_c SE\{\hat{\beta}\}$ but smaller than $\hat{\beta} + t_c SE\{\beta\}$, where t_c is the t value associated with the significance level of α_2. Appropriate values of t_c for different confidence levels and degrees of freedom are shown in Table III-2. As an illustration, consider the parameter estimate for the number of employee's in Equation (III-7a). In that case the parameter estimate is 22.98 and the t statistic (for the null hypothesis that the true parameter value was zero) was 2.79. (The sample size was 16 and there were 12 degrees of freedom.) Using the general formulation shown in Equation (III-8), we see that

$$2.79 = \frac{22.98 - 0}{SE\{\hat{\beta}\}} \qquad \text{(III-13)}$$

and, therefore, that $SE\{\hat{\beta}\}$ is 22.98/2.79 = 8.24. Substituting this last value into Equation (III-12), we obtain the confidence interval for the true parameter value (β) with a probability level of $1 - \alpha_2$. Thus,

$$22.98 - t_c \times 8.24 < \beta < 22.98 + t_c \times 8.24 \qquad \text{(III-14)}$$

For a "95% confidence interval," or $1 - \alpha_2 = 0.95$, the significance level α_2 is equal to 0.05, and the associated t_c value (for 12 degrees of freedom) is 2.18 from Table III-2. Therefore, there is a 95% probability that the true parameter value is between 5.02 and 40.94, even though the *single* best estimate of the true value is 22.98. Another way of interpreting this information is to say that the absolute error associated with the estimated $\hat{\beta}$ value is less than 2.18×8.24 or 17.96 with a probability of 95%.

III-4 ERRORS IN FORECASTS OF DEPENDENT VALUES

In models of demand or costs, it is often the case that the level of demand or cost at some value of the explanatory factors is of interest. Such a forecast may be obtained by substituting values of the explanatory variables into the model with a set of estimated parameter values. For example, an estimate of C would be 2028 with a value of $E = 77$ for the model in Equation (III-7b):

$$C_{\text{est}} = -7.83 + 26.44E = -7.83 + 26.44 \times 77 = 2028 \qquad \text{(III-15)}$$

In this section we will consider how reliable such an estimate might be.

It is of primary importance to estimate the error stemming from our regression equation (e.g., what is the probability that the error in our estimate, represented by the difference between Y_i (or C_{est} in this case) and the true value μ_i, or $Y_i - \mu_i$, is less than some specified amount). For this purpose, the estimated standard deviation of Y_i, or $SE\{Y_i\}$, provides an estimate of the error between the estimating regression and the true function. Specifically, the statistic [shown in Eq. (III-16)] below is distributed according to the Student's t distribution; thus,

$$t = \frac{Y_i - \mu_i}{SE\{Y_i\}} \qquad \text{(III-16)}$$

has a Student's t distribution with $n - k - 1$ degrees of freedom (DF). In turn, and using the notation shown in Table III-2, we can say that for DF degrees of freedom, the probability is $1 - \alpha_2$ that the t statistic will fall between the associated plus and minus t_c values, or

$$1 - \alpha_2 = \Pr\left\{ -t_c < \frac{Y_i - \mu_i}{SE\{Y_i\}} < +t_c \right\} \qquad \text{(III-17)}$$

Thus, there is a probability of $1 - \alpha_2$ that the *error* from the estimating function (or $Y_i - \mu_i$) will be less than $\pm t_c SE\{Y_i\}$, where t_c is the critical t value associated with a probability level of α_2 and DF $= n - k - 1$ degrees of freedom. Similarly, there is a probability of $1 - \alpha_2$ that the true mean μ_i will fall within the interval from $Y_i - t_c SE\{Y_i\}$ to $Y_i + t_c SE\{Y_i\}$. This, of course, would be the *confidence interval* for the true regresison value μ_i with a probability of $1 - \alpha_2$.

To compute either the error or confidence interval at any probability level requires us to first calculate the estimated standard deviation of Y_i or $SE\{Y_i\}$. With a single explanatory variable [as in Eq. (III-1a)], an unbiased estimator for the variance of Y_i (which is simply the square of the estimated standard deviation) would be as follows:

$$\text{Vâr}[Y_i] = \frac{s^2}{n} + \frac{s^2(x_i - \bar{x})^2}{\sum\limits_{i=1}^{n} x_i^2 - n\bar{x}^2} \tag{III-18}$$

$$= \frac{s^2}{n} + (x_i - \bar{x})^2 \text{Vâr}[\beta] \tag{III-19}$$

where s is the standard error of the estimate and $\text{Vâr}[\beta]$ is $s^2/[\Sigma x_i^2 - n\bar{x}^2]$; an unbiased estimator for σ^2, or s^2, is

$$s^2 = \frac{\sum\limits_{i=1}^{n}(y_i - Y_i)^2}{n - k - 1} = \frac{\sum\limits_{i=1}^{n}(y_i - \hat{\alpha} - \hat{\beta}x_i)^2}{n - k - 1}$$

$$= \frac{\sum\limits_{i=1}^{n} y_i^2 - n(\hat{\alpha} + \hat{\beta}\bar{x})^2 - \hat{\beta}^2\left(\sum\limits_{x=1}^{n} x_i^2 - n\bar{x}^2\right)}{n - k - 1} \tag{III-20}$$

This latter variance estimator is an estimate of the variability of an individual *observed* y_i value with respect to the estimated regression line. Recall that the ordinary least-squares regression technique assumes that the observed y_i values were normally distributed about the regression line.

Of no little importance, it can be seen [from Eq. (III-18)] that the variability of the estimate Y_i, and thus its error, is dependent upon the value of x_i; as x_i moves farther away from $\bar{x}$ (the mean observed value of x_i for all i), the variance of Y_i and the error will increase. (That is, when x_i is equal to $\bar{x}$, then the second term of Equation (III-18) or (III-19) drops out, thus minimizing the variance of Y_i.) With more than one explanatory variable, calcuation of the variance of Y_i becomes more

complicated.[3] However, it is well within the capability of modern computers to compute, and most statistical analysis packages provide this
capability.

The preceding discussion dealt with the difference between our estimate of the expected value of the true function and the expected value
itself or $Y_i - \mu_i$. In any particular case the actual observed value of the
dependent variable (y_i) would be the sum of the expected value (μ_i) plus a
random error term, the latter reflecting the random fluctuations of
observed y_i values about the expected value of y_i. Again, our best estimate
of the expected value of y_i would be Y_i, but the variance of the random
error term, or s^2, should be added to the variance of Y_i to obtain the
variance of any individual forecast value. (Here, the distinction is made
between the variability of a single estimate and that of the average of all
possible estimates.)

To apply these error measures, let us make use of the estimated regression shown in Equation (III-7b). The first question will be: How good an
estimate of the total annual system operating costs will result from using
the regression? To repeat, there is a probability of $1 - \alpha_2$ that the error
from the estimating function (or $Y_i - \mu_i$) will be less than $\pm t_c(\mathrm{V\hat{a}r}[Y_i])^{1/2}$
$= \pm t_c SE\{Y_i\}$, where t_c is the critical t value associated with that probability and DF $= n - k - 1$ degrees of freedom. To calculate $\mathrm{V\hat{a}r}[Y_i]$, we first
need s^2, $\bar{x}$, $\mathrm{V\hat{a}r}[\beta]$ or $(SE\{\hat{\beta}\})^2$, x_i and n. As noted in the discussion
following Equation (III-8), the value of $SE\{\hat{\beta}\}$ is simply the estimated β
coefficient value divided by the t statistic shown in parentheses below the
coefficient; thus, for Equation (III-7b) or (III-15), $SE\{\hat{\beta}\}$ is 26.44/7.57, or
3.49. The square of this last value, or 12.2, is $\mathrm{V\hat{a}r}[\beta]$. The value of s^2 can be
calculated using the formulation shown in Equation (III-20); for the data
in Table III-1 which were used to estimate the regression, the s^2 value is
2.32×10^6. Finally, using Equation (III-19), we get

$$\mathrm{V\hat{a}r}[Y_i] = \frac{2.32 \times 10^6}{16} + (x_i - \bar{x})^2 12.2 = 145{,}000 + (x_i - \bar{x})^2 12.2 \quad \text{(III-21)}$$

where $\bar{x}$ is 356.31. When x_i equals $\bar{x}$, then the value of Y_i will be 9413 and
that of $SE\{Y_i\}$ will be 381.

In our instance, and using the data in Table III-1, we can say the
following when x_i equals $\bar{x}$ (or 356.31) and DF $= 14$:

For a probability of 95% (or α_2 of 0.05), the t_c value is 2.15; thus there is
a 95% chance that the estimated annual cost of \$9413 (in thousands)
has an error of less than \$819; or the 95% confidence interval for the
true cost is from \$8594 to \$10,232.

---

[3] Using matrix notation, the estimated value of $\mathrm{Var}(Y_i)$ becomes $s^2 X_F'(X'X)^{-1}X_F$ where X_F is a
vector of forecast values of the explanatory variables and X is a matrix of all the data used in
estimation.

For a probability of 90% (or α_2 of 0.10), the t_c value is 1.76; thus, there is a 90% chance that the estimated annual cost of $9413 has an error of less than $671; or the 90% confidence interval for the true cost is from $8742 to $10084.

These conclusions regarding a confidence interval for the expected value of y_i are true for $x_i = \bar{x}$. A 95% confidence interval plot of the dependent variable in Equation (III-7b) is shown in Figure III-2; points on this were calculated in the same manner as for the case $x_i = \bar{x}$ and with the use of Equation (III-21). As can be seen, the uncertainty associated with our cost forecasts becomes greater as we examine employee levels further away from the mean value of E in the estimation data. We should also mention that the confidence range shown in Figure III-2 assumes that a linear model relating cost to employee numbers [Eq. (III-7b)] is correct.

Whether or not this estimating function is considered to be sufficiently accurate to be used for its intended purposes depends, of course, on the

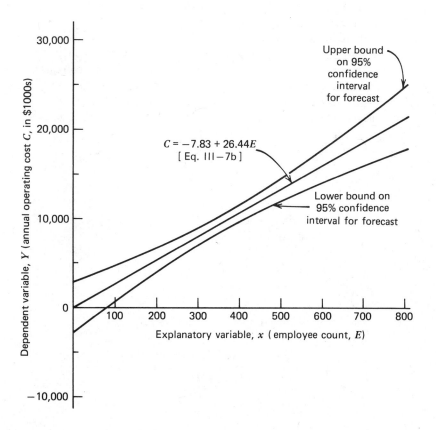

Figure III-2. A 95% confidence interval on forecast mean values from a regression equation.

particular circumstances (e.g., what levels of accuracy can be tolerated, what levels of employment are to be considered, etc.). Thus, at this point, the analysis ends and the judgment begins.

III-5 HYPOTHESIS TEST FOR ZERO INTERCEPT

For the regression in Equation (III-7b), Y_i is -7.83 when x_i is 0 (that is, $C = -7.83$ when $E = 0$). Thus, it is apparent that this regression line *almost* goes through the origin as can be seen from Figure III-2. In turn, we can test the hypothesis that the true cost μ_i is 0 when x is 0. This test can be accomplished in several fashions.

First, we can simply test whether or not the estimated parameter $\hat{\alpha}$ is significantly different from 0. Following the procedure in Section III-2 the estimated parameter value is -7.83 with a t-statistic of -0.01 and $16 - 1 - 1 = 14$ degrees of freedom. With this t-statistic and degrees of freedom there is a greater than 40% chance that an estimated parameter of -7.83 or less arose due to random variations, even if the true parameter value was 0. Accordingly, there is little reason to reject the hypothesis that the constant parameter α equals 0.

A second test is also possible using the hypothesis that cost, C, is 0 when employment, E, is zero. This test is slightly more powerful and robust than the single parameter test on α since it also considers the uncertainty in the parameter $\hat{\beta}$. The test can be accomplished by making use of the relationship described in Equation (III-16). That is, for μ_i equal to 0, the t-statistic shown below has a Student's t distribution with $n - k - 1$ degrees of freedom:

$$t \text{ statistic} = \frac{Y_i}{SE\{Y_i\}} \tag{III-22}$$

If μ_i is hypothesized to be 0 when x_i is 0, the associated Y_i and $\text{V\^ar}[Y_i]$ values [from Eq. (III-7b) and (III-19)], will be

$$Y_i = -7.83$$

$$\text{V\^ar}[Y_i] = \frac{s^2}{n} + (0 - \bar{x})^2 \text{V\^ar}[\beta]$$

$$= 145{,}000 + (-356.31)^2 12.2$$

$$= 1.69 \times 10^6$$

and

$$SE\{Y_i\} = 1302$$

Thus, the t statistic [using Eq. (III-22)] will be $-7.83/1302$, or -0.00601, for 14 degrees of freedom.

From Table III-3 it can be seen that the probability of a t value being larger (in absolute terms) than -0.00602 due to pure chance is much greater than 84% (since for DF = 14 and $t = 0.2$, $1 - F(t) = 0.422$ and, therefore, $\alpha_2 = 0.844$), thus leading one to conclude that there is very little reason to reject the null hypothesis (that the intercept is zero).[4] Also, when x_i is zero, the 95% confidence interval for the true cost is $-7.83 \pm 2.15 \times 1302$, or from -2807 to $+2791$.

In all, then, one might conclude that the estimator in Equation (III-7b) should be rejected in favor of an equation without a constant term, or $Y = \hat{\beta}x$. When estimated, the result of this model is $Y = 26.42x$. For the two estimators the sums of the squared residuals were virtually identical, as are the r^2 values and coefficients for the employee count. Moreover, the statistical tests for the two parameter regression [Eq. (III-7b)] strongly supported the null hypothesis that the regression goes through the origin. Given this conclusion, one would be inclined to say that medium-sized bus systems tended to have constant returns to scale with respect to the employee count, represented by a cost function of the form $Y = \hat{\beta}x$.

III-6 EFFECTS OF VIOLATIONS OF THE ASSUMPTIONS OF LEAST-SQUARES REGRESSION

The foregoing discussion considered the reliability of the results of a regression expression under some fairly restrictive assumptions. In this section we shall briefly mention some common ways in which these assumptions are violated.

Incorrect Model Form

Any regression model must assume a particular algebraic form, even though the parameters of the model are to be estimated. An example of a model form is the linear equation (III-7a). It is often the case that the model form chosen is inappropriate or incorrect. Poor statistical properties of a model are a primary indication of a poor model; such properties include large prediction errors and large confidence intervals on parameter estimates. Prediction of dependent variables outside of the range of data used for estimation is particularly prone to error with incorrect model forms.

---

[4]Using exact calculations, rather than the values tabulated in Table III-3, we determine that the probability of a t value larger than -0.00602 (in absolute terms) occurring due to pure chance is 99.53%.

Multicollinearity

It may be the case the particular explanatory or independent variables are highly correlated. For example, travel time and cost tend to be positively correlated since longer trips both take more time and cost more. The effect of such positive correlation is to make it difficult to disentangle the independent effects of the individual variables. An indication of such confounding problems occurs when confidence intervals for two or more explanatory variables are quite large. A correction for this problem is to gather more data in which the variables are not as highly correlated.

Serial Correlation

In estimation of models from time series or over space, it is often the case that subsequent or adjacent observations are similar in nature. While parameter estimates are not biased by this phenomenon, the standard errors of parameters are calculated to be lower than their true value. This bias in the estimate of parameter uncertainty occurs because there is less variation in the sample than would occur with a completely random sample. Whenever time series or spatially adjacent data are used, there may be a problem with serial correlation. There are sophisticated tests and corrections available to handle such problems; readers are urged to consult an appropriate statistics or econometrics text such as those cited earlier.

Simultaneity

As discussed earlier, there are both performance and demand relationships between the volume and price of travel on a particular facility. In estimating a function from a set of observations of volumes and prices, an analyst may be estimating a demand function, a supply or performance function, or some combination thereof. This is one form of the problem of identification, in which two or more relationships exist between dependent and explanatory variables. To determine which function is estimated in the simple case of volume and price observations, one must decide whether the set of observations trace out a demand or performance function. That is, if the demand function was constant and a series of policy changes affected the performance function, then the set of observations traces out the demand function. Conversely, a constant facility operation policy with changing demand results in identification of a performance function. In addition to these methods, direct experimentation or some sophisticated econometric techniques can be used to overcome the problems of simultaneity.

Function Instability

As noted earlier in the text, there is often no reason to assume that functions are constant over time or from one locale to another. Demand functions in particular might be expected to shift over time as population increases, auto ownership increases, or other changes occur. To the extent that these changes are not explicitly included in a model, then the demand function will be inappropriate if it is applied to the different conditions.

TABLE III-2. Critical t Values for the t Distribution for Various Confidence Levels (α_1 or α_2)[a]

α_2	α_1	Number of Degrees of Freedom									
		1	2	3	4	5	6	7	8	9	10
1.0	0.5	0.00	0.00	0.00	0.00	0.00	0.00	0.00	0.00	0.00	0.00
0.8	0.4	0.33	0.29	0.28	0.27	0.27	0.27	0.26	0.26	0.26	0.26
0.6	0.3	0.73	0.62	0.58	0.57	0.56	0.55	0.55	0.55	0.54	0.54
0.4	0.2	1.38	1.06	0.98	0.94	0.92	0.91	0.90	0.89	0.88	0.88
0.2	0.1	3.08	1.89	1.64	1.53	1.48	1.44	1.42	1.40	1.38	1.37
0.1	0.05	6.31	2.92	2.35	2.13	2.02	1.94	1.90	1.86	1.83	1.81
0.05	0.025	12.7	4.30	3.18	2.78	2.57	2.45	2.37	2.31	2.26	2.23
0.02	0.01	31.8	6.97	4.54	3.75	3.37	3.14	3.00	2.90	2.82	2.76
0.01	0.005	63.7	9.93	5.84	4.60	4.03	3.71	3.50	3.36	3.25	3.17
0.002	0.001	318.3	22.3	10.2	7.17	5.89	5.21	4.79	4.50	4.30	4.14

α_2	α_1	Number of Degrees of Freedom									
		11	12	13	14	15	16	17	18	19	20
1.0	0.5	0.00	0.00	0.00	0.00	0.00	0.00	0.00	0.00	0.00	0.00
0.8	0.4	0.26	0.26	0.26	0.26	0.26	0.26	0.26	0.26	0.26	0.26
0.6	0.3	0.54	0.54	0.54	0.54	0.54	0.54	0.53	0.53	0.53	0.53
0.4	0.2	0.88	0.87	0.87	0.87	0.87	0.87	0.86	0.86	0.86	0.86
0.2	0.1	1.36	1.36	1.35	1.35	1.34	1.34	1.33	1.33	1.33	1.33
0.1	0.05	1.80	1.78	1.77	1.76	1.75	1.75	1.74	1.73	1.73	1.73
0.05	0.025	2.20	2.18	2.16	2.15	2.13	2.12	2.11	2.10	2.09	2.09
0.02	0.01	2.72	2.68	2.65	2.62	2.60	2.58	2.57	2.55	2.54	2.53
0.01	0.005	3.11	3.06	3.01	2.98	2.95	2.92	2.90	2.88	2.86	2.85
0.002	0.001	4.03	3.93	3.85	3.79	3.73	3.69	3.65	3.61	3.58	3.55

TABLE III-2. (Continued)

α_2	α_1	Number of Degrees of Freedom									
		22	24	26	28	30	40	50	100	200	∞
1.0	0.5	0.00	0.00	0.00	0.00	0.00	0.00	0.00	0.00	0.00	0.00
0.8	0.4	0.26	0.26	0.26	0.26	0.26	0.26	0.26	0.25	0.25	0.25
0.6	0.3	0.53	0.53	0.53	0.53	0.53	0.53	0.53	0.53	0.53	0.52
0.4	0.2	0.86	0.86	0.86	0.86	0.85	0.85	0.85	0.85	0.84	0.84
0.2	0.1	1.32	1.32	1.32	1.31	1.31	1.30	1.30	1.29	1.29	1.28
0.1	0.05	1.72	1.71	1.71	1.70	1.70	1.68	1.68	1.66	1.65	1.65
0.05	0.025	2.07	2.06	2.06	2.05	2.04	2.02	2.01	1.98	1.97	1.96
0.02	0.01	2.51	2.49	2.48	2.47	2.46	2.42	2.40	2.37	2.35	2.33
0.01	0.005	2.82	2.80	2.78	2.76	2.75	2.70	2.68	2.63	2.60	2.58
0.002	0.001	3.51	3.47	3.44	3.41	3.39	3.31	3.26	3.17	3.13	3.09

Source: Modified from Table All in E. Kreyszig, *Advanced Engineering Mathematics*, 4th ed., Wiley, New York, 1979.

[a]For a one-sided, upper-tail or lower-tail test

$$\alpha_1 = 1 - F(t_c) = \Pr(t > t_c) = \Pr(t < -t_c)$$

where t_c is the critical value of t as tabulated above. For a two-sided, equal-tail test,

$$\alpha_2 = 1 - F(t_c) + F(-t_c) = \Pr(t > t_c) + \Pr(t < -t_c)$$

Example: (one sided) $t_c = 2.02$ for $\alpha_1 = 0.05$, DF = 5
(two sided) $t_c = 2.57$ for $\alpha_2 = 0.05$, DF = 5

TABLE III-3. α_1 Significance Levels for Various t Statistic Values[a]

Degrees of Freedom	Values of the t Statistic								
	0.2	0.4	0.6	0.8	1.0	1.2	1.4	1.6	1.8
1	.437	.379	.328	.285	.250	.221	.197	.178	.161
2	.430	.364	.305	.254	.211	.177	.148	.125	.107
3	.427	.358	.295	.241	.196	.158	.128	.104	.085
4	.426	.355	.290	.234	.187	.148	.117	.092	.073
5	.425	.353	.287	.230	.182	.142	.110	.085	.066
6	.424	.352	.285	.227	.178	.138	.106	.080	.061
7	.424	.351	.284	.225	.175	.135	.102	.077	.057
8	.423	.350	.283	.223	.173	.132	.100	.074	.055
9	.423	.349	.282	.222	.172	.130	.098	.072	.053
10	.423	.349	.281	.221	.170	.129	.096	.070	.051
12	.422	.348	.280	.220	.169	.127	.093	.068	.049
14	.422	.348	.279	.219	.167	.125	.092	.066	.047
16	.422	.347	.278	.218	.166	.124	.090	.065	.045
18	.422	.347	.278	.217	.165	.123	.089	.064	.044
20	.422	.347	.278	.217	.165	.122	.088	.063	.043
30	.421	.346	.277	.215	.163	.120	.086	.060	.041
40	.421	.346	.276	.214	.162	.119	.085	.059	.040
50	.421	.345	.276	.214	.161	.188	.084	.058	.039
70	.421	.345	.275	.213	.160	.117	.083	.057	.038
∞	.421	.345	.274	.212	.159	.115	.081	.055	.036

TABLE III-3. (Continued)

Degrees of Freedom	Values of the t Statistic									
	2.0	2.4	2.8	3.2	3.8	4.4	5.0	6.0	7.0	8.0
1	.148	.126	.109	.096	.082	.071	.063	.053	.045	.040
2	.092	.069	.054	.043	.031	.024	.019	.013	.010	.008
3	.070	.048	.034	.025	.016	.011	.008	.005	.003	.002
4	.058	.046	.024	.016	.010	.006	.004	.002	.001	.001
5	.051	.031	.019	.012	.006	.004	.002	.001	.000	.000
6	.046	.027	.016	.009	.004	.002	.001	.000		
7	.043	.024	.013	.008	.003	.002	.001	.000		
8	.040	.022	.012	.006	.003	.001	.001	.000		
9	.038	.020	.010	.005	.002	.001	.000			
10	.037	.019	.009	.005	.002	.001	.000			
12	.034	.017	.008	.004	.001	.000				
14	.033	.015	.007	.003	.001	.000				
16	.031	.014	.006	.003	.001	.000				
18	.030	.014	.006	.002	.001	.000				
20	.030	.013	.006	.002	.001	.000				
30	.027	.011	.004	.002	.000					
40	.026	.011	.004	.001	.000					
50	.025	.010	.004	.001	.000					
70	.025	.010	.003	.001	.000					
∞	.023	.008	.003	.001	.000					

[a]Table entries represent $1 - F(t)$, the probability of a t variable exceeding the value of t shown for the degrees of freedom (DF) indicated. Example: $\Pr(t > 1.8) = 0.066$ with DF = 5.

INDEX

Abandonment of facilities, 154-155, 319
Acceptability of alternatives, *see*
    Feasibility or acceptability
Accounting cost estimation:
  by aggregating unit costs, 254-256
  by allocation, 259-260
Accuracy:
  of demand forecasts, 249-251
  statistical, 356-360
Adjusted rate of return, 339, 344-346
Aggregate data, 237
Aggregate demand:
  elasticity, 18-21
  models, 15-16
  see also Demand; Demand functions
Air pollution, 53n, 220-222. *See also*
    Externalities
Air travel:
  fares for, 39
  forecasting of, 251
Allocation:
  of costs for estimation, 259-260
  of taxi costs, 300-302
Alternatives analysis, *see* Benefit-cost
    analysis
Altshuler, A., 13n
Analysis period, 156-157. *See also*
    Planning horizon
Annual costs:
  capital recovery factor for computing, 61
  equivalent, 168-171
Ascher, W., 25n
Asher, N. J., 57n
Atherton, T., 248n
Au, T., 169n, 191n, 225n, 300n, 302n, 339n,
  341n
Au, T. P., 169n, 191n, 339n, 341n
Automobile:
  availability of, 248
  demand for travel by, 248
  ownership costs of, 54
  roadway costs for, 297

Average total cost:
  for the long run, 73
  for the short run, 62
  see also Cost functions
Average variable cost:
  as pricing strategy, 103-108, 112-116,
    122-123
  short run, 62
  see also Cost functions
Avoided costs, 154-155, 313-314

Backward-bending situations, 117-123
Baerwald, J. E., 316n
BART (Bay Area Rapid Transit), 154-155
Baumann, D., 300n, 302n
Beckmann, M., 50n
Ben-Akiva, M., 248n
Benefit-cost analysis:
  basic steps, 155-167
  common errors, 308-317
  vs. cost-effectiveness analysis, 2
  and incremental principle, 199
  vs. long run economic planning, 153
  methods, 167-183
    benefit-cost ratio, 173-176
    equivalent annual costs, 168-171
    inconsistencies of, 182-183
    internal rate of return, 176-192,
      325-347
    net present value, 171-173
  ordering of alternatives for, 168, 173,
    177, 188-189
  and point of view, 308-310
  see also Economic efficiency; Internal
    rate of return
Benefits:
  calculated from logit demand model, 245
  and costs avoided, 313-314
  and demand functions, 80
  differences in definitions, 82
  economic definition, 87
  expected, 150

369